中学英语语法练习 3000 题

（第四版）

朱茂忠　编

上海交通大学出版社

内容提要

　　本书归纳了历年高考真题和各地的模拟试题,从中选出了 3000 句最基本又最具代表性的句子,汇编成册,供中学各年级学生使用。

图书在版编目(CIP)数据

中学英语语法练习 3000 题 / 朱茂忠编. —4 版
—上海:上海交通大学出版社,2016
ISBN 978-7-313-03604-9

Ⅰ. 中... Ⅱ. 朱... Ⅲ. 英语—语法—中学—习题集 Ⅳ. G634.415

中国版本图书馆 CIP 数据核字(2013)第 148591 号

中学英语语法练习 3000 题
(第四版)

编　　者:朱茂忠
出版发行:上海交通大学出版社　　　　地　　址:上海市番禺路 951 号
邮政编码:200030　　　　　　　　　　电　　话:021-64071208
出 版 人:郑益慧
印　　制:常熟市文化印刷有限公司　　　经　　销:全国新华书店
开　　本:880mm×1230mm　1/32　　　印　　张:16.25
字　　数:524 千字
版　　次:2003 年 12 月第 1 版　2016 年 6 月第 4 版　　印　　次:2016 年 12 月第 20 次印刷
书　　号:ISBN 978-7-313-03604-9/G
定　　价:28.00 元

出版社的话

朱茂忠老师编著的《中学英语语法练习 3000 题》出版已十多年，十多次的反复印刷说明该书深受上海和全国各地初、高中广大师生的欢迎，确实已成为中学生学习英语的好帮手，自学英语者的好老师，也是中学英语老师的好参谋。

朱茂忠老师是上海市延安中学教学经验极为丰富的老教师，为了跟上时代的步伐和新形势的需要，他在第四版中补充了新的内容。

《中学英语语法练习 3000 题》将再版，我社为此感到高兴，也是全社会的宝贵财富。但愿这两本书能成为广大师生的良师益友，更愿读者成为英语学习的佼佼者。

上海交通大学出版社

序　言

在经济全球化的时代，英语作为国际交流的语言尤显重要，对于每个中学生来说学好一门外语重在中学时代掌握好语言学习的规律并通过相互交流、阅读与持之以恒的运用。只有这样才能不断提升外语能力，为走在改革开放、面向世界的前列奠定语言基础，更为建设好美丽中国的事业打好自己的发展基础。

朱老师是我校的优秀教师，在长期的英语教学过程中积累了丰富的教学经验，并在指导学生学好英语方面有着丰硕的实践成果，为延安中学培养了大批优秀学生。同时他更是一位热爱学生、关心学生、乐于帮助学生的优秀老师和班主任。他把三十余年的教学经验，经过提炼与总结汇编成册，使一批又一批的学生不断受益。许多学生在教师的关爱下，从喜欢朱老师到喜爱英语学习，最后成为一名品学兼优的延安毕业生。学好英语，朱老师经常强调要"五多"，即：多听、多说、多读、多写、多用。各类得到朱老师指导的学生均有收获。

虽然朱老师早过退休年龄，但他对英语教学的热爱和追求永不退休，希望有更多的中学生通过阅读朱老师的研究成果从中受益，本书适合想要学习英语的学生使用。

延安中学校长　**郭　雄**

一封学生的感谢信

敬爱的朱老师：

今天是您献给我们的最后一堂课。在您即将退休的时候，回顾这学期来您对我们的鞭策与教诲，关心与付出，我们有太多太多的感动和感激。在此，我谨代表全班53名同学，向您表示我们最衷心的感谢。

半年以前，您来到我们这个班级，还记得当时我们的英语成绩惨不忍睹，一半同学不及格。而短短的五个月后，我们班的成绩有了奇迹般的飞跃，基本上消除了不及格现象。高分越来越多，整体水平有了很大的提高。同学们都说，现在做英语卷有了感觉，不再是像猜谜语一样碰运气，也不再凭着所谓的语感去蒙一个说不清道理的答案。这翻天覆地的变化中固然有我们的努力，但更重要的是您日日夜夜为我们洒下的汗水。我们不会忘记在这一个学期内您为我们的学习成绩和成长过程所付出的一切。

还记得我们望着可怜的摸底考分数，欲哭无泪的时候，是您鼓励我们，只要配合您的教学，就一定可以迎头赶上。

还记得您那浅显易懂的讲课，条理清晰的笔记，还有那些很有针对性的训练，让我们在心中重新找回了自信，让我们燃起了希望的火焰。

还记得您把每次测验的高分进行全班表扬。但同样会对不争气的我们进行丝毫不留情的批评。然而我们知道，没有您的鞭策与指正，我们不会有今天的成绩。

还记得您那天吃力地趴在讲台上的身影，记得您那虚弱的身体和病历卡上危险的信号，记得您卧在床上批改着我们的试卷,记得连夜为我们赶出来的一份份笔记。朱老师,我们不会忘记这些,您是用自己的言行诠释着"教师"两字。您是用自己的生命创造高三(1)班的奇迹。

如今,当我们欣喜地看到自己在英语成绩上的巨变时,我们却发现,您要退休了。我们真有些依依不舍,我们多么希望朱老师您能留下来,带我们走完高三这最后一段路。但我们也知道您的身体状况不允许您再为我们呕心沥血。我们希望天天听到您的谆谆教诲,但我们也得关心您的身体,尊重您的选择。

您说过我们是您最后一届学生,您希望我们能为您那漫长而光辉的教师生涯画上一个圆满的句号。您也说过,今天是您最后一次站在讲台前,最后一次传授您的知识。对您来说,短短的五个月,在您的教师生涯中是那样的短暂,这五个月的成绩也许算不上很大的辉煌,但这五个月毕竟是结局而显得特别和永恒。而对我们来说,这五个月内所学会的、所收获的,将是我们高三征途上的砝码,也是我们人生道路上毕生的财富。望着您离去的背影,想着您的那些教导,我们有些留恋,但没有伤感;我们有些不舍,但没有遗憾。因为我们已从您身上学到了最珍贵的东西。

朱老师,您是成功的。因为几十年的耕耘,已让您桃李满天下。而您的成功也将是圆满的。因为在今年的七月,您将收到一份让您最满意的答卷。

最后,让我再次代表全班向您——我们敬爱的朱老师,道一声:谢谢! 同时送上全班的祝福,祝您能在以后的日子里身体健康,万事如意!

高三(1)班全体成员
代表:裴秉正(班长)
2002年2月

目 录

单项练习

第一讲　三种基本句型

1. Which sentence is right?
   A. There seems to have a spelling mistake in this sentence.
   B. If you are convenient tomorrow, please help me with my English.
   C. It is possibility that you will reach the railway station in time.
   D. What happened to you yesterday?
2. We don't care if a hunting dog smells _____, but we really don't want him to smell _____.
   A. well, well   B. bad, bad
   C. well, badly   D. badly, bad
3. Only _____ he would succeed in the end.
   A. Jane believe   B. Jane believed
   C. believed Jane   D. did Jane believe
4. _____ to stay up to let me in; just give me a key.
   A. There's no need for you   B. You don't have
   C. You are unnecessary   D. It doesn't need
5. Indeed, your knife looks _____, but it cuts _____.
   A. nice, bad   B. nicely, badly
   C. nice, badly   D. nicely, bad
6. The flower smells _____.
   A. pleased   B. sweetly
   C. sweetness   D. pleasant
7. _____ used to be an orphanage here, but we can't find it now.
   A. There   B. There was
   C. It   D. It was
8. _____ no need to tell him all about it.
   A. It is   B. It has

C. There has   D. There is
9. A teacher is _____ correct.
    A. not necessary always   B. necessary not always
    C. necessarily not always   D. not necessarily always
10. The football team has done well this year. _____ have trained very hard.
    A. All players   B. All their players
    C. All its players   D. All of players
11. Did you really think that his sister looked _____ that night?
    A. ugly   B. beautifully
    C. eagerly   D. anxiously
12. There are many _____ in our library.
    A. old American interesting history books
    B. interesting old American history books
    C. interesting American old history books
    D. American interesting old history books
13. _____ came from the second-hand bookstore.
    A. All these old stories   B. These all old stories
    C. All old these stories   D. These old all stories
14. Those who participated in the experiment had to remain _____ all night.
    A. awaken   B. awake
    C. awaked   D. awoken
15. We have not had _____ as this for many weeks.
    A. so cold a day   B. how cold a day
    C. a day so cold   D. a such cold day
16. Radio _____ in our life.
    A. widely is used   B. is used widely
    C. is widely used   D. is wide used
17. As some famous singers will appear at the pop concert, _____ likely to be a large audience.
    A. it's   B. here's
    C. there's   D. that's
18. A holiday is very _____ after a long period of work.

A. welcomed   B. welcome
C. a welcome   D. welcoming
19. Only _____ to have escaped being fined by the policeman.
    A. did some of the drivers seem
    B. some of the drivers seemed
    C. did seem some of the drivers
    D. seemed some of the drivers
20. — Who shall we choose to make up our baseball team?
    — Well, _____ Harry, but he is not a very good player, I
      suppose.
    A. it's   B. he's
    C. there's   D. that's
21. — _____ doesn't seem to be any possibility that they will win
      the game.
    — No, _____ what I can't understand.
    A. It, that's   B. There, that's
    C. That, there's   D. There, here's
22. He ran towards the seaside and _____ into the water.
    A. dived   B. diving
    C. headed   D. heading
23. They're not very good, but we like _____.
    A. anyway to play basketball with them
    B. to play basketball with them anyway
    C. to play with them basketball anyway
    D. with them to play basketball anyway
24. — Do you like the material?
    — Yes, it _____ very soft.
    A. is feeling   B. felt
    C. feels   D. is felt
25. What a pity that my computer doesn't work! _____ must be
    something wrong with it.
    A. It   B. There
    C. This   D. That
26. The Art Museum _____ since last Monday.

A. has opened   B. has been opened

C. has been open   D. had been open

27. _____ looked up in alarm.

    A. All the present women   B. All the women present

    C. The all present women   D. The all women present

28. _____ is no doubt that the manager has made the right decision.

    A. It   B. This

    C. There   D. That

29. There was _____ to weigh the elephant.

    A. big enough nothing   B. big nothing enough

    C. nothing big enough   D. nothing enough big

30. _____ in history when remarkable progress was made in relatively short periods of time.

    A. There has time   B. It has time

    C. It is time   D. There has been a time

31. Alice is proud of having _____ bed.

    A. a beautiful old Chinese wooden

    B. an old beautiful Chinese wooden

    C. a beautiful Chinese old wooden

    D. a beautiful old wooden Chinese

32. The _____ student standing at the gate speaks very good Chinese.

    A. tall young American   B. young tall American

    C. American tall young   D. American young tall

33. We visited some schools and spent the _____ days at the seaside.

    A. few last sunny   B. last few sunny

    C. last sunny few   D. few sunny last

34. Mary studies at a _____ school.

    A. famous medical Chinese   B. famous Chinese medical

    C. medical Chinese famous   D. Chinese medical famous

35. Tom set out to do the work not long after breakfast _____ it two hours later. Then he had a short rest.

A. finishing   B. so as to finish
C. having finished   D. and finished

36. Go two blocks, and you'll find a _____ building.
   A. tall grey stone   B. stone grey tall
   C. grey stone tall   D. tall stone grey

37. We're glad you've _____ a fine brave young man.
   A. grown up   B. grown
   C. brought up   D. brought out

38. Tom and John are going swimming with _____ boys this afternoon.
   A. little two other   B. two other little
   C. two little other   D. little other two

39. _____ that Wilson treats all his employees fairly.
   A. It is aware   B. It awares
   C. I am awared   D. I am aware

40. _____ a time in the 1960s _____ young people liked wearing army uniforms.
   A. It was, that   B. It was, since
   C. There was, when   D. For, when

41. _____ often speak highly of his modern paintings.
   A. His a few friends   B. Few friends of his
   C. His few friends   D. A few his friends

42. _____ a hole in one of the walls. Otherwise, we couldn't have seen what was going on inside the room.
   A. There happened to be   B. It happened to be
   C. There happened to have   D. It happened to have

43. _____ seems to be something wrong with this recorder. _____ going to be repaired.
   A. It, There   B. There, It's
   C. It, There's   D. There, There's

44. — What's that noise?
   — Oh, _____ the wind shaking the windows.
   A. there's   B. it's
   C. must be   D. here's

45. The report made by our general manager _____ encouraging.
   A. was heard   B. was sounded
   C. sounded   D. heard
46. Nearly all the foreign friends said that the Chinese dishes tasted
   _____.
   A. quite well   B. pretty wonderfully
   C. just perfect   D. rather sweetly
47. A round-clock shop is a shop which _____ all day.
   A. keeps opened   B. remains opened
   C. keeps open   D. goes on opening
48. _____ a long time since I saw her last.
   A. For   B. There is
   C. During   D. It is
49. I felt in _____ and took out some money.
   A. a pocket my coat   B. my coat's pocket
   C. my pocket coat   D. my coat pocket
50. The piece of silk _____ quite _____.
   A. is feeling, smoothly   B. is felt, smooth
   C. feels, smooth   D. is felt, smoothly
51. Anson set out after dark _____ home an hour later.
   A. arriving   B. to arrive
   C. having arrived   D. and arrived
52. _____ speak French very well.
   A. These both students   B. Both of they
   C. Both of students   D. Both these students
53. The father has kept _____ letters he received from his son.
   A. the all   B. all the
   C. all of   D. each
54. She showed us the gift she had got, which was a _____ pencil-box.
   A. red beautiful wooden   B. wooden red beautiful
   C. beautiful red wooden   D. beautiful wooden red
55. _____ wonder that Tom lost his way yesterday as he came
   here for the first time.
   A. It is   B. It is not

C. It is no   D. There is no

56. I have been to the doctor's about my headache. He says there is
    _____, but I must lie up for a few days.
    A. something serious   B. anything serious
    C. not serious   D. nothing serious

57. This _____ girl is Mary's cousin.
    A. pretty little Swedish   B. Swedish pretty little
    C. Swedish little pretty   D. little pretty Swedish

58. _____ draw very well.
    A. These both children   B. Both of they
    C. Both they   D. Both these girls

59. There's _____ about the affair.
    A. something funny   B. something fun
    C. fun something   D. funny something

60. Pears from that part of the country do not taste as _____ as
    those from our hometown.
    A. nice   B. well
    C. satisfied   D. deliciously

61. Jack bought _____ apples and presented them to me.
    A. five big red   B. big five red
    C. five red big   D. red five big

62. His suggestion sounded _____ but nobody agreed to it.
    A. reasonable   B. reasonably
    C. unreasonably   D. unreasonable

63. Do you like those _____ flowers?
    A. little lovely red paper   B. lovely little paper red
    C. paper lovely little red   D. lovely little red paper

64. Which of the following is wrong?
    A. Cakes that look nice don't necessarily taste good.
    B. No one least of all the children paid attention.
    C. It is no need to book the tickets in advance.
    D. Mary shares in her husband's troubles as well as his joys.

65. Tony is going on the picnic with _____ friends.
    A. two little other   B. two other little

C. other little two   D. other two little

66. — Have you got everything ready for the meeting?

     — Yes, but we need _____.

     A. three other chair   B. other three chairs

     C. another three chairs   D. three another chairs

67. He said he _____ my gift very much.

     A. delighted   B. thanked

     C. appreciated   D. welcome

68. _____ is doubt _____ we can finish the work in three weeks.

     A. There, if   B. It, whether

     C. It, that   D. There, whether

69. Whether people can live on another star _____ as a secret now.

     A. is remained   B. has remained

     C. remains   D. is remaining

70. There _____ too much homework to do tomorrow.

     A. seems to have   B. seem to be

     C. seems not to have   D. doesn't seem to be

71. To tell you the truth, your plan _____ to be improved further.

     A. need   B. kept

     C. must   D. remains

72. Are _____ often accessible _____ in your school?

     A. you, to the labs   B. the labs, to you

     C. you, for the labs   D. the labs, for you

73. There _____ every possibility that business will get better.

     A. seems to be   B. seem not to be

     C. don't seem to be   D. seem to be

74. He sent her a _____ shirt as a birthday present.

     A. Chinese fine silk   B. fine silk Chinese

     C. silk fine Chinese   D. fine Chinese silk

75. _____ is no possibility _____ Bob can win the first prize in the match.

     A. There, that   B. It, that

     C. There, whether   D. It, whether

第二讲 倒装句

1. Just in front of our house _____ with a history of 1,000 years.
   A. does a tall tree stand   B. stands a tall tree
   C. a tall tree is standing   D. a tall tree stands

2. — Did you see who the driver was?
   — No, so quickly _____ that I couldn't get a good look at his face.
   A. did the car speed by   B. the car sped by
   C. does the car speed by   D. the car speed by

3. _____ tomorrow, our ship will sail for Macao.
   A. However the weather is like
   B. However is the weather like
   C. Whatever is the weather like
   D. Whatever the weather is like

4. Higher and higher _____ and then it was out of sight.
   A. flew it   B. it flew
   C. did it fly   D. was it flying

5. — How was the televised debate last night?
   — Super! Rarely _____ so much media attention.
   A. debate attracted   B. did a debate attract
   C. a debate did attract   D. attracted a debate

6. — Do you know if Terry will go camping this weekend?
   — Terry? Never! She _____ tents and fresh air!
   A. has hated   B. hated
   C. will hate   D. hates

7. So much of interest _____ that most visitors simply run out of time before seeing it all.
   A. offers Beijing   B. Beijing offers
   C. does Beijing offer   D. Beijing does offer

8. _____ well prepared you are, you still need a lot of luck in

mountain climbing.
   A. However   B. Whatever
   C. No matter   D. Although
9. Hearing the dog barking fiercely, away _____.
   A. fleeing the thief   B. was fleeing the thief
   C. the thief was fleeing   D. fled the thief
10. Never _____ Lisa would arrive but she turned up at last minute.
   A. did we think   B. have we thought
   C. we thought   D. we have thought
11. _____ you may have, you should gather your courage to face
    the challenge.
    A. However a serious problem
    B. What a serious problem
    C. However serious a problem
    D. What serious a problem
12. Only with the greatest of luck _____ to escape from the rising
    flood waters.
    A. managed she   B. she managed
    C. did she manage   D. she did manage
13. _____ difficulties they may come across, they will help one
    another to get them over.
    A. However   B. Whatever
    C. Whichever   D. Since
14. Only when the war was over _____ to his hometown.
    A. did the young soldier return
    B. the young soldier returned
    C. returned the young soldier
    D. the young soldier did return
15. The little time we have together we try _____ wisely.
    A. spending it   B. to spend it
    C. to spend   D. spending that
16. No sooner _____ than the fire broke out.
    A. he had left   B. had he left
    C. his leaving   D. he left

17. Not until the late 1940s _____ China's history _____ a great turning point.
    A. did, come to
    B. had, come to
    C. that, came to
    D. was, brought
18. Only after she got off the bus, _____ that _____ her handbag on the seat.
    A. she found, she had lost
    B. did she find, had she lost
    C. did she realize, she had left
    D. she realized, had she left
19. Not only _____ polluted but _____ crowded.
    A. was the city, were the streets
    B. the city was, were the streets
    C. was the city, the streets were
    D. the city was, the streets were
20. Only after he came back _____ what had happened.
    A. I knew
    B. I did know
    C. did I know
    D. I had known
21. Hardly ever _____ get a job these days without a good education.
    A. people can
    B. do people
    C. people might
    D. have people
22. _____ , the young man didn't dare to walk alone at night.
    A. As he was brave
    B. As brave he was
    C. Brave as he was
    D. Brave as was he
23. _____ your arrival, I'd have met you at the airport.
    A. If I knew
    B. If I know
    C. Had I known
    D. Should I know
24. _____ after the heavy rain.
    A. Out did the flowers come
    B. Came out the flowers
    C. Out coming the flowers
    D. Out came the flowers
25. _____ my eyes when I began to imagine the most fantastic shapes.
    A. Not until I closed
    B. No sooner had I closed

C. Hardly did I close   D. Scarcely had I closed

26. As the lion is the king of beasts, _____ is the eagle king of birds.
    A. as   B. so
    C. like   D. and

27. Only _____ solve the problem.
    A. can my father and uncle
    B. my father and uncle can
    C. are my father and uncle able to
    D. is my father and uncle able to

28. He listened so carefully that not a word _____.
    A. did he miss   B. he missed
    C. he never missed   D. did he never miss

29. Never _____ so much protest against the pollution. It won't be long before we have a better environment.
    A. has there been   B. there has been
    C. has it been   D. it has been

30. Unable to win the match _____, the players had done their best.
    A. which they did   B. which did they
    C. as were they   D. as they were

31. No sooner had I started off _____ it began to rain.
    A. then   B. than
    C. that   D. as

32. — The weather forecast says it will clear up in the afternoon.
    — _____. Then we'll play outdoors.
    A. So will it   B. So it will
    C. It will, too   D. Also it will

33. Man can't live without air or water. _____ it is with animals.
    A. Neither   B. Nor
    C. Either   D. So

34. — Isn't his wife at home?
    — _____
    A. I've been so told.   B. I've so been told.

C. So have I been told.   D. So I have been told.

35. — They are tired of the experiment, but they have to work at it.

— _____

A. So are we.   B. So are and nor we.
C. Nor do we.   D. It is the same with us.

36. We didn't have them repaired. _____.
A. Nor do we know who did
B. We do not know who did it, either
C. Nor we know who did it
D. Nor we had idea who did it

37. _____ the plane flies, _____ on the ground.
A. The higher, the less clearly we see things
B. The more highly, the less clearly we see things
C. The more highly, the less we see things clearly
D. The higher, the less we see things clearly

38. Not a single song _____ at yesterday's party.
A. she sang   B. sang she
C. did she sing   D. she did sing

39. Hardly had he finished his speech _____ the audience started cheering.
A. than   B. before
C. when   D. as

40. In recent years travel companies have succeeded in selling us the idea that the further we go, _____.
A. our holiday will be better
B. our holiday will be the better
C. the better our holiday will be
D. the better will our holiday be

41. As far as I am concerned, education is about learning and the more you learn, _____.
A. the more for life are you equipped
B. the more equipped for life you are
C. the more life you are equipped for
D. you are equipped the more for life

42. Only when your identity has been checked, _____.
    A. you are allowed in   B. you will be allowed in
    C. will you show in   D. will you be allowed in
43. _____, you must show your card and walk your bike.
    A. No matter whoever you are
    B. Whomever you are
    C. Whoever you are
    D. No matter whom you are
44. Only by telling him the truth right now _____ to stop him from making such a stupid mistake.
    A. you are able   B. you will be able
    C. can you be able   D. will you be able
45. _____ you do, _____ they will do to you.
    A. The more exercises, the more
    B. The better, the more
    C. The more exercises, the more good
    D. The better, the more good
46. So much _____ about his studies that he couldn't sleep at night.
    A. worrying he was   B. he was worried
    C. did he worry   D. he did worry
47. So difficult _____ it to live in an English-speaking country that I determined to learn English well.
    A. I have felt   B. have I felt
    C. I did feel   D. did I feel
48. — You forgot your purse when you went out.
    — Good heavens, _____.
    A. so did I   B. so I did
    C. I did so   D. I so did
49. On top of the books _____ the photo album you're looking for.
    A. is   B. are
    C. has   D. have
50. After the war we never saw the farmer again, _____ from him.

A. nor did we hear   B. neither we heard
C. not did we hear   D. either didn't hear

51. _____ , he still couldn't afford it.
    A. Cheap although the jacket was
    B. Cheap as the jacket was
    C. As the jacket was cheap
    D. How cheap was the jacket

52. Only after _____ his work _____ to see his grandfather.
    A. finishing, did he go   B. he finishes, did he go
    C. he finished, he went   D. having finished, he went

53. _____ , I have to put it away and focus my attention on study this week.
    A. However the story is amusing
    B. No matter amusing the story is
    C. However amusing the story is
    D. No matter how the story is amusing

54. So often _____ in recent years that it has almost become a rule.
    A. has this happened   B. this has happened
    C. is this happening   D. for this to happen

55. Only in this way _____ to get over so many difficulties.
    A. can we expect   B. we can expect
    C. can we expected   D. we can expected

56. Not until he got off the bus _____ he find that he had had his money stolen.
    A. had   B. did
    C. then   D. has

57. _____ appear, they are really large heavenly bodies.
    A. As the small stars   B. Small as the stars
    C. The stars as small   D. The small stars as

58. Not until _____ from London _____ Britain.
    A. did he come, did I leave   B. he came, I left
    C. he had come, did I leave   D. had he come, I left

59. Only at the party _____ her smile happily.

A. we saw   B. had we been
C. did we see   D. are we seeing
60. He promised to help us with our job if he finished his, and _____.
A. he did either   B. so did he
C. so he did   D. too he did
61. Only at my school _____ such a good goal-keeper.
A. one finds   B. does one find
C. that one finds   D. where one finds
62. _____ he goes to see a doctor, _____ he will get well.
A. Sooner, sooner   B. Earlier, sooner
C. The sooner, the sooner   D. The later, the sooner
63. Warren is fond of working out hard problems. He thinks that
_____ they are, _____ they do to him.
A. the harder, the better
B. the harder, the more good
C. the more hard, the better
D. much hard, more good
64. _____ you get to the top of the mountain, _____ you feel it
to breathe.
A. The closer, the more difficult
B. The more closely, the more difficultly
C. More closer, more difficulty
D. More closely, less difficult
65. _____ treated in such a rude way in this part of the world.
A. We have seldom been   B. Seldom have we been
C. Seldom we have been   D. Have we been seldom
66. The nearer an object is to us, _____.
A. the bigger it looks   B. it will look much bigger
C. the biggest it looks   D. it will look very big
67. Only after a baby seal is pushed into the sea by its mother
_____ to swim.
A. how will it learn   B. will it learn how
C. it will learn how   D. and it will learn how
68. — Will the girls play volleyball after class?

— No, and _____.
    A. neither the boys will   B. the boys won't, too
    C. nor will the boys   D. so won't the boys

69. Jane promised to go shopping with me, and _____.
    A. she did so   B. so she did
    C. so did she   D. she did it

70. — My father doesn't like spicy food.
   — _____.
    A. So does me   B. Neither does me
    C. So does mine   D. Nor does mine

71. Then _____ we had been looking forward to.
    A. came the hour   B. the hour came
    C. comes the hour   D. the hour is coming

72. _____ for your help, we might have got lost in the forest.
    A. Had it not   B. Had it not been
    C. If it were not   D. If we had not been

73. He watched that play on TV last night. And _____.
    A. so did I   B. I did so
    C. so I did   D. so I was

74. _____ the expense, I _____ a round-the-world tour.
    A. Were it not for, would take
    B. If it were not, take
    C. Weren't it for, will take
    D. If it hadn't been, would have taken

75. In the room _____ window is wide open _____.
    A. which, does our teacher live
    B. whose, does our teacher live
    C. whose, lives our teacher
    D. which, live our teacher

76. Not until yesterday _____ the experiment.
    A. he started   B. did he start
    C. would he start   D. had he started

77. _____, Mother will wait for him to have dinner together.
    A. However late is he   B. However he is late

C. However is he late   D. However late he is
78. Much _____ I like the picture, I don't want to buy it.
    A. because   B. though
    C. since   D. as
79. So fast _____ it is difficult for us to imagine its speed.
    A. light travels that   B. does light travel that
    C. travels light that   D. light travels so that
80. It was not until the end of last month _____ the cost of the project.
    A. did I know   B. that I knew
    C. I have known   D. I did know
81. — My teacher is very strict with us students.
    — _____. He never lets off a single mistake of ours.
    A. He is so   B. So is he
    C. So he is   D. So does he
82. Never before _____ in greater need of modern public transport than it is today.
    A. has this city been   B. this city has been
    C. was this city   D. this city was
83. Bob can hardly drive a car, _____.
    A. so can Tom   B. either can Tom
    C. Tom can't too   D. neither can Tom
84. Not until Mr. Smith came to the school _____ what kind of school it was.
    A. he knew   B. that he knew
    C. he didn't know   D. did he know
85. Little _____ about what others think.
    A. he cares   B. is he caring
    C. does he care   D. he has cared
86. No sooner _____ to the company than they began their work.
    A. did they get   B. have they got
    C. would they get   D. had they got
87. _____ a high building with some trees around it.
    A. There are   B. There has

C. There stand   D. There stands

88. _____ received law degrees as today.
    A. Never have so many women
    B. Never have women ever
    C. Never so many women have
    D. Never have there been so many women

89. Only then _____ the importance of mastering a foreign language.
    A. he understood   B. did he realized
    C. did he realize   D. he came to understand

90. _____, he always found time to study.
    A. Busy was he   B. Busy as he was
    C. He was busy   D. Busy as was he

91. — I like to watch football games, but I don't play it.
    — _____.
    A. So do I   B. So it is with me
    C. So I do   D. I do so

92. Never in my life _____ in that manner.
    A. have I been spoken   B. have I been spoken to
    C. I have been spoken   D. I have been spoken to

93. Young _____ he is, he's going very grey.
    A. although   B. even though
    C. though   D. when

94. — What did you think of the film? Did you like it?
    — I'm afraid not. And _____.
    A. my father, either   B. neither was my father
    C. my father didn't too   D. nor did my father

95. — It was careless of you to have left your clothes outside all night.
    — My God! _____.
    A. So did I   B. So I did
    C. So were you   D. So did you

96. Rarely _____ such a silly thing.
    A. have I heard of   B. I have been heard of
    C. have I been heard of   D. I have heard of

97. So badly _____ in the accident that he was kept in hospital for treatment.
    A. did he injure   B. he was injured
    C. was he injured   D. he did injure
98. Here _____ you.
    A. is a ticket of   B. a ticket is for
    C. is a ticket for   D. has a ticket of
99. Now _____ your turn to keep guard.
    A. there is   B. is going
    C. comes   D. has come
100. Spring begins in March. Then _____.
    A. April and May come   B. April is coming
    C. come April and May   D. is April coming

第三讲　十六种时态和它们的时间状语

1. We _____ our new neighbors yet, so we don't know their names.
   - A. don't meet
   - B. won't meet
   - C. haven't met
   - D. hadn't met

2. Send my guards to your lovely wife when you _____ home.
   - A. wrote
   - B. will write
   - C. have written
   - D. write

3. The unemployment rate in this district _____ from 6% to 5% in the past two years.
   - A. has fallen
   - B. had fallen
   - C. is falling
   - D. was falling

4. — Did you tidy your room?
   — No, I was going to tidy my room but I _____ visitors.
   - A. had
   - B. have
   - C. have had
   - D. have

5. Population experts predict that most people _____ in cities in the near future.
   - A. live
   - B. would live
   - C. will live
   - D. have lived

6. Mary went to the box office at lunch time, but all the tickets _____ out.
   - A. would sell
   - B. had been sold
   - C. have sold
   - D. was selling

7. During the period of the recent terrorist activities, people _____ not to touch any unattended bag.
   - A. had always been warned
   - B. were always being warned
   - C. are always warning
   - D. always warned

8. We _____ on our project day and night in the past two weeks.
   A. had worked   B. have worked
   C. will be working   D. had been working
9. Every few years, the coal workers _____ their lungs X-rayed to ensure their health.
   A. are having   B. have
   C. have had   D. had had
10. Did you predict that many students _____ up for the dance competition?
    A. would sign   B. signed
    C. have signed   D. had signed
11. Before I began this job, I _____ a baby-sitter for two years.
    A. have been   B. was
    C. would be   D. had been
12. — I hear that Jason is planning to buy a car.
    — I know. By next month, he _____ enough for a used one.
    A. will have saved   B. will be saving
    C. has saved   D. saves
13. I'm sorry you've been waiting so long, but it'll still be some time _____ Nancy gets back.
    A. before   B. since
    C. till   D. after
14. — How long have you been here?
    — Only about five minutes. Henry and Simon _____ here with me.
    A. have walked   B. were walking
    C. had walked   D. walked
15. — You mean your gas and electricity bill isn't correct. _____ you still _____ it?
    — No.
    A. Are, going to pay   B. Had, paid
    C. Were, paying   D. Would, have paid
16. — You've been telephoning for ages. Aren't you going to finish it?

— I _____ through yet. The line has been busy all morning.

A. haven't got   B. don't get
C. hadn't got   D. didn't get

17. — It'll be the first time I _____ the subject.
— Don't worry. It'll be a bit difficult the first time you _____ it.

A. have taught, teach   B. teach, have taught
C. will teach, will teach   D. have taught, will teach

18. — Is Tim a good manager?
I think he lacks the experience he _____ for such a job.

A. should have   B. should have had
C. need have   D. must have had

19. He gave us warning to stay from the machine while it _____.

A. had worked   B. was working
C. would work   D. would be working

20. I _____ the book on the reading list before I attended the lecture.

A. have read   B. would have read
C. had read   D. read

21. He is ill. He _____ in bed for 3 weeks.

A. is lying   B. has been lying
C. has lain   D. lay

22. My uncle _____ until he was forty-five.

A. married   B. didn't marry
C. was not marrying   D. would marry

23. He will have learned English for eight years by the time he _____ from the university next year.

A. will graduate   B. will have graduated
C. graduates   D. is to graduate

24. — Will you go skiing with me this winter vacation?
— It _____.

A. all depend   B. all depends
C. is all depended   D. is all depending

25. The new suspension bridge _____ by the end of last month.

A. has been designed   B. had been designed
C. was designed   D. would be designed

26. When Jack arrived he learned Mary _____ for almost an hour.
    A. had gone   B. had set off
    C. had left   D. had been away

27. — Do you know our town at all?
    — No, this is the first time I _____ here.
    A. was   B. have been
    C. came   D. am coming

28. — We could have walked to the station; it was so near.
    — Yes. A taxi _____ at all necessary.
    A. wasn't   B. hadn't been
    C. wouldn't be   D. won't be

29. Tom _____ into the house when no one _____.
    A. slipped, was looked   B. had slipped, looked
    C. slipped, had looked   D. was slipping, looked

30. — Oh, it's you! I _____ you.
    — I've just had my hair cut, and I'm wearing new glasses.
    A. didn't recognize   B. hadn't recognized
    C. haven't recognized   D. don't recognized

31. — Can I join your club, Dad?
    — You can when you _____ a bit older.
    A. get   B. will get
    C. are getting   D. will have got

32. She set out soon after dark _____ home an hour later.
    A. arriving   B. to arrive
    C. having arrived   D. and arrived

33. — I'm sorry to keep you waiting.
    — Oh, not at all. I _____ here only a few minutes.
    A. have been   B. had been
    C. was   D. will be

34. I don't really work here; I _____ until the new secretary arrives.
    A. just help out   B. have just helped out

C. am just helping out   D. will just help out

35. If a man _____ succeed, he must work as hard as he can.
    A. will   B. is to
    C. is going to   D. should

36. It is believed that if a book is _____, it will surely _____ the reader.
    A. interested, interest
    B. interesting, be interested
    C. interested, be interesting
    D. interesting, interest

37. You _____ the umbrella. Don't you think it silly to carry an umbrella on such a fine day?
    A. mustn't have brought   B. didn't have to bring
    C. needn't have brought   D. didn't need to bring

38. I'd rather you _____ anything about it for the time being.
    A. do   B. didn't do
    C. don't do   D. not did

39. _____ from school for almost two weeks, so she is working harder to make up for the lost time.
    A. Being absent
    B. Having been absent
    C. Because she has been absent
    D. She has been absent

40. The earlier _____ start work tomorrow, the sooner _____ finish.
    A. we'll, we   B. we, we'll
    C. we'll, we'll   D. we, /

41. In addition to John and Helen, their father _____ visit us tomorrow.
    A. is coming to   B. are coming to
    C. are to   D. is likely

42. — You look happy today, Jane.
    — I like my new dress and Mother _____, too.
    A. likes   B. does

C. do   D. is

43. Because of the shortage of coal in England, attempts _____ to use natural gas as a source of power.
    A. have made   B. having made
    C. are being made   D. will be making

44. He is late again today. I'll _____ that he will not be late tomorrow.
    A. be sure   B. hope for
    C. see to it   D. make it to

45. _____, it went off unexpectedly.
    A. While cleaning the gun
    B. While he was cleaning the gun
    C. To clean his gun
    D. Cleaning his gun

46. "There _____ the bell. Class begins," said the teacher.
    A. will go   B. go
    C. would go   D. goes

47. The happy moment I had looked forward to _____ at last.
    A. came   B. coming
    C. come   D. to come

48. Tom has just arrived, but I didn't know he _____ .until yesterday.
    A. had come   B. was coming
    C. came   D. will come

49. When I _____ across a new word, I look it up in the dictionary.
    A. come   B. will come
    C. have come   D. came

50. The museum he paid a visit _____ at the end of the street.
    A. stand   B. stands
    C. to stand   D. to stands

51. We have to go to the seaside in his car because ours _____ fixed.
    A. wasn't   B. haven't
    C. hasn't been   D. hadn't been

52. He said he felt bad because he _____ late the night before.
   A. sit up   B. was sitting up
   C. has sit up   D. had been sitting up
53. Until he was married, he _____ any new clothes.
   A. has not had   B. doesn't have
   C. has not   D. did not have
54. By the end of the 18th century the city's population _____ about two million.
   A. was   B. were
   C. had been   D. being
55. — Excuse me, where could I find Mr. Cook?
   — He _____ in his office at the moment.
   A. should work   B. should be working
   C. could work   D. must have worked
56. — Did Billy play well in the first half?
   — I'm afraid he _____. I expect he'll do better in the next half.
   A. was disappointing   B. is disappointed
   C. disappointed   D. would disappoint
57. When the film _____, a crowd of people stopped to watch it so that traffic came to a stop.
   A. was being shot   B. was shot
   C. was shooting   D. shot
58. Wang Li, I don't think you _____ Feng Yang, a newcomer to our class.
   A. having met   B. to have met
   C. have met   D. had met
59. — Have you brought my book?
   — Oh no! I _____ again. That was stupid of me.
   A. forgot   B. have forgotten
   C. had forgotten   D. forget
60. The Palmers chose to buy the house as its surroundings _____ clean and quiet.
   A. was   B. being

C. had been   D. were

61. I _____ TV when the light went out.
    A. watched   B. would watch
    C. was watching   D. had watched

62. We _____ the roof of our house last night, and we're going to complete it today.
    A. repaired   B. had repaired
    C. would repair   D. were repairing

63. — Oh, Mary. What shall we do with our son? He _____ things about.
    — It's really annoying.
    A. is always leaving   B. has always left
    C. always leaves   D. always left

64. The flower show, which _____ until 5 p. m. every day, has been a complete success.
    A. opens   B. is open
    C. opening   D. is opened

65. Although he has lived with us for years, he _____ us much impression.
    A. hadn't left   B. didn't leave
    C. doesn't leave   D. hasn't left

66. Roman Empire _____ for centuries.
    A. has existed   B. had existed
    C. existed   D. was existed

67. — What's the trouble?
    — Dr. William, yesterday we were playing basketball when I fell on my knee. It _____ ever since then.
    A. had hurt   B. had been hurt
    C. has hurt   D. has been hurt

68. I was _____ for the beach, forgetting my appointment with the dentist, when my mother reminded me.
    A. to leave   B. to be leaving
    C. about to leave   D. to have left

69. He knew I collected stamps and coins and asked me whether my

28

collection _____.
A. was growing B. was grown
C. grew D. had been grown

70. We hurried to the school gate, amazed to see that our school bus _____ already _____ out in the street.
A. had, waited B. /, waited
C. was, waiting D. /, waiting

71. Doctors, it seems that I _____ my breath. It has been like that for weeks.
A. always catch B. have always caught
C. will always catch D. am always catching

72. In Japan when we spent the night at a small country, we _____ so low on the floor before.
A. haven't ever slept B. wouldn't have slept
C. hadn't ever slept D. couldn't have slept

73. — Mr. Jones, this is Carlo. I _____ because I'm going to the movie after school. So I'll be absent for dinner.
— That's OK.
A. phone B. have phoned
C. am phoning D. was phoning

74. — You see we've been invited to Kathy's party. Don't forget to call for me tonight, and we'll go together.
— Oh, _____. Thank you for reminding me.
A. I'd almost forgotten
B. I've almost forgotten
C. I'd have almost forgotten
D. I almost forgot

75. Sir, I'll have your luggage brought in while you _____ in this form.
A. are filling B. have filled
C. have been filling D. will fill

76. — I'm so sorry. I _____ some coffee on your book.
— That's all right.
A. had spilled B. have spilled

C. having spilled   D. spill

77. After the interview, she realized that she had no useful skill that
_____ her boss.
A. was interesting   B. interested
C. would be interested   D. interested in

78. _____ the people rose up.
A. Long before   B. It was before long
C. It was not long before   D. It was not before long

79. Now _____ your turn to be on duty.
A. come   B. comes
C. there is   D. is coming

80. I _____ for Beijing tomorrow.
A. am leaving   B. leaves
C. will have been leaving   D. left

81. We have _____ the city for a week. Now it's time for us
_____.
A. been in, to leave   B. been in, leaving
C. come to, to leave   D. come to, leaving

82. All of us have come to understand that knowledge _____ only
from practice.
A. has come   B. came
C. comes   D. is coming

83. It _____ them only two years to build such a great bridge.
A. took   B. cost
C. spent   D. paid

84. I wonder if he _____. If he _____, please let me know as
soon as possible.
A. will come, arrives   B. comes, arrives
C. comes, will arrive   D. will come, will arrive

85. — Your father has come to school.
— I _____ he _____.
A. don't think, is coming   B. didn't think, will come
C. don't think, will come   D. didn't think, was coming

86. I really didn't know whether he _____ anything about it.

A. had told   B. has spoken
C. had said   D. has talked
87. Everything _____ by the time you get there.
    A. will have been ready   B. was ready
    C. had been ready   D. has been ready
88. There _____ the bell.
    A. goes   B. is going
    C. to go   D. has gone
89. How many people does the doctor know _____ of the disease?
    A. are dying   B. dying
    C. has died   D. dies
90. I _____ a novel _____ by O. Henry at seven yesterday evening.
    A. read, written   B. would read, to write
    C. was reading, written   D. was to read, writing
91. It is the second time that I _____ here.
    A. had been   B. am
    C. have been   D. will be
92. The police _____ the thief three days before yesterday.
    A. have arrested   B. has arrested
    C. arrested   D. had arrested
93. He said he _____ all day last Saturday.
    A. worked   B. would work
    C. was working   D. had worked
94. I _____ hardly _____ when the quarrel started.
    A. have, left   B. had, left
    C. would, leave   D. did, leave
95. I waited until he _____ speaking before I made the suggestion.
    A. has finished   B. would finish
    C. had finished   D. would have finished
96. I assure you that next time I come here I'll make sure my watch _____ well.
    A. will work   B. will be working
    C. works   D. has worked

97. The boy _____ non-stop for the past hour seems to be _____.
   A. cried, ill seriously
   B. who has been crying, seriously ill
   C. crying, seriously ill
   D. having been crying, ill seriously

98. It _____ a long time before I see you again.
   A. will be   B. is being
   C. has been   D. is

99. Mary _____ to wait in the room from ten o'clock, but nobody came.
   A. began   B. has begun
   C. had begun   D. was beginning

100. I _____ the classroom as soon as I _____ what I _____.
   A. was leaving, finished, did
   B. left, finished, had to do
   C. left, had finished, did
   D. had left, finished, had done

101. How nice to see you here again! I _____ you _____ still sick in bed.
   A. think, are   B. thought, were
   C. think, have been   D. thought, would be

102. Can you help me? I _____ this TV set last Sunday, and now it _____.
   A. have bought, hasn't worked
   B. bought, won't work
   C. had bought, didn't work
   D. bought, doesn't work

103. As Tom _____ with his toys, his baby-sitter _____ asleep.
   A. played, was falling
   B. was playing, fell
   C. was playing, was falling
   D. had played, fell

104. — Would you please repeat it?
    — Sorry that I _____ quite catch it.
    A. didn't   B. don't
    C. wouldn't   D. can't
105. Is this the first time that you _____ to this part of the country?
    A. come   B. will come
    C. have come   D. came
106. When Jack arrived, he was told Jane _____ for almost an hour.
    A. had gone   B. had set off
    C. had left   D. had been away
107. Call me for help when you _____ in trouble, and I _____ to you at once.
    A. will be, will come   B. are, come
    C. shall be, shall come   D. are, will come
108. Dick _____ that he _____ in two weeks, and I'm sure he will.
    A. said, will return   B. will say, returns
    C. has said, will return   D. said, returns
109. Please go back and make sure that all the lights _____ off.
    A. will be   B. are
    C. had been   D. would be
110. Don't you remember that we _____ to the theatre tonight?
    A. would go   B. are going
    C. go   D. will be gone
111. London _____ on the River Thames.
    A. is standing   B. stood
    C. stands   D. has stood
112. Could you tell me something about the accident _____ this morning?
    A. that happened   B. which was happened
    C. that was happened   D. which had happened
113. Dick _____ to be quite honest and hard-working.

A. says   B. said
C. has said   D. is said

114. I believe I _____ a letter from her soon.
    A. receive   B. will receive
    C. have received   D. had received

115. The year 2002 _____ remarkable changes in Shanghai's landscape.
    A. sees   B. has seen
    C. saw   D. had seen

116. It _____ every day so far this week.
    A. rains   B. will rain
    C. rained   D. has been raining

117. What _____ you _____ when the fire broke out?
    A. have, done   B. were, doing
    C. are, doing   D. did, do

118. Your mother _____ when you finish the work here.
    A. has arrived   B. arrived
    C. will have arrived   D. had arrived

119. She said she would send me a present, but she _____.
    A. didn't send   B. never sent
    C. never did   D. did

120. While I _____ near the lake, I saw children swimming there.
    A. walked   B. took a walk
    C. was walking   D. had walked

121. She thought she _____ the film, so she gave the ticket to Mary.
    A. would see   B. had not seen
    C. was seeing   D. had seen

122. Let's go to the cinema as soon as school _____.
    A. will be over   B. be over
    C. was over   D. is over

123. Because she _____ in the sun, she got a bad sunburn.
    A. had lain   B. had laid
    C. has lain   D. had lay

124. — What _____ the farming population of China?

34

— Oh, I am not quite sure. Maybe China _____ a farming population of 800,000,000.

A. is, is B. are, are

C. are, has D. is, has

125. He _____ all his money to the poor people, and from that time he _____ a happy life.

A. will give, has led B. has given, has led

C. gave, led D. gives, has been leading

126. Mr. Smith _____ to have got a reward _____ the police _____ the robbers.

A. said, to help, to find B. is said, for helping, find

C. said, and helped, find D. was said, helping, to find

127. Sugar _____ of carbon, hydrogen and oxygen.

A. consist B. consists

C. consisted D. is consisted

128. The old man _____ out his key and _____ the door.

A. had taken, opened B. took, opened

C. would take, opened D. took, had opened

129. When Tom _____ into the room, I _____ a telephone call.

A. came, was making B. would come, made

C. had come, was making D. came, would make

130. By the time he _____ from Australia, his daughter _____ school.

A. had returned, finished B. returned, had finished

C. returned, finished D. would return, finished

131. "I _____ your plan," _____ the businessman.

A. am understanding, said B. understand, says

C. understood, says D. understand, said

132. The first use of atomic weapons was in 1945, and their power _____ increased enormously ever since.

A. is B. was

C. has been D. had been

133. You won't know if the dress _____ you until you _____ it on.

A. fits, will try   B. will fit, will try
C. fits, have tried   D. will fit, will have tried

134. The old woman _____ three weeks after she _____ to the hospital.
    A. dies, is sent   B. died, had been sent
    C. died, would be sent   D. had died, was sent

135. From then on they _____ along very well with each other.
    A. got   B. have got
    C. had got   D. were getting

136. If the sportsman _____ next week, he _____ eight races since three years ago.
    A. wins, will win   B. wins, will have won
    C. will win, will win   D. will win, has won

137. Why _____ the change of the plan?
    A. wasn't I informed of   B. didn't I inform of
    C. I wasn't informed   D. no one informed me

138. Don't use the telephone unless it _____ necessary.
    A. /   B. is
    C. will be   D. was

139. I _____ the report since early morning, but I haven't finished it yet.
    A. have written   B. have been written
    C. write   D. have been writing

140. Tim _____ of paying them a visit, but he was too busy then.
    A. had thought   B. thought
    C. thinks   D. have thought

141. My birthday _____ in two weeks' time.
    A. would be   B. was
    C. is   D. will have been

142. We _____ for you there at 8 tomorrow morning.
    A. will write   B. will be writing
    C. will have written   D. write

143. They _____ their task so far.
    A. will finish   B. have finished

C. finished   D. had finished

144. The teacher told us last week that the moon _____ around the earth.
    A. moves   B. move
    C. moved   D. will move

145. I think he _____ the novel at the age of 52.
    A. wrote   B. had wrote
    C. was writing   D. has written

146. At present many scientists _____ living things in the sea.
    A. study   B. will study
    C. studied   D. are studying

147. By next year, he _____ twenty years old.
    A. will have been   B. will be
    C. had been   D. is to be

148. We were late. When we got to the playground, the football match _____.
    A. had started   B. was starting
    C. started   D. would start

149. Today is Monday and tomorrow _____ Tuesday.
    A. will   B. shall be
    C. is   D. are

150. We _____ at the school by and by.
    A. will gather   B. gathered
    C. is gathering   D. have gathered

第四讲 虚拟语气

1. — Guess what! I have got A for my term paper.
   — Great! You _____ read widely and put a lot of work into it.
   A. must   B. should
   C. must have   D. should have

2. — Sorry, Professor Smith. I didn't finish the assignment yesterday.
   — Oh, you _____ have done it as yesterday was the deadline.
   A. must   B. mustn't
   C. should   D. shouldn't

3. Oh, my goodness! You are still working on the assignment. It _____ two days ago.
   A. must have been handed in
   B. can't have been handed in
   C. should have been handed in
   D. shouldn't be handed in

4. — Linda hasn't come yet. I wonder whether she has received our invitation.
   — She _____ it because I didn't write her address clearly enough.
   A. couldn't receive   B. may not have received
   C. can't have received   D. mustn't have received

5. Once again Dick failed in the exam. He _____ since he was quite a good student.
   A. should not fail   B. should not have failed
   C. needn't fail   D. needn't have failed

6. Had you attended the meeting, you _____ surprised how much time they had wasted in the useless discussion.
   A. would have   B. would have been
   C. must have   D. will have been

7. — Here is your key, sir. Your room number is 311. By the way, _____ keep anything valuable in your room.

— Thank you.

    A. you'd better not   B. you'd not better

    C. you'd rather not   D. you'd not rather

8. The law requires that anyone working in restaurants _____ a medical check-up twice a year.

    A. has   B. must have

    C. have   D. shall have

9. — I hear the maths teacher failed you in the test.

    — Yes. When I got the paper, I _____.

    A. was able to cry   B. could cry

    C. could have cried   D. may have cried

10. — I don't understand why Jim is always late for class.

    — He _____ if he got up earlier.

    A. wasn't   B. wouldn't

    C. won't   D. weren't

11. If the letter had been sent to the wrong address, it _____ returned to the post office.

    A. would have been   B. will have been

    C. must have been   D. must be

12. If it wasn't an accident, he _____ it on purpose.

    A. must do   B. must have done

    C. had meant to do   D. should have done

13. Our boss ordered a survey to learn how many people _____ the local newspaper.

    A. would read   B. could read

    C. must read   D. read

14. I _____ be very grateful if you _____ mail this parcel for me.

    A. should, should   B. might, could

    C. ought to, might   D. would, could

15. Had he passed the entrance examinations, he _____ in the university now.

    A. would have been   B. would be

    C. will have been   D. must have been

16. _____ it not for the fact that you _____ ill, I would ask you to do the work again right now.
    A. Was, were   B. Were, are
    C. Is, are   D. Were, were

17. — Did you go to Spain on holiday?
    — I _____ to go, but I got sick at the last minute.
    A. wish   B. had planned
    C. would like   D. was planning

18. If only I _____ busy then, I _____ you with the problem.
    A. hadn't been, would have helped
    B. weren't was able to help
    C. wasn't, could help
    D. hadn't been, would be able to help

19. _____ for his great care and love, she might never have recovered from her illness.
    A. If it were not   B. Not having it been
    C. If it had been   D. Had it not been

20. There was a lot of fun at yesterday's party. You _____ come, but why didn't you?
    A. must have   B. should
    C. need have   D. ought to have

21. I wish I _____ to the cinema with them last night.
    A. had gone   B. went
    C. would go   D. should

22. They suggested that he _____ a taxi.
    A. calls for   B. calls up
    C. call for   D. must call for

23. I still haven't got the letter Maggie sent me a week ago. I wonder if the letter _____ wrongly delivered.
    A. might be   B. might have been
    C. should be   D. should have been

24. If only I _____ the book on the reading list before I attended the lecture!
    A. have read   B. had read

C. would read   D. read

25. Jack _____ yet, otherwise he would have telephoned me.
    A. mustn't have arrived   B. shouldn't have arrived
    C. can't have arrived   D. need not have arrived

26. My sister met him at the Grand Theatre yesterday afternoon, so he _____ your lecture.
    A. couldn't have attended   B. needn't have attended
    C. mustn't have attended   D. shouldn't have attended

27. If only he _____ quietly as the doctor instructed, he would not suffer so much now.
    A. lies   B. lay
    C. had lain   D. should lie

28. What would have happened _____, as far as the river bank?
    A. Bob had walked farther   B. if Bob should walk farther
    C. had Bob walked farther   D. if Bob walked farther

29. It is hard for me to imagine what I would be doing today if I _____ in love, at the age of seven, with the Melinda Cox Library in my hometown.
    A. wouldn't have fallen   B. had not fallen
    C. should fall   D. were to fall

30. He hesitated for a moment before kicking the ball, otherwise he _____ a goal.
    A. had scored   B. scored
    C. would score   D. would have scored

31. — Shall we go skating or stay at home?
    — Which _____ do yourself?
    A. do you rather   B. would you rather
    C. will you rather   D. should you rather

32. Yesterday, Jane walked away from the discussion. Otherwise, she _____ something she would regret later.
    A. had said   B. said
    C. might say   D. might have said

33. Tom ought not to _____ me your secret, but he meant no harm.

A. have told   B. tell
C. be telling   D. having told
34. — If he _____, he _____ that food.
   — Luckily he was sent to the hospital immediately.
   A. was warned, would not take
   B. had been warned, would not have taken
   C. would be warned, had not taken
   D. would have been warned, had not taken
35. The pen I _____ I _____ is on my desk, right under my nose.
   A. think, lost   B. thought, had lost
   C. think, had lost   D. thought, have lost
36. I told Sally how to get here, but perhaps I _____ for her.
   A. had to write it out
   B. must have written it out
   C. should have written it out
   D. ought to write it out
37. I didn't see your sister at the meeting. If she _____, she would have met my brother.
   A. has come   B. did come
   C. came   D. had come
38. _____ for the free tickets, I would not have gone to the films so often.
   A. If it is not   B. Were it not
   C. Had it not been   D. If they were not
39. I would have come to your party had it been possible, but I _____ so busy.
   A. had been   B. were
   C. was   D. would be
40. My suggestion is that he _____ at the meeting this afternoon.
   A. attends   B. should attend
   C. be present   D. will be present
41. From what I hear about their hotel and the weather, they _____ their holiday very much.

A. would have enjoyed   B. should have enjoyed
C. needn't have enjoyed   D. can't have enjoyed

42. — I don't see Tom. I wonder why he's late.
— Well, he _____ his train, or maybe he overslept.
A. might have missed   B. might miss
C. should have missed   D. should miss

43. _____ now if you had lost your watch?
A. Hadn't you been upset   B. Wouldn't you be upset
C. Weren't you upset   D. Wouldn't you have upset

44. I was writing my report last Sunday, otherwise I _____ you to the zoo.
A. would take   B. took
C. should take   D. could have taken

45. Susan might have come to school in time for Professor Browning's lecture, _____.
A. but he got up rather late   B. but he had got up so late
C. if he got up earlier   D. unless he had got up earlier

46. If we hadn't been caught in a traffic jam, we _____ ahead of you.
A. would have got there   B. would be there
C. would arrive   D. would be reached

47. What he had said suggested that he _____ against the idea.
A. was   B. were
C. should fight   D. be fighting

48. He insisted that he _____ in good health and _____ to work there.
A. was, be sent   B. was, was sent
C. be, be sent   D. be, must be sent

49. I _____ talk about this problem any more.
A. should like to   B. would like to
C. would rather not   D. would rather not to

50. Your suggestion that he _____ till next week is reasonable.
A. will wait   B. waits
C. wait   D. waited

51. The Chinese government has found it necessary that consumption _____ so as to speed up production.
    A. is encouraged   B. be encouraged
    C. must be encouraged   D. should be discouraged
52. If you didn't nap after dinner you _____ to take a sleeping pill.
    A. shouldn't feel the need   B. shouldn't feel a need
    C. wouldn't feel the need   D. wouldn't feel need
53. My friend said to me on the bus, "It's quite warm here, so you _____ so many clothes."
    A. shouldn't take   B. needn't take
    C. shouldn't have taken   D. needn't have taken
54. Tom is a polite boy. He _____ so rudely.
    A. couldn't act   B. can't have acted
    C. mustn't have acted   D. ought not have acted
55. Why didn't you let me know your trouble? You _____ that, you know.
    A. can do   B. must have done
    C. should have done   D. would do
56. It is strange that the car _____ down at exactly the same place where it broke down yesterday.
    A. break   B. broke
    C. had broken   D. would break
57. It is about time that you _____ the medicine.
    A. took   B. taking
    C. will take   D. can take
58. Sue would rather leave for San Francisco _____ in Los Angeles.
    A. to stay   B. than stay
    C. staying   D. than staying
59. Mr. Carl, who I _____ to _____ south of England, is still living in America.
    A. thought, had moved   B. think, has moved
    C. thought, have moved   D. think, has moved the

60. — It is better _____ him the bad news.
    — Yes, better _____ it as a secret.
    A. not to tell, to keep   B. not to tell, keep
    C. not tell, keep   D. not tell, to keep
61. Whom would you rather _____ the trousers?
    A. have ment   B. have mended
    C. have mend   D. had mended
62. She _____ here now if she hadn't done so well in her interview.
    A. wouldn't work   B. wouldn't have worked
    C. wouldn't be working   D. doesn't work
63. Since the ground is covered with thick snow, it _____ heavily last night.
    A. must be snowing   B. must have snowed
    C. had snowed   D. must have been snowed
64. The flower is dead. I _____ it more water.
    A. would have given   B. must give
    C. could have given   D. should have given
65. It is desired that he _____ his plan right away.
    A. carried out   B. had carried out
    C. would carry out   D. carry out
66. I would have come earlier, but I _____ that you were waiting.
    A. wouldn't know   B. hadn't known
    C. didn't know   D. haven't known
67. — He _____ here for two weeks.
    — Really, then he _____ have known the town quite well.
    A. stayed, should   B. has been, must
    C. got, can   D. had come, may
68. I helped him out, but I'd rather _____ it.
    A. not do   B. not to do
    C. haven't done   D. not have done
69. I was assured by the doctor that my daughter only had a bad cold. I _____ about it.
    A. didn't need worry   B. needn't have worried
    C. don't have to worry   D. needed not to worry

70. The careless man received a ticket for speeding. He _____ have driven so fast.
    A. can't   B. wouldn't
    C. mustn't   D. shouldn't
71. Mary _____ my letter, otherwise she would have replied earlier.
    A. has received   B. ought to have received
    C. can't have received   D. shouldn't have received
72. I would rather _____ tell you. You'd better _____ ask me any longer.
    A. not, to   B. not, not to
    C. not to, not to   D. not, not
73. Bob's doctor suggests _____ for a few days.
    A. that he is resting   B. he resting
    C. him to rest   D. that he rest
74. Mary got up early, but she _____ so, because she had no work to do that morning.
    A. can not have done   B. must not have done
    C. shouldn't have done   D. needn't have done
75. It is essential that human _____ ways and means to protect the environment.
    A. adopt   B. have adopted
    C. will adopt   D. will have adopt
76. — What did you think of the food?
    — Well, it _____ worse.
    A. couldn't have been   B. couldn't be
    C. might not have been   D. might not be
77. Since you didn't use a postcode, it's no good complaining your letter _____ sooner.
    A. should arrive   B. should have arrived
    C. must arrive   D. must have arrived
78. You went to the wrong store. You _____ to the store next to the restaurant, but you went to the store by the bank.
    A. might go   B. will have gone

C. ought to go   D. ought to have gone

79. I still haven't received the Christmas card he sent me a week ago. It _____ sent to the wrong address.
    A. could have been   B. should have been
    C. could be   D. might be

80. _____ a hole in one of the walls. Otherwise, we couldn't have seen what was going on inside the room.
    A. There happened to be   B. It happened to be
    C. There happened to have   D. It happened to have

81. I _____ there since I wasn't asked to, but I did.
    A. needn't have gone   B. didn't need to go
    C. couldn't have gone   D. couldn't go

82. I didn't go to the concert yesterday, but I do wish I _____ there.
    A. went   B. have been
    C. go   D. had been

83. The boy was at a loss what to say. He _____ my question.
    A. might not understand
    B. wouldn't understand
    C. might not have understood
    D. wouldn't have understood

84. — Billy, you didn't hand in your assignment again. You _____ to me while I was assigning homework.
    — I'm terribly sorry, Mrs. Smith.
    A. must be listening   B. might be listening
    C. might have listened   D. would have listened

85. I _____ many mistakes in the test. I'm sure I was careful enough.
    A. couldn't make   B. shouldn't
    C. couldn't have got   D. mustn't have made

86. The two climbers _____ down the mountain if they _____ by a big rock.
    A. would have fallen, had not been blocked
    B. would fall, had not been blocked

47

C. would have fallen, were not blocked

D. will fall, aren't blocked

87. We suggested that our class meeting _____ the next week.

A. was held   B. would be held

C. be held   D. must hold

88. If it _____ so late we could have a cup of coffee.

A. isn't   B. weren't

C. not be   D. wasn't

89. — The meeting begins at 3 p. m. It's still too early.

— You _____ here so early.

A. needn't have come   B. needn't come

C. didn't have to come   D. shouldn't have come

90. Surely I would never have believed, _____ it with my own eyes.

A. if I didn't see   B. if I had not seen

C. if I don't see   D. if I haven't seen

91. I would rather _____ at home than _____ today.

A. to stay, to go to the movies

B. stay, go to the movies

C. stayed, go to the movies

D. staying, going to the movies

92. He _____ healthy, but he takes little exercise.

A. will be   B. should be

C. would be   D. must be

93. _____ tomorrow, he would help us with our work.

A. He would come   B. If he will

C. If he should come   D. Will he come

94. Would you give Corky the picture if you _____ to meet him this week?

A. will happen   B. happen

C. would happen   D. happened

95. I would go with you _____ not so busy.

A. will I be   B. if I am

C. if I were   D. would I be

48

96. I thanked him for what he _____.
    A. did   B. had done
    C. has done   D. was doing
97. Oh, I'm sorry. Juliet went out a minute ago. You ____ five
    minutes earlier.
    A. should have come   B. should come
    C. would have come   D. would come
98. My teacher treats me dearly as if I _____ his own child.
    A. am   B. were
    C. will be   D. have been
99. I wish I _____ your telephone number. Otherwise I _____
    you.
    A. knew, would phone
    B. had known, would have phoned
    C. knew, would have phoned
    D. know, will phone
100. It is high time we _____ effective action to stop it.
    A. are taking   B. take
    C. will take   D. took

第五讲 被动语态

1. When he turned professional at the age of 11, Mike _____ to become a world champion by his coach and parents.
   A. expected
   B. was expecting
   C. was expected
   D. would be expected

2. John had to have his car repaired in a garage because it _____ seriously.
   A. damaged
   B. was being damaged
   C. had damaged
   D. had been damaged

3. With the help of high technology, more and more new substances _____ in the past years.
   A. discovered
   B. have discovered
   C. had been discovered
   D. have been discovered

4. Officials say that few parents _____ with the virus owing to the effective prevention.
   A. infected
   B. are infected
   C. have infected
   D. be infected

5. In recent years many football clubs _____ as business to make a profit.
   A. have run
   B. have been run
   C. had been run
   D. will run

6. The employees _____ that they should renew their contracts within a week.
   A. advise
   B. have advised
   C. are advised
   D. had been advised

7. The church tower which _____ will be open to tourists soon. The work is almost finished.
   A. has restored
   B. has been restored
   C. is restoring
   D. is being restored

8. After getting lost in a storm, a member of the navy team _____

for days later.
A. rescued   B. was rescued
C. has rescued   D. had been rescued

9. The diamond mine _____ accidentally by a little boy when he was playing hide-and-seek.
A. discovered   B. was discovered
C. has been discovered   D. would discover

10. Is honesty the best policy? We _____ that it is when we are little.
A. will teach   B. teach
C. are taught   D. will be taught

11. You can lead a horse to water, but you can't make it _____.
A. drinking   B. to drink
C. drink   D. drunk

12. A lot of people _____ in yesterday's car crash.
A. badly hurted   B. were badly hurted
C. were badly hurting   D. were badly hurt

13. He was _____ clever but dishonest.
A. thought as   B. thought of to be
C. thought of as   D. thought of

14. We bought a box of apples last week, but half of them in the box _____ eaten since then.
A. were   B. have been
C. was   D. has been

15. _____ silk feels soft _____.
A. That, has been proved   B. That, has proved
C. If, has been proved   D. Whether, has proved

16. He used to _____ his teaching when he was young.
A. devote to   B. be devoted to
C. devoting to   D. being devoted to

17. Why haven't you finished your homework yet? You _____ to have finished it by last Sunday!
A. are supposed   B. were supposed
C. are supposing   D. were supposing

18. This is the first time that he _____ the first prize in the maths contest.
   A. will award   B. is awarded
   C. has awarded   D. has been awarded
19. Cleaning women in big cities usually get _____ by the hour.
   A. pay   B. paying
   C. paid   D. to pay
20. Paper _____ by the Chinese long before its use _____ in Europe.
   A. invented, known   B. invented, was known
   C. was invented, known D. was invented, was known
21. The thief got _____ as he was caught picking a lady's pocket in the bus.
   A. beat   B. being beaten
   C. beaten   D. beating
22. The computer will tell what the result will be when information _____ into it.
   A. feeds   B. is fed
   C. is feeding   D. is being fed
23. As soon as everyone _____ the examination _____, the test papers were given out.
   A. taking, was seated B. took, seated
   C. taking, seated   D. taken, was seated
24. Secondary and higher education _____ available to all high school graduates in this country so far.
   A. have made   B. have been made
   C. have made themselves D. have made it
25. Worries _____ all kinds of illness, from high blood pressure to stomachache.
   A. believe to have caused B. are believed to be causing
   C. are believed to cause   D. believe to cause
26. In western countries, teenagers _____ to more drug education, but drug use is still on the rise.
   A. are exposed   B. expose

C. are exposing   D. have exposed

27. Jia Ming feels heavy pressure as he _____ by his parents to work harder so that he can have a wonderful life.
    A. is always being told   B. had always been told
    C. was always being told   D. having always been told

28. There appear new words and expressions in our life, and many of them _____ by the public.
    A. have been accepted   B. are accepted
    C. having been accepted   D. to have been accepted

29. The pilot asked all the passengers on board to remain _____ as the plane was making a landing.
    A. seat   B. seating
    C. seated   D. to be seating

30. Experiments proved that sea water _____ at a lower temperature than fresh water.
    A. is freezing   B. was frozen
    C. froze   D. freezes

31. The cruel boss wouldn't _____ his employees rest for a while during the business hours.
    A. promise   B. allow
    C. let   D. permit

32. This pair of shoes _____.
    A. has sold   B. have sold
    C. has been sold   D. have been sold

33. Much attention has to _____ the work.
    A. be paid to do   B. pay to doing
    C. be paid to doing   D. pay to do

34. More than a dozen students in that school _____ abroad to study medicine last year.
    A. sent   B. were sent
    C. had sent   D. had been sent

35. The football team _____ eleven members.
    A. consists of   B. is consisted of
    C. makes up of   D. is made up

36. Plastic parts can _____ metals in a lot of machines, but they don't last long.

    A. be substituted for   B. substitute to

    C. substitute with   D. be substituted by

37. According to the Chinese Herbal Medicine a lot of plants _____ different diseases.

    A. can be used to treating   B. can be used to treat

    C. are used treating   D. used to treat

38. An iron and steel works, with some satellite factories, _____ here.

    A. are to build   B. is to build

    C. is to be built   D. are to be built

39. The British _____ not to be very good at cooking.

    A. says   B. say

    C. is said   D. are said

40. Vehicles _____ through that area on Saturday night.

    A. are let not pass   B. are not let to pass

    C. don't let pass   D. don't let to pass

41. Every possible use has been _____ his spare time.

    A. made for   B. done for

    C. made of   D. done of

42. To his surprise, he found the office _____ the night before.

    A. was broken into   B. had broken into

    C. was being broken into   D. had been broken into

43. The food _____ in that shop _____ very well as it _____ good.

    A. made, sells, tastes   B. makes, is sold, tastes

    C. made, is sold, tastes   D. made, sells, is tasted

44. The number of deaths from heart disease will be reduced greatly if people _____ to eat more fruit and vegetables.

    A. persuade   B. will persuade

    C. be persuaded   D. are persuaded

45. The old mother _____ that her grandson _____ in the school.

A. told, was taken good care
B. was told, had taken good care of
C. has told, is taken good care of
D. was told, was taken good care of

46. This dictionary _____ to you; yours _____ by someone else.
    A. is not belonged, has been taken
    B. doesn't belong, has taken
    C. doesn't belong, has been taken
    D. doesn't belong, will have been taken

47. Margaret proudly showed her mother the toy cat she had _____ in the competition.
    A. gained   B. won
    C. caught   D. rewarded

48. The money the lady spent on clothes last year _____ more than 10,000 *yuan*.
    A. added to   B. added up to
    C. added up   D. was added to

49. The planes _____ nearly a month to plant the seeds.
    A. did   B. made
    C. took   D. was taken

50. Although Mr. Smith is _____ a famous writer, he still talks very little about himself.
    A. known of   B. known as
    C. knowing as   D. known to

51. His debts ____ six thousand *yuan* and took him two years to pay off.
    A. add   B. add to
    C. add up to   D. add up

52. Once the plan gets _____, a student may get as much as US$ 50,000 as an education abroad loan.
    A. approving   B. to approve
    C. to be approved   D. approved

53. News about the World Cup, which is _____, _____ all

over the world.

A. in the progress, spreads   B. in progress, is spreaded

C. in progress, is spreading   D. in the progress, spreads

54. The Olympic Games of 2008 _____ in Beijing.

A. held   B. were taken place

C. took place   D. took the place

55. Is it announced that he _____ the first prize in the maths competition?

A. was warded   B. has been rewarded

C. was won   D. has been awarded

56. The parents' absence _____, so the kids invited their friends home to have a party.

A. take advantage of   B. take the advantage of

C. was taken advantage of   D. were taken advantage of

57. The lights in the kitchen _____ all night.

A. has left on   B. had left on

C. have been left on   D. left on

58. It _____ that suspension bridges _____ from steel cables.

A. is said, are hanged   B. is said, is hung

C. says, hung   D. is said, hang

59. No harm _____ your health if you dream a little when you are sleeping.

A. does to   B. does for

C. is done to   D. is done for

60. It _____ me that he didn't like the food like this.

A. occurred   B. was occurred

C. occurred to   D. was occurred to

第六讲 主谓语一致的规则

1. Attending concerts on the campus _____ part of the pleasure of college life.
   A. are   B. is
   C. it is   D. being

2. E-mail, as well as telephones, _____ an important part in daily communication.
   A. is playing   B. have playing
   C. are playing   D. play

3. Books of this kind _____ well.
   A. sell   B. sells
   C. are sold   D. is sold

4. — Each of the students, working hard at his or her lessons, _____ to go to university.
   — So do I.
   A. hope   B. hopes
   C. hoping   D. hoped

5. _____ of the land in that district _____ covered with trees and grass.
   A. Two fifth, is   B. Two fifth, are
   C. Two fifths, is   D. Two fifths, are

6. As a result of destroying the forests, a large _____ of desert _____ covered the land.
   A. number, has   B. quantity, has
   C. number, have   D. quantity, have

7. Xiao Lin, just like me, _____ fond of folk songs.
   A. is   B. are
   C. am   D. were

8. The computers on the table _____ Professor Smith.
   A. belongs   B. are belonged to

C. belongs to   D. belong to

9. One of the new books _____ several pages _____.
    A. has, missed   B. have, missing
    C. has, missing   D. have, missed

10. Lots of advice _____ to them on how to fight against sandstorms.
    A. has given   B. are given
    C. was given   D. already gave

11. Writing stories and articles _____ what I enjoy most.
    A. is   B. have been
    C. was   D. are

12. I can't help you. _____ of my hands are full of mud.
    A. Both   B. Each
    C. All   D. Every

13. Every year around the end of October, this kind of _____ because they will get rotten quickly.
    A. orange is on sale   B. oranges are for sale
    C. the oranges are on sale   D. oranges sells well

14. The visiting team _____.
    A. are having a wonderful dinner
    B. is having a wonderful dinner
    C. is having wonderful dinner
    D. are having wonderful dinner

15. Every boy and every girl _____ Mr. Wang as he devoted himself _____.
    A. likes, to teaching   B. liked, to teach
    C. like, to teaching   D. like, to teach

16. Lots of rubbish _____ every day.
    A. is thrown   B. are thrown away
    C. has thrown away   D. throws

17. I've told you that the third and last part of the story _____ most interesting.
    A. is   B. are
    C. was   D. were

18. All but one _____ to see him off at the airport.

58

A. have been   B. has been
C. have gone   D. go

19. The _____ are collecting money, food, clothing and medicines for the flooding areas.

  A. official   B. public
  C. Red Cross   D. organization

20. The police _____ every reason to arrest him.

  A. has   B. needs
  C. have   D. believe

21. _____ have a racing car.

  A. Each   B. Each of them
  C. Every of them   D. They each

22. The police _____ on the scene a few minutes after the murder occurred.

  A. had been   B. were
  C. having been   D. being

23. The trousers _____ the boy sitting over there.

  A. belongs to   B. belong to
  C. is belong to   D. are belong to

24. One million pounds _____ a large sum of money.

  A. are   B. is
  C. have been   D. has been

25. Mr. Iglesias, the famous Spanish singer, together with his girl friend and his father, _____ visiting Shanghai now.

  A. is going to   B. are
  C. are to   D. is

26. His *Selected Poems* _____ in 1990.

  A. was first published   B. has been first published
  C. were first published   D. have been first published

27. _____ students have visited the exhibition.

  A. A great many   B. A great many of
  C. A good many of   D. The great number of

28. Every boy and every girl in the club _____ invited to attend the evening party.

A. have been   B. has been
C. are   D. have not

29. John as well as I _____ your plan.
A. agree to   B. agrees to
C. agree with   D. agrees with

30. I want two of you to clean the window. The rest _____ sweep the floor.
A. is to   B. will be to
C. are to   D. is going to

31. Mrs. Jackson, together with her husband and daughter _____ the palace ball.
A. has gone to   B. have gone to
C. are going to   D. have been to

32. Professor Smith along with his assistants _____ on the project day and night to meet the deadline.
A. work   B. working
C. is working   D. are working

33. Zhang's family _____ rather big, with twelve people in all.
A. is   B. are
C. being   D. was

34. "Every magazine except these two _____," said the librarian.
A. has been borrowed   B. has been lent
C. have been borrowed   D. have been lent

35. Mary as well as two of her friends _____ during the concert the day before yesterday.
A. invited   B. was invited
C. were invited   D. had been invited

36. I have three brothers. One is in Beijing, _____ together with my parents, _____ in Nanjing.
A. the others, are   B. the other, is
C. other, are   D. other, is

37. _____ object to the plan.
A. The teacher rather than the students
B. Not only the teacher but also the students

C. Not only the students but also the teacher

D. The teacher in addition to the students

38. _____ the students _____ the teacher _____ to see the film again.

Λ. Not only, but also, want

B. Either, or, want

C. Both, and, wants

D. Not, but, wants

39. The police _____ every reason to arrest Tim.

A. has   B. needs

C. have   D. believes

40. Bread and butter, which most westerners usually eat, _____ not greatly accepted by us Chinese.

A. is   B. are

C. has   D. have

41. When he pushed his way off the crowded bus, he found about half of his eggs _____ broken.

A. was   B. were

C. are   D. have

42. The number of tickets sold yesterday _____ much bigger than we had expected.

A. is   B. was

C. are   D. were

43. Telephone messages for the manager _____ on her desk but she didn't notice them.

A. were left   B. was left

C. was leaving   D. were leaving

44. Reading books _____ the only habit that he developed when he was in the university.

A. were   B. was

C. formed   D. have been

45. All _____ ready for the celebration, and all _____ eager to have a good time.

A. was, was   B. were, were

C. was, were   D. were, was

46. Her family _____ quite large, and all her family _____ pop fans.
    A. is, is   B. are, are
    C. is, are   D. are, is

47. I should say the first five questions were quite easy, but the rest _____ hard.
    A. were   B. was
    C. are   D. is

48. I don't think that five hundred pounds _____ a big sum for a rich man like you.
    A. are   B. is
    C. were   D. is to be

49. Not even one of the hundred students who took the test _____ passed.
    A. have   B. has
    C. was   D. were

50. Dick, _____ his students, was at the party. He said to me that he did not know anyone _____ me there.
    A. together with, besides   B. along with, except
    C. rather than, except   D. instead of, besides

51. 30% of the cattle _____ thin, but the rest _____ fat.
    A. are, are   B. is, is
    C. is, are   D. are, is

52. Can you tell me the number of the students who _____?
    A. is going to attend the sports meeting
    B. are going to attend the lecture
    C. has taken part in the lecture
    D. wants to take part in the sports meeting

53. Miss White _____ her parents is going to pay a visit to the Great Wall.
    A. not   B. and
    C. or   D. nor

54. Two thirds of the people there _____ that more than two

thirds of their time _____ spent on reading.
A. have said, is   B. said, were
C. have said, are   D. will say, have been

55. Life there _____ quite comfortable in the last century.
A. said to be   B. was said to be
C. was to say   D. had been said

56. You _____ to work for 40 hours a week if you _____ the job.
A. expect, will take   B. are expected, take
C. will expect, have taken   D. expect, take

57. The sports meet will _____ off if it _____.
A. put, rains   B. put, will rain
C. be put, is rained   D. be put, rains

58. The boy learned that all his toys _____ while he _____ out.
A. were put away, was   B. had put away, was
C. would put away, was   D. were put away, would be

59. Great changes _____ place since our reform _____ some twenty years ago.
A. took, were started   B. had taken, started
C. were taken, started   D. have taken, started

60. Many a man _____ swimming in the river, but only _____ can swim across it.
A. go, a few   B. goes, a few
C. go, few   D. goes, few

61. Mr. Mefan, together with his wife and daughter, _____ going to Japan next month.
A. are   B. is
C. will be   D. would be

62. What he says and what he does _____.
A. do not agree   B. does not agree
C. don't agree with   D. not agree

63. Only a knife and fork _____ on the table. There is nothing else.

A. are
B. are left
C. is
D. was

64. Shanghai Book Traders _____ an enterprise _____ in the import and export of publications and stationery.
    A. is, to specialize
    B. are, specializing
    C. is, specializing
    D. are, being specialized

65. Large amounts of money _____ a new airport.
    A. were spent building
    B. was spent building
    C. were cost to build
    D. was cost building

66. _____ going to the exhibition.
    A. All but he and me is
    B. All but he and me are
    C. All but he and I are
    D. All but he and I am

67. About _____ in that country _____ out of work.
    A. 20 percent people, is
    B. 20 percent of people, are
    C. 20 percent of the people, are
    D. 20 percent people, are

68. Six times three _____ eighteen.
    A. equal
    B. is equal
    C. equals
    D. equals to

69. Every boy and every girl _____ present _____ the farewell party yesterday.
    A. was, to
    B. was, at
    C. were, at
    D. were, to

70. This kind of glasses manufactured by experienced craftsmen _____ comfortably.
    A. is worn
    B. wears
    C. wearing
    D. are worn

71. Many a girl _____ to play football in the past few years.
    A. have learnt
    B. learnt
    C. learns
    D. has learnt

72. He is the one of the students who _____ always praised by the teacher.
    A. is
    B. are

C. have been   D. has
73. How close parents are to their children _____ a strong influence on the character of the children!
    A. have   B. has
    C. having   D. to have
74. Sports and games _____ one healthy while reading books _____ one wise.
    A. make, make   B. makes, make
    C. makes, makes   D. make, makes
75. The cashier and storeman _____ found _____ in the store.
    A. was, lain   B. were, lying
    C. were, lain   D. was, lying
76. My bicycle is all right. _____ repairing.
    A. Both of the wheels need B. Neither of the wheels needs
    C. All the wheels need   D. None of the wheels needs
77. No one in the department but Tom and I _____ that the director is going to resign.
    A. knows   B. know
    C. have known   D. am to know
78. Actually twenty miles _____ a long way to go.
    A. are   B. have been
    C. is   D. has been
79. The football team, _____ the first game, will immediately prepare their training for the next one.
    A. who has won   B. that won
    C. who have won   D. who won
80. All _____ ready for the party, I am sure _____ guests will have a good time.
    A. is, all   B. are, all the
    C. is, all the   D. are, all of the
81. That he has got so many prizes these years _____ him famous.
    A. made   B. make
    C. makes   D. had made
82. The teacher is very strict with his students. He requests that

every student _____ class.
A. be not late for
B. is not late for
C. don't be late for
D. not be late for

83. Tom is one of the boys who _____ always on time.
A. is
B. am
C. are
D. was

84. The singer and dancer _____ our evening.
A. is to attend
B. are to attend
C. were to attend
D. is attend

85. I, who _____ your friend, will try my best to help you.
A. am
B. be
C. is
D. being

86. He said that _____ plenty of room for everybody.
A. there were
B. they were
C. it was
D. there was

87. Two hours _____ enough for us.
A. is
B. are
C. have
D. were

88. Neither Bill nor his parents _____ at home.
A. is
B. are
C. has
D. was

89. *The Canterbury Tales* _____ written by Chaucer.
A. has been
B. were
C. was
D. had been

90. The singer and dancer _____ to make a speech this afternoon.
A. is
B. are
C. is about
D. are about

91. The audience in the theatre _____ in a variety of ways, some in suits and dresses, some in jeans last night.
A. has dressed
B. had dresses
C. dress
D. were dressed

92. _____ of the students are girls, and the rest _____ boys.
A. Two third, is
B. The two third, are
C. Two thirds, are
D. Two thirds, is

93. The beautiful _____ not always the same as the good.
    A. are   B. be
    C. is   D. it is
94. Jin Mao Building in Pudong Area is one of the most beautiful buildings in Shanghai. Many a wonderful night _____ there by me.
    A. have been spent   B. has been spent
    C. have spent   D. has spent
95. There _____ a bottle of wine and a half left at home.
    A. is   B. are
    C. have been   D. has had

第七讲 四种疑问句

1. If you talk nice and polite, people listen to you. If you shout, this is no good, _____?
   A. do you   B. don't you
   C. is it   D. isn't it

2. You didn't use to like him much when we were at school, _____?
   A. were we   B. weren't we
   C. did you   D. didn't

3. Sally's never seen a play in the Shanghai Grand Theatre, _____?
   A. hasn't she   B. has she
   C. isn't she   D. is she

4. It doesn't matter if they want to come to your party, _____?
   A. doesn't it   B. does it
   C. don't they   D. do they

5. — _____ do you think it'll be before I can go back to work?
   — Well, you'll be feeling much better by next weekend.
   A. How soon   B. How fast
   C. How long   D. How much

6. — Alice says Jack may be here all next week.
   — If so, he'd be able to go to the football game with us on Saturday, _____?
   A. won't he   B. hadn't he
   C. wouldn't he   D. couldn't he

7. The news that they failed their driving test discouraged him, _____?
   A. did they   B. didn't they
   C. did it   D. didn't it

8. I don't suppose anyone will volunteer, _____?
   A. do I   B. don't I
   C. will they   D. won't they

68

9. Mrs. Black doesn't believe her son is able to design a digital camera, _____?
   A. is he   B. isn't he
   C. doesn't she   D. does she

10. He comes late sometimes, _____?
    A. is he   B. isn't he
    C. comes he   D. doesn't he

11. How _____ can you finish the drawing?
    A. often   B. soon
    C. long   D. rapid

12. Which is _____ country, Canada or Australia?
    A. a large   B. larger
    C. a larger   D. the larger

13. If I knew the answer, I wouldn't be asking, _____?
    A. didn't I   B. did I
    C. would I   D. wouldn't I

14. — Wasn't it Dr. Wang who spoke at the meeting just now?
    — _____.
    A. I didn't know he was   B. Yes, it was
    C. No, he wasn't   D. Yes, he did

15. I think Miss Cooper is unfit for her job as a secretary, _____?
    A. isn't she   B. do I
    C. is she   D. don't I

16. _____ did you visit besides the new stadium?
    A. Where else   B. What else
    C. Where   D. When

17. For a long time scientists believed the atom was unbreakable, _____?
    A. did they   B. didn't they
    C. was it   D. wasn't it

18. — How many scientists did you see in the conference room?
    — _____.
    A. No ones   B. No
    C. None   D. Not one

19. He _____ last weekend, didn't he?
    A. didn't do anything   B. did nothing
    C. hardly did anything   D. failed to do anything
20. Chinese must have the largest number of speakers, _____?
    A. mustn't they   B. haven't they
    C. don't they   D. doesn't it
21. Few of us have studied German, _____?
    A. have they   B. don't they
    C. haven't we   D. have we
22. — Can you come on Saturday or Sunday?
    — I'm afraid _____ day is possible for me.
    A. either   B. neither
    C. some   D. any
23. — _____ wants to buy my Yongjiu bicycle?
    — John wants to buy _____.
    A. Which of you, it   B. Who of you, yours
    C. Who of you, it   D. Who do you think, that
24. — Does she study her subjects well?
    — No, _____ well.
    A. she studies all   B. any isn't studied
    C. she studies none   D. she studies neither
25. — Is he a professor?
    — No. He is _____ a professor _____ a writer, a famous
      writer.
    A. both, and   B. not, but
    C. neither, nor   D. either, or
26. Ask those women carrying babies to come in first, _____?
    A. won't they   B. will they
    C. will you   D. shall you
27. We had to wait a long time to get our visa, _____?
    A. don't we   B. didn't we
    C. couldn't we   D. shouldn't we
28. He _____ that morning, did he? Which one is wrong?
    A. did nothing

B. hardly did anything

C. failed in the exam

D. did not do as he was instructed

29. What great changes, _____?

A. aren't they   B. are they

C. will they   D. don't they

30. — Will three people be enough?

— Another three _____.

A. will be   B. will do

C. can do   D. must be

31. What he said is impossible, _____?

A. is he   B. isn't he

C. is it   D. isn't it

32. — She goes to Beijing on business at least twice a year.

— I beg your pardon. I didn't quite follow you. _____?

A. How often   B. How long

C. How soon   D. What time

33. This is the first time that your grandpa has been to America, _____?

A. isn't he   B. isn't it

C. hasn't he   D. hasn't it

34. — Which hotel did he say he would stay in, Sunlight or Rome?

— Sorry, I can't remember _____.

A. where   B. anywhere

C. which   D. either

35. I can imagine you are satisfied with your students, _____?

A. are you   B. can't I

C. aren't you   D. don't I

36. — Dr. Martin, I have toothache when I am eating.

— OK. Does it just come when you eat cold foods _____ is it constant for any types of food?

A. but   B. otherwise

C. or   D. and

37. I don't think it is going to rain tomorrow, _____?

A. do I   B. isn't it
C. don't I   D. is it

38. If you can't find your pen in your pocket, why _____?
    A. not look for it everywhere else
    B. not look for it anywhere else
    C. you don't look for it somewhere else
    D. don't you look for it somewhere else

39. Henry had to tell the truth, _____?
    A. did he   B. hadn't he
    C. didn't he   D. had he

40. Everybody thinks she is a famous singer, _____?
    A. isn't she   B. don't they
    C. do they   D. is she

41. _____ have you been to the city of Guangzhou?
    A. How often   B. How many times
    C. How long   D. How much time

42. _____ the teachers in the university do you know?
    A. Which of   B. How many
    C. Who are   D. What of

43. There is no light in the dormitory. They must have gone to the
    lecture, _____?
    A. didn't they   B. don't they
    C. mustn't they   D. haven't they

44. — _____ are the Olympic Games held?
    — They _____ once every four years.
    A. How often, occur   B. How soon, occur
    C. How long, are held   D. How far, are held

45. They must have come to school, _____?
    A. mustn't they   B. shouldn't they
    C. have they   D. didn't they

46. I hear that it won't be long before you leave for France,
    _____?
    A. don't I   B. will it
    C. don't you   D. will you

47. — _____ did you get to school yesterday?
    — By taxi.
    A. When   B. How
    C. Who   D. Where
48. — _____ your uncle?
    — He is a teacher.
    A. Who is   B. What is
    C. Which is   D. Whom
49. _____ is your school from here?
    A. How long way   B. How far
    C. How much far   D. How long
50. — How _____ was Smith driving when the policeman stopped him?
    — Ninety miles an hour.
    A. rapid   B. long
    C. far   D. fast
51. You never told us why your son applied to Fudan University, _____?
    A. did he   B. didn't he
    C. did you   D. didn't you
52. Clever boys need never work very hard, _____?
    A. needn't they   B. don't they
    C. do they   D. need they
53. There was a loud scream from the backstage immediately after the concert ended, _____?
    A. wasn't there   B. was there
    C. didn't it   D. did it
54. She said she was well already, _____?
    A. was she   B. wasn't she
    C. did she   D. didn't she
55. _____ take a camera with us so that we can take photos there?
    A. Why don't   B. Why not
    C. Why not to   D. Why shouldn't
56. He didn't think you would succeed, _____?

A. did he   B. would you
C. didn't he   D. wouldn't you

57. Bill's aim is to inform the viewers that cigarette advertising on TV is illegal, _____?
A. isn't it   B. is it
C. isn't he   D. is he

58. You don't think that he is likely to succeed this time, _____?
A. do you   B. don't you
C. is he   D. isn't he

59. You had a hot bath just now, _____?
A. hadn't you   B. had you
C. did you   D. didn't you

60. Something has to be done to stop our rivers from being polluted, _____?
A. doesn't it   B. hasn't it
C. don't they   D. haven't they

61. They dared not ask the librarian for help, _____ they?
A. did   B. dare
C. dared   D. will

62. — Have you not finished reading the novel?
     — No, I _____.
A. did   B. have
C. have not   D. have finished

63. There's not much news in today's paper, _____?
A. isn't it   B. are there
C. is there   D. aren't there

64. How _____ from Nanjing to Beijing?
A. far is there   B. long is there
C. far is it   D. long way is

65. He must have watched the TV play the other day, _____?
A. mustn't he   B. didn't he
C. haven't he   D. did he

66. _____ that a society like the National Society for the Prevention of Cruelty to Children is still needed in a civilized country?

A. How come   B. How it comes

C. How did it come about   D. How did it come

67. Beer bottles can be recycled, but they need cleaning thoroughly, _____ they?

    A. don't   B. mustn't

    C. needn't   D. can't

68. The doctor must have been there the other day, _____?

    A. mustn't he   B. haven't he

    C. didn't he   D. wasn't he

69. He's supposed to do the washing-up tonight, _____?

    A. hasn't he   B. does he

    C. isn't he   D. is he

70. — You don't think the dictionary is expensive, do you?

    — _____. It's expensive.

    A. No, I don't   B. No, I do

    C. Yes, I do   D. Yes, I don't

第八讲　否 定 句

1. It was due to luck _____ judgment that the driver succeeded in avoiding an accident.
   A. better than   B. other than
   C. more than   D. rather than

2. While I say I agree to most of your ideas, I don't approve of _____.
   A. anything   B. everything
   C. something   D. nothing

3. — Is there _____ peace and quiet in this noisy room? Quiet down, everyone!
   — Sorry, we didn't know you were working.
   A. not   B. no
   C. none   D. nothing

4. — My ten dollars isn't enough for the workbook. Have you got any money on you?
   — _____ at all.
   A. None   B. Not
   C. Nothing   D. No

5. We'll drink coffee without sugar _____ put you to the trouble of fetching some.
   A. otherwise   B. instead
   C. rather than   D. or rather

6. — Will Mary enter for the speech contest?
   — _____.
   A. Possibly not   B. Not possibly
   C. Not possible   D. Possible not

7. _____ amount of money can buy true friendship.
   A. No   B. Not
   C. Never   D. Not only

8. — In the future, the computer will be part of our life.
   — Yes. People just can't do without computer in the office
   _____ at home _____ even in cars.
   A. and, and   B. either, nor
   C. or, or   D. nor, nor
9. — Have you received a Christmas card from the Johns?
   — We haven't got _____ yet this Christmas.
   A. many mails   B. any mail
   C. much of mail   D. any of mails
10. — You didn't play well in the football season, did you?
    — No, we lost most of the games, but not _____.
    A. all   B. at all
    C. everyone   D. each
11. The destruction of the ancient building was a loss that _____
    could make up for.
    A. no amount of money   B. not amount of money
    C. no number of money   D. not number of money
12. "Life begins at forty" is more often an expression of hope _____
    a statement of fact.
    A. instead of   B. than
    C. rather than   D. other than
13. _____ nobody can tell how they _____ the bridge ten years
    ago.
    A. Nearly, built   B. Almost, built
    C. Hardly, built   D. Scarcely, built
14. As I know, there is _____ car in this neighborhood.
    A. no such   B. no a
    C. not such   D. no such a
15. — Will you give this message to Mr. White, please?
    — Sorry, I can't. He _____.
    A. doesn't any more work here
    B. doesn't any longer here work
    C. doesn't work any more here
    D. doesn't work here any longer

16. — Is _____ here?
    — No, Bob and Tim have asked for leave.
    A. anybody   B. somebody
    C. everybody   D. nobody
17. Rather than _____ on a crowded bus, he always prefers
    _____ a bicycle.
    A. ride, ride   B. riding, ride
    C. ride, to ride   D. to ride, riding
18. I will do it myself _____ ask him to do it.
    A. rather than   B. other than
    C. more than   D. would rather
19. Though he is not bright, he has _____ trouble in solving the
    question.
    A. not a bit   B. not a little
    C. no least   D. none less
20. She felt lonely when she first arrived because she had _____ to
    talk to.
    A. somebody   B. anyone
    C. nobody   D. anybody
21. We know little about London, because _____ of us has
    _____ been to England.
    A. all, never   B. any, never
    C. none, ever   D. no one, ever
22. He was _____ pleased when he heard the bad news.
    A. something but   B. nothing but
    C. everything but   D. anything but
23. This book is no better than that one. I like _____ of them.
    A. either   B. both
    C. each   D. neither
24. They couldn't eat in a restaurant, because _____ of them had
    _____ money on them.
    A. all, no   B. any, no
    C. none, any   D. everyone, any
25. I have two sisters but _____ of us have ever been to Beijing.

A. neither   B. both
C. none   D. no one

26. Because it was snowing hard, buses could _____ get through _____ did taxis appear on the street.
   A. both, and   B. either, or
   C. not only, but also   D. neither, nor

27. — Are you still going to Hawaii for holidays?
   — Yes, but I really _____ because I don't have much money.
   A. shouldn't   B. can't
   C. mustn't   D. won't

28. Asked what else he liked to eat, he said he preferred chicken to _____ meat.
   A. some other   B. some more
   C. any more   D. any other

29. If you agree with me, I don't expect you simply to agree and do _____ more. Instead, I expect you to give your reasons.
   A. something   B. nothing
   C. any   D. not

30. — How many times have you read that poem?
   — Oh, at least ten times, if _____ more.
   A. no   B. not
   C. any   D. yet

31. I prefer to stay in the seaside town, _____ because of its job opportunities, _____ because of its low living expenses.
   A. not, but   B. both, as well as
   C. no more, than   D. not, instead

32. The great use of school education is _____ to teach you things _____ to teach you the art of learning.
   A. not, but   B. would rather, than
   C. not so much, as   D. no more, than

33. If you want to grow grass here, the ground must be just right— _____ too wet _____ too dry.
   A. either, or   B. both, and
   C. or, or   D. neither, nor

34. Is anybody feeling cold? If _____ , let's put the central heating off.
    A. not   B. no
    C. none   D. any
35. — You have seen all those paintings, haven't you?
    — Not quite. Some I _____ .
    A. hadn't   B. didn't
    C. haven't   D. weren't
36. I'm thirsty. I want to drink some water, but there was _____ in the bottle.
    A. nothing   B. none
    C. not   D. no
37. _____ of the boys can play football.
    A. Not every   B. Not all
    C. No each   D. No one
38. I agree with most of what you said, but I don't agree with _____ .
    A. everything   B. anything
    C. something   D. nothing
39. — Is Professor Luo going to give us a lecture this afternoon?
    — _____ . He's gone to Nanjing.
    A. I'm afraid so   B. I'm afraid not
    C. I don't think it   D. I think so
40. I don't have _____ time for the preparation.
    A. plenty of   B. a lot of
    C. enough   D. many
41. You are not allowed to ask _____ questions during the examination.
    A. any   B. some
    C. no   D. a
42. The man over there is _____ the famous Mr. Victor Hazal.
    A. no other but   B. none other than
    C. no one than   D. none but
43. — That piano player did play loud.

— I was bothered by his lack of talent _____ by his loudness.

A. but   B. so much as

C. even   D. rather than

44. It was a lovely Saturday afternoon in July, but Ann was _____ swimming _____ fishing.

A. both, and   B. either, or

C. neither, nor   D. not only, but also

45. I gave him warning, but he took _____ notice of it.

A. not   B. none

C. not any   D. little

46. The children were catching butterflies in the garden. Some caught a lot, and others caught _____ at all.

A. nothing   B. none

C. no one   D. no

47. Mr. Wang was _____ tired and went to sleep at once.

A. not a little   B. not a few

C. not a least   D. not a bit

48. — It is worth doing, isn't it?

— I suppose _____.

A. that   B. it does

C. so   D. it

49. Would you please _____ spoil your child? He has destroyed all the greens in our garden.

A. not   B. not to

C. to   D. don't

50. I've got only one ticket for you two. So you can't go to the concert _____; _____ of you can go.

A. either, either   B. both, either

C. both, both   D. neither, neither

51. _____ us could understand what he said.

A. Someone of   B. Anyone of

C. None of   D. Nobody

52. The Palace Museum in Beijing is _____ inaccessible to ordinary people.

A. not longer   B. not long
C. no long   D. no longer

53. — Will it rain on the day of our departure?
— _____.
A. I hope not   B. I don't hope so
C. I hope not so   D. I hope it wouldn't

54. I came _____ as a teacher _____ as a student.
A. no, but   B. not, but
C. neither, but   D. nor, but

55. The hard truth is that _____ Tom _____ his twin sister has
yet done enough to get a passing grade for the course.
A. both, and   B. whether, or
C. either, or   D. neither, nor

56. Joan told me that _____ nothing important had ever happened.
A. almost   B. hardly
C. nearly   D. scarcely

57. _____ of his parents is short-sighted, but he is.
A. None   B. Either
C. Neither   D. Both

58. He has two sons, and _____ looks like him.
A. all of them   B. both of them
C. each of them   D. neither of them

59. Don't spit _____.
A. anywhere   B. somewhere
C. nowhere   D. everywhere

60. He _____ answer those questions openly.
A. dares not   B. don't dare to
C. didn't dare   D. dares

第九讲 感 叹 句

1. The little boy come riding full speed down the motorway on his bicycle. _____ it was!
   A. What a dangerous scene   B. What dangerous a scene
   C. How a dangerous scene   D. How dangerous the scene

2. _____ it is!
   A. What a good piece of advice
   B. What a piece of good advice
   C. How good piece of advice
   D. How piece of good advice

3. _____ he wishes to be a useful man!
   A. What   B. What much
   C. How hard   D. How

4. _____ they are!
   A. How good students   B. What good students
   C. What a good student   D. How good a student

5. _____ Mr. Smith has bought!
   A. How nice a car   B. How a nice car
   C. What nice a car   D. What nice car

6. _____ weather we are having today!
   A. What a fine   B. How a lovely
   C. What fine   D. How lovely

7. _____ we have had today!
   A. How wonderful time   B. What wonderful time
   C. How wonderful a time   D. What wonderful a time

8. You've got a nice house. _____ it looks!
   A. How beautiful   B. How nicely
   C. What beautiful house   D. What a beautiful house

9. _____ to knock over the ink bottle!
   A. What careless you are   B. How careless of you

C. How careless for you   D. What a careless man are you

10. _____ fun it is to swim in a hot summer day!
A. How great   B. What great
C. How great a   D. What a great

·11. _____ I regretted telling you the news!
A. How well   B. What
C. How   D. What a

12. _____ from Beijing to London!
A. How long way it is   B. What a long way is it
C. How long way is it   D. What a long way it is

13. _____ news at home and abroad we have had these days!
A. What inspired   B. How inspiring
C. How inspired   D. What inspiring

14. _____ to go swimming in a river in summer!
A. How pleasant is   B. How pleased it is
C. Such a pleasure   D. How pleasant it is

15. _____ look is at the sight of the terrible scene!
A. How frightening her frightened
B. What her frightened
C. How her frightening frightened
D. What frightening her

第十讲　祈使句和命令句

1. I'll look into the matter as soon as possible. Just _____ a little patience.
   - A. having
   - B. to have
   - C. have
   - D. has
2. One more week，_____ we will accomplish the task.
   - A. or
   - B. so that
   - C. and
   - D. if
3. _____ quiet or go out.
   - A. To keep
   - B. Keep
   - C. Keeping
   - D. Kept
4. _____ , or you'll bump into the shop window.
   - A. Looking out
   - B. Look out
   - C. Look around
   - D. Looking round
5. _____ blood if you can and many lives will be saved.
   - A. Giving
   - B. Give
   - C. Given
   - D. To give
6. _____ down the radio—the baby's asleep in the next room.
   - A. Turning
   - B. To turn
   - C. Turned
   - D. Turn
7. Be sure to write to us，_____?
   - A. will you
   - B. aren't you
   - C. can you
   - D. mustn't you
8. Let us explain all this to you later this afternoon. _____?
   - A. shall we
   - B. will you
   - C. shan't we
   - D. won't you
9. _____ it or not, his discovery has created a stir in scientific circle.
   - A. Believe
   - B. To believe
   - C. Believing
   - D. Believed

10. Can't the community do _____ to help the aged?
    A. something   B. everything
    C. anything   D. nothing
11. Don't forget to bring the dictionary when you come next time,
    _____?
    A. do you   B. will you
    C. don't you   D. mustn't you
12. To do well in the test, _____.
    A. the four choices should be looked at carefully before you make
       a choice
    B. don't answer anything before a careful look at the four
       choices
    C. before you choose an answer, carefully look at the four
       choices
    D. look at the four choices carefully before choosing an answer
13. Can _____ help me to carry these boxes?
    A. somebody   B. anybody
    C. some one   D. any one
14. Would you _____ to lift the bag of books upstairs?
    A. do me the favour   B. do me a favour
    C. do a favour for me   D. do the favour to me
15. _____ believe _____ reject anything just because any other
    person has rejected or believed it.
    A. Neither, nor   B. Whether, or
    C. Either, or   D. Not, or
16. _____ the bookstore at the corner — perhaps you'll find the
    book you want.
    A. Trying   B. Try
    C. To try   D. Have tried
17. Let's meet at the Shanghai Railway Station, _____?
    A. shall we   B. will you
    C. shan't we   D. won't you
18. Let me try again, _____?
    A. don't I   B. shall we

C. won't you   D. will you
19. Class is over. _____ a rest, everybody.
    A. Do you have   B. Have
    C. Have you   D. Please you have
20. Come, and sit down. Have a cup of tea, _____?
    A. wouldn't you   B. will you
    C. haven't you   D. do you
21. Please let us go, _____?
    A. shall we   B. will you
    C. will not you   D. shan't we
22. Hurry up and you _____ the experiment in a few minutes.
    A. finish   B. have finished
    C. will finish   D. are finishing
23. He has trouble getting to sleep. Just a little noise, _____ he
    will stay awake all night.
    A. or   B. and
    C. so   D. for
24. Let us take a look at the photo of your son, _____?
    A. do you   B. will you
    C. shall we   D. will we
25. Please let us take a holiday tomorrow, _____?
    A. shall we   B. will you
    C. shall we not   D. will you not
26. Would you please show me _____ pictures?
    A. any   B. some
    C. something   D. anything
27. You'll catch cold without your coat. _____.
    A. Take on it   B. Take it on
    C. Put on it   D. Put it on
28. Hurry up, _____ you'll miss the early bus.
    A. and   B. or
    C. until   D. but
29. _____ more physical exercise, or you won't be strong enough.
    A. Doing   B. Do

C. To do   D. Having done
30. _____ the best use is made of time in class.
    A. Be sure to   B. Be sure of
    C. Make sure of   D. Make sure that
31. Please _____ what you are listening to _____ miss the key
    points.
    A. concentrate on, or you'll
    B. concentrate to, and you'll
    C. concentrate for, unless you'll
    D. concentrate with, otherwise you'll
32. _____ books and you will make sure which _____ suitable
    _____ your purpose.
    A. Browsing through, is, to
    B. To browse among, may be, to
    C. Browse through, is, for
    D. Browse, may be, for
33. Another word from you _____ I will kill you.
    A. or   B. but
    C. and   D. yet
34. Another sound from me _____ the snake might strike.
    A. or   B. but
    C. and   D. yet
35. — English has a large vocabulary, hasn't it?
    — Yes. _____ more words and expressions and you will find
    it easier to read and communicate.
    A. Know   B. Knowing
    C. To know   D. Known

第十一讲 情态助动词

1. You know he is not going to let us leave early if we _____ get the work done.
   A. can't   B. may not
   C. shouldn't   D. mustn't

2. Black holes _____ not be seen directly, so determining the number of them is a rough task.
   A. can   B. should
   C. must   D. need

3. The boss has given everyone a special holiday, so we _____ go to work tomorrow.
   A. can't   B. mustn't
   C. needn't   D. shouldn't

4. When I was young, I was told that I _____ play with matches.
   A. wouldn't   B. needn't
   C. mustn't   D. daren't

5. According to the air traffic rules, you _____ switch off your mobile phone before boarding.
   A. may   B. can
   C. would   D. should

6. It _____ have been Tom that parked the car here, as he is the only one with a car.
   A. may   B. can
   C. must   D. should

7. It is important to know about the cultural differences that _____ cause problems.
   A. must   B. dare
   C. need   D. may

8. I _____ worry about my weekend—I always have my plans ready before it comes.

A. can't   B. mustn't
C. daren't   D. needn't

9. You _____ bring your identification when you open a bank account.
   A. may   B. can
   C. must   D. will

10. The new law states that people _____ drive after drinking alcohol.
    A. wouldn't   B. needn't
    C. won't   D. mustn't

11. — My e-dictionary is nowhere to be found. Who _____ have taken it?
    — I don't know. But keep looking for it and you will find it.
    A. should   B. could
    C. need   D. shall

12. The climbers _____ reach the top of the mountain, but because of the sudden snowstorm, they _____ come down.
    A. could, weren't able to   B. were able to, couldn't
    C. could, couldn't   D. were possible to, couldn't

13. — I hear your neighbour next door has recently sold their house.
    — Yes, they _____ sell it. They both lost their jobs a couple of months ago.
    A. had to   B. had meant to
    C. were about to   D. would like to

14. — Mary is fond of talking, isn't she?
    — Yes, if no one interrupts her, she _____ go on talking all night.
    A. shall   B. should
    C. will   D. would

15. I've been sick quite a few times just because I can't _____ to the cold weather in the south.
    A. have been used   B. get used
    C. have used   D. use

16. I'll call for the police if he _____ again.

A. dares gamble   B. dared gamble
C. dare to gamble   D. dares to gamble

17. The eleven-month-old boy _____ walk on his own.
A. was able to   B. could
C. can be able to   D. could be able to

18. — Could I call you by your first name?
— Yes, you _____.
A. will   B. could
C. may   D. might

19. You can't imagine that a well-behaved gentleman _____ be so rude to a lady.
A. might   B. need
C. should   D. would

20. It has been announced that candidates _____ remain in their seats until all the papers have been collected.
A. can   B. will
C. may   D. shall

21. You _____ return the magazine to me now. You may keep it until next Friday.
A. can't   B. needn't
C. mustn't   D. may not

22. Mr. Bush is on time for everything. How _____ it be that he was late for the opening ceremony?
A. can   B. should
C. may   D. must

23. — Could I borrow your dictionary?
— Yes, of course you _____.
A. might   B. will
C. can   D. should

24. When he was there, he _____ go to that coffee shop at the corner after work every day.
A. would   B. should
C. had better   D. might

25. Sir, you _____ be sitting in this waiting room. It is for women

and children only.

    A. oughtn't to   B. can't

    C. won't   D. needn't

26. According to the local regulations, anyone who intends to get a driver's licence _____ take an eye test.

    A. can   B. must

    C. would   D. may

27. — Shall I tell John about it?

    — No, you _____. I've told him already.

    A. needn't   B. wouldn't

    C. mustn't   D. shouldn't

28. I wonder how he _____ that to the teacher.

    A. dare to say   B. dare saying

    C. not dare say   D. dared say

29. You _____ get a prize if you win.

    A. shall   B. need

    C. must   D. have to

30. — Must I renew the book now?

    — No, you _____, but you _____ that yesterday.

    A. mustn't, should do

    B. may not, should do

    C. needn't, should have done

    D. can't, should have done

31. Since you need to catch an early bus tomorrow morning, we _____ now.

    A. might as well leave   B. ought to have left

    C. had better to leave   D. should have to leave

32. I _____ at our teacher's remarks.

    A. cannot help but to wonder

    B. cannot help but wonder

    C. cannot but wondering

    D. can not help but wondering

33. — How much is that computer?

    — It _____ $400. I'm sure it is.

A. may be   B. must be
C. might be   D. can't be

34. — I didn't hear the cell phone. Did you call me just now?
    — You _____ have heard it when you were in such a noisy
    crowd.
    A. should   B. couldn't
    C. must   D. might

35. — It has not been raining for days and the flowers need _____.
    — No, they _____. I have just watered them.
    A. watering, needn't water
    B. being watered, needn't any water
    C. to water, don't need any water
    D. to be watered, don't need any water

36. Difficult as the task was, we _____ finish it ahead of time and
    therefore we were highly praised for it.
    A. could   B. had to
    C. were able to   D. would

37. They _____ be at home. You see, the door is locked from the
    outside.
    A. may   B. must
    C. mustn't   D. can't

38. After they were given several terrible blows, the enemy did not
    _____ out after dark.
    A. dared to come   B. dared come
    C. dare coming   D. dare to come

39. Just as I was hurrying to class, there _____ come Tom with a
    long story to tell me.
    A. could   B. must
    C. might   D. would

40. _____ I repeat the question?
    A. Will   B. Shall
    C. Ought   D. Can

41. — Where's the knife?
    — It _____ on the plate. I put it there just now.

A. could be
B. may be
C. would be
D. should be

42. — Travelling is usually expensive.
— You _____ be right but I should say it depends on how you
do it.

A. can
B. must
C. will
D. may

43. He was so shy that he _____ strangers the way.

A. not dared ask
B. dared not ask
C. dared not to ask
D. not dared to ask

44. We realized that we _____ if we wished to catch the bus.

A. must hurry
B. must have hurried
C. might hurry
D. might have hurried

45. You went to the wrong store. You _____ to the store next to
the restaurant, but you went to the store by the bank.

A. might go
B. will have gone
C. ought to go
D. ought to have gone

46. — Do you think the rain will affect the results of the football
game?
— Well the players are accustomed to such rainy weather, so it
_____ make any difference to them.

A. shan't
B. shouldn't
C. needn't
D. needn't to

47. — Is he complaining?
— _____, but I don't care.

A. He may be
B. He may do so
C. So he does
D. So is he

48. Bert was so forgetful that he _____ show up for work on
Sunday thinking it was Monday.

A. might
B. should
C. could
D. would

49. She _____ chat for hours on end if you give her a chance.

A. shall
B. should
C. must
D. will

50. — Does your class teacher know what has really happened to the monitor?
    — No, but I think he _____ the truth.
    A. needs to be told   B. needs be told
    C. needs to tell   D. is needed telling
51. Don't work too hard and put yourself under stress if _____ avoid it.
    A. you are possible to   B. it is possibility to
    C. you can possibly   D. you make possible to
52. To our relief, we _____ into touch with the tourists trapped underground.
    A. could get   B. were able to get
    C. could have got   D. would have got
53. Seeing a poisonous snake, I _____ .
    A. dared not to move   B. didn't dare to move
    C. not dared move   D. not dared to move
54. I do not particularly like my next door neighbour though he _____ be very helpful.
    A. should   B. might
    C. must   D. can
55. "_____ I wrap it up for you?" the salesgirl asked me.
    A. May   B. Shall
    C. Can   D. Need
56. Bobby _____ be at home because I met him in the library a minute ago.
    A. mustn't   B. may not
    C. can't   D. won't
57. — That must be a mistake.
    — Oh, no, it _____ a mistake.
    A. cannot be   B. mustn't be
    C. won't be   D. needn't be
58. Professor Hill, many students want to see you. _____ they wait here or outside?
    A. Do   B. Will

C. Shall   D. Can

59. You _____ to school, if you don't feel quite well.
   A. needn't to come   B. don't need come
   C. needn't come   D. don't need coming

60. You might just as well tell the manufacturer that male customers _____ not like the design of the furniture.
   A. must   B. shall
   C. may   D. need

61. — Would you please stay with us for lunch, Mrs. Jones?
   — Sorry, I _____. My children are waiting for me at home.
   A. wouldn't   B. won't
   C. needn't   D. can't

62. The boss has promised that every player in NBA _____ have a rise in income.
   A. would   B. might
   C. shall   D. can

63. The man you want to see has arrived. _____ he come at once?
   A. Does   B. Will
   C. Shall   D. Is

64. I parked my car right under the big tree, but now it's gone. Where _____ it be?
   A. may   B. could
   C. will   D. must

65. Children under 12 years of age in that country _____ be under adult supervision when in a public library.
   A. must   B. may
   C. can   D. need

66. We _____ be polite to the customers. How _____ you be so rude to them?
   A. may, can   B. should, could
   C. can, would   D. can't, should

67. The small girl says that she _____ touch the snake though it is dead now.
   A. dares to   B. dare not

C. dare not to   D. dares not to

68. You _____ go there with me if you feel too tired to do so.
A. need to   B. don't need
C. needn't   D. needn't have to

69. The city _____ be very dirty, but things are different now.
A. must   B. couldn't
C. might   D. used to

70. — _____ I finish drinking the cup of coffee at once?
— No, you needn't.
A. Must   B. Shall
C. May   D. Can

71. You _____ not have swum across the lake. It was too dangerous.
A. may   B. would
C. could   D. should

72. — _____ what he has said be true?
— Yes, it _____ be true.
A. May, may   B. Can, can
C. May, must   D. Can, must

73. Each time my uncle came from New York, he _____ bring me a lot of useful books.
A. should   B. might
C. would   D. could

74. There _____ be any difficulty about passing the road test since you have practiced a lot in the driving school.
A. mustn't   B. shan't
C. shouldn't   D. needn't

75. This piece of information has not been made public yet. You _____ never mention it to anyone else.
A. might   B. must
C. could   D. will

76. You _____ to the meeting tomorrow if you have something important to do.
A. don't need come   B. don't need coming

C. needn't to come   D. needn't come

77. You _____ go there with us since you are not in good health.
A. don't need   B. need not to
C. needn't   D. needn't have to

78. How _____ you say that you really understand the whole story if you have covered only part of it?
A. can   B. must
C. need   D. may

79. Tom _____ do a lot of housework as his mother is sick and she _____ taking care of.
A. need to, need   B. needs, needs
C. needn't, needn't   D. needs to, needs

80. — Remember to return the magazine to Mary.
— _____.
A. Of course   B. I will
C. I won't   D. Why not

81. He's just joking. I don't think you _____ it seriously.
A. need to take   B. need taking
C. need take   D. need in taking

82. You _____ be mistaken about his ability. He _____ solve the hard problem alone.
A. can, must   B. must, can
C. could, may   D. must, might

83. The kid is crying, for he _____ jump over the ditch.
A. dares not   B. dares not to
C. dare not to   D. doesn't dare to

84. When they were living together at that time, they _____ tell each other jokes.
A. must   B. could
C. would   D. might

85. — _____ it rain heavily this afternoon?
— No, there isn't any possibility of having a heavy rain.
A. Must   B. Shall
C. Can   D. May

86. "_____ you give me a room for the night?" I asked, on arriving at the hotel.
    A. Should   B. Can
    C. Might   D. May
87. I _____ tell her the truth. I have no other choice.
    A. could not   B. may not help
    C. cannot but   D. cannot help
88. You can't imagine that a good student _____ be so rude to his teacher.
    A. might   B. need
    C. should   D. would
89. I don't think he _____ a new TV set.
    A. needs buy   B. need
    C. need to buy   D. need buy
90. The fire spread through the hotel very quickly but everyone _____ get out.
    A. had to   B. would
    C. could   D. was able to

第十二讲　并　列　句

1. Which sentence is wrong?
   A. I have three pens, they are all in my pencil-box.
   B. I have three pens, and they are all in my pencil-box.
   C. I have three pens, which are all in my pencil-box.
   D. I have three pens. They are all in my pencil-box.

2. Tom looked upon the test as an obstacle _____ his classmates regarded it as a challenge.
   A. while   B. because
   C. unless   D. if

3. The child picks up English from their parents, _____ an adult language-learner has to attend classes.
   A. while   B. so
   C. contrary   D. though

4. The bear gave birth to four babies last night, but _____ died soon after birth.
   A. two of which   B. the two of them
   C. both of them   D. two of them

5. Will you mend the cleaner yourself _____ shall we ask someone else to fix it?
   A. and   B. but
   C. or   D. so

6. Little Willie can be very annoying, _____ generally he is a good boy.
   A. however   B. but
   C. in spite   D. first of all

7. _____, but they couldn't breathe a sigh of relief.
   A. The exam being over   B. The exam was over
   C. The exam to be over   D. The exam over

8. They appeared to have done well in the contest, _____ they

all came out of the hall, chatting happily.
A. so   B. but
C. for   D. when
9. _____ for a long time, so I wrote to my friend again.
A. Having not heard from him
B. Not having heard from her
C. I hadn't heard from her
D. Not having been received her letter
10. Any significant social change brings its problems and _____ is essential to work out the proper solutions.
A. it   B. which
C. that   D. there
11. She thought I was talking about her son, _____, in fact I was talking about my daughter.
A. whom   B. where
C. which   D. while
12. Tommy caught the school bus, _____.
A. and Jane did neither   B. but so did Jane
C. and Jane didn't either   D. but Jane didn't
13. My name is Robert, _____ most of my friends call me Bob for short.
A. then   B. instead
C. however   D. but
14. Fishing is his favourite hobby, and _____.
A. he'd like to collect coins as well
B. he feels like collecting coins, too
C. to collect coins is also his hobby
D. collecting coins also gives him great pleasure
15. They were surprised that a child should work out the problem _____ they themselves couldn't.
A. once   B. then
C. while   D. if
16. — I don't like chicken _____ fish.
— I don't like chicken, _____ I like fish very much.

A. and, and   B. and, but
C. or, and   D. or, but

17. — Would you like to come to dinner tonight?

    — I'd like to, _____ I'm too busy.

    A. and   B. so

    C. as   D. but

18. Tom took the first prize, _____ was a wonderful achievement for a small child.

    A. and it   B. this

    C. that   D. and which

19. _____ from school for almost two weeks, so she is working harder to make up for the lost time.

    A. Being absent

    B. Having been absent

    C. Because she has been absent .

    D. She has been absent

20. Someone must have left the tap on, _____ the water was running over and flooding the bathroom.

    A. for   B. therefore

    C. moreover   D. however

21. Susan might have come to school in time for Professor Browning's lecture, _____.

    A. but she got up rather late

    B. but she had got up so late

    C. if she got up earlier

    D. unless she had got up earlier

22. They believe that the spirit stays with the body for three days, _____ someone always stays with the dead person.

    A. so during this time   B. so during which

    C. during this time   D. so when

23. Peter is far from perfect, _____ there is much good in him than you think.

    A. unless   B. but

    C. or   D. for

24. The thief kept trying to escape and _____ time he was caught and brought back.
    A. each   B. any
    C. some   D. either
25. In the north, summer is short and cool at night, _____ winter is not so bad with heating.
    A. while   B. though
    C. if   D. for
26. He speaks German fluently, _____ he prefers to chat in English.
    A. and yet   B. so anyhow
    C. but also   D. and therefore
27. The new type of air conditioner will cost you a lot of money, _____ it will save electricity in the long run.
    A. for   B. since
    C. or   D. but
28. — What's wrong, Bob?
    — Oh, Dad, I'm trying hard, but the car _____ start.
    A. mustn't   B. shan't
    C. won't   D. can't
29. Nowadays many people long for an adventure to a place where few people, _____ at least no one they know, have gone before.
    A. whom   B. or
    C. and   D. for
30. People thought Romona was a quiet girl, but _____ wasn't quite true.
    A. which   B. as
    C. she   D. it
31. Hard work _____ success and failure often _____ laziness.
    A. lies in, leads to   B. leads to, lies in
    C. lies to, leads in   D. lies for, leads into
32. Sir, you'd better check in your luggage quickly, _____ you'll miss your flight.
    A. and   B. or

C. so   D. for

33. The professor has a large collection of stamps, _____ are foreign stamps.
    A. and more than half of them
    B. and more than half of which
    C. more than half
    D. more than half of that

34. You must hurry _____ you will miss the train.
    A. if   B. or
    C. either   D. unless

35. The weather was bad, and _____ we postponed our trip.
    A. however   B. therefore
    C. moreover   D. nevertheless

36. We _____ bed _____ we heard a knock at the door.
    A. were prepared for, when
    B. were preparing for, and at that time
    C. prepared a, then
    D. were prepared for a, and suddenly

37. Feathers fall to the ground slow, _____ stones fall much faster.
    A. yet   B. however
    C. though   D. for

38. There must have been no oil in the tank, _____ the car has suddenly stopped.
    A. because   B. as
    C. since   D. for

39. The bus suddenly stopped _____ there was no petrol in the tank. Which of the following is wrong?
    A. because   B. as
    C. since   D. for

40. Tom was badly ill that day, _____, he couldn't go to school.
    A. so   B. because
    C. therefore   D. for

第十三讲 宾 语 从 句

1. These shoes look very good. I wonder _____ .
   A. how much cost they are   B. how much do they cost
   C. how much they cost   D. how much are they cost
2. He spoke proudly of his part in the game, without mentioning _____ his teammates had done.
   A. what   B. which
   C. why   D. while
3. By improving reading skills, you can read faster and understand more of _____ you read.
   A. that   B. what
   C. which   D. whether
4. As his best friend, I can make accurate guesses about _____ he will do or think.
   A. what   B. which
   C. whom   D. that
5. As a new diplomat, he often thinks of _____ he can react more appropriately on such occasions.
   A. what   B. which
   C. that   D. how
6. Tina was hesitating about the job offer as she did not know _____ the company was an established one.
   A. whether   B. what
   C. until   D. although
7. When changing lanes, a driver should use his turning signal to let other drivers know _____ .
   A. he is entering which lane   B. which lane he is entering
   C. is he entering which lane   D. which lane is he entering
8. The message you intend to convey through words may be the exact opposite of _____ others actually understand.

105

A. why   B. that
C. which   D. what

9. Portable videophones will show us _____ is happening at the end of the line.
   A. which   B. what
   C. how   D. why

10. Contrary _____ we had expected, he didn't try his best.
    A. to what   B. as
    C. to that   D. on which

11. — Which car do you think _____ presently?
    — The most expensive one.
    A. will she buy   B. would she buy
    C. she will buy   D. she would buy

12. In order to find out the escaped prisoner, the police decided to question _____ lives in the neighbourhood.
    A. who   B. whom
    C. whoever   D. whomever

13. Manners are just a formal expression of _____ you treat people.
    A. how   B. what
    C. why   D. who

14. It was a matter of _____ would take the position.
    A. who   B. whoever
    C. whom   D. whomever

15. _____ be sent to work there?
    A. Who do you suggest
    B. Who do you suggest that should
    C. Do you suggest who should
    D. Do you suggest whom should

16. I wonder how _____ the letter would reach him. In a week, I hope.
    A. long   B. soon
    C. fast   D. quick

17. Little Tommy was reluctant to tell the schoolmaster _____ he

had done the day before.

A. that   B. how

C. where   D. what

18. I remember _____ this used to be a quiet village.

A. when   B. how

C. where   D. what

19. — Do you remember _____ he came?

— Yes, I do. He came by car.

A. how   B. when

C. that   D. if

20. Sarah hopes to become a friend of _____ shares her interests.

A. anyone   B. whomever

C. whoever   D. no matter who

21. _____ you have seen both fighters, _____ will win?

A. Since, do you think who   B. As, who you think

C. When, whoever   D. Since, who do you think

22. The grand hotel has been completed, but we don't know _____ come into use.

A. how long it will   B. how long will it

C. how soon will it   D. how soon it will

23. Shanghai has taken on a new look. It isn't like _____ it used to be.

A. what   B. how

C. which   D. that

24. The students are all interested in _____ Miss Brown managed to do it.

A. which   B. what

C. that   D. how

25. With his camera, he kept taking pictures _____ he did and saw.

A. where   B. which

C. of which   D. of what

26. With a lot of school time being devoted to non-academic activities, parents might wonder _____ their children would

have time for traditional learning.
A. that if   B. though
C. when   D. since

27. His grandfather was among the first to settle in _____ is now the famous holiday place.
A. what   B. which
C. where   D. that

28. It is better to have half of _____ than nothing at all.
A. one wants   B. what one wants
C. which one wants   D. that one wants

29. Mr. Baker comes from either Harvard or Yale, but I can't remember _____.
A. which   B. where
C. there   D. that

30. The old man takes a walk every morning _____ it rains.
A. except   B. except that
C. except for   D. except when

31. I lost my way in the new town and _____ made matters worse was that I had my wallet stolen.
A. that   B. it
C. which   D. what

32. I am surprised _____ Henry _____ have been fooled by such a simple trick.
A. that, should   B. when, should
C. because, must   D. that, would

33. It is generally considered unwise for students to ask teachers _____ they don't understand without any thinking.
A. however   B. whichever
C. whatever   D. whoever

34. _____ objected to the plan at the meeting yesterday?
A. Do you know who   B. Who you think
C. Whom do you believe   D. Do you suppose who

35. We asked the doorman _____ the office would still be open at five.

A. that   B. when
C. where   D. whether

36. He was born in _____ is now known as Xiangyang.
    A. what   B. that
    C. where   D. there

37. George Washington was born in 1732 in a very rich family in _____ is now the state of Virginia.
    A. which   B. where
    C. that   D. what

38. Give the message to _____ is at the desk.
    A. who   B. whom
    C. whomever   D. whoever

39. He was lucky enough to sell his car for exactly _____.
    A. where he had paid for it   B. what he had paid for it
    C. what he was paid for it   D. which he had paid for it

40. The situation in Kosovo changes so often that you cannot tell _____ it would be like the following day.
    A. whether   B. how
    C. why   D. what

41. It is generally considered unwise to give a child _____ he or she wants.
    A. however   B. whatever
    C. whichever   D. whenever

42. There are many computers in the office. Make sure _____ the door before you leave.
    A. you will lock   B. you lock
    C. for locking   D. locking

43. Miss Lin felt _____.
    A. an honour that she was a teacher
    B. that she was a teacher an honour
    C. it an honour when she was a teacher
    D. it an honour that she was a teacher

44. My husband said that I could choose _____ dress looked nice on me.

A. the   B. any
C. whichever   D. which

45. Our teacher suggests active reading, and he says it will result in a better understanding of what _____.
    A. to read   B. to be read
    C. is being read   D. is to read

46. I wonder _____ we shall have to walk _____ we shall catch the last bus.
    A. whether, or else   B. either, or
    C. that, or that   D. whether, or whether

47. Looking about him, Crook wondered why _____, rich or not, would choose to live in such surroundings.
    A. anyone   B. someone
    C. any   D. some

48. There aren't many seats left for this concert; you had better make sure _____ one today.
    A. getting   B. to have got
    C. that you get   D. that you would get

49. We should carefully remove _____ might be harmful to young people.
    A. what   B. whatever
    C. that   D. anything

50. There will be a special price for _____ buys things in large numbers here.
    A. who   B. whom
    C. whoever   D. whomever

51. Do you think _____ watching TV all the time is a nice way of relaxation?
    A. whether   B. if
    C. why   D. that

52. This is the small village in _____ not long ago.
    A. we stayed at   B. where we stayed
    C. which we stayed   D. where we stayed in

53. You can imagine _____ to settle down to work on the newspaper

at two pounds a week, when I knew that I could earn as much as that in a single day as a beggar.

    A. how hardly was it   B. what hard was it

    C. how hard it was   D. what hard it was

54. We, Chinese people, always mean _____.

    A. that we said   B. which we said

    C. what we said   D. whether we said

55. Nobody could tell _____ those fishermen would be back again.

    A. how long   B. how soon

    C. how far   D. how much

56. When they first arrived in _____ a famous tourist city, it was only a small town with a population of about five hundred.

    A. what is now   B. what it is now

    C. which now is   D. now is

57. You'd better give the ticket to _____ wants it.

    A. who   B. whoever

    C. whom   D. whomever

58. Free film tickets will be sent to _____ are interested in the film.

    A. whomever   B. whoever

    C. no matter who   D. whichever

59. _____ do you suppose _____ will take charge of our class next term?

    A. Who, that   B. Who, /

    C. Whom, /   D. Whom, that

60. When the European settlers arrived in _____ is now the United States, they brought their holidays like Christmas.

    A. that   B. which

    C. what   D. where

61. The prize will go to _____ of them writes the best composition.

    A. whatever   B. whichever

    C. whoever   D. whomever

62. It was only a small seaside town then compared to _____ now.

    A. that it is   B. what is

C. it is   D. what it is
63. Don't put off till tomorrow _____ you can do today.
    A. what   B. that
    C. which   D. when
64. What _____ would happen if we met with a serious flood?
    A. you suppose   B. would you suppose
    C. you would suppose   D. do you suppose
65. She wondered _____ she could get back very soon.
    A. that   B. if
    C. or   D. so
66. What do you think _____?
    A. should I do   B. I should do
    C. to do   D. for me to do
67. Of course you may invite _____ you like to.
    A. who   B. whom
    C. whomever   D. whoever
68. He never told us _____.
    A. where did he live   B. whom he lived with
    C. how could he live   ·   D. why was he living alone
69. I can't tell _____ they hope will come to be their new class
    teacher.
    A. who   B. whom
    C. what   D. that
70. I didn't know _____ water they wanted.
    A. how much   B. how many
    C. how wonderful   D. how beautiful
71. What do you think _____ left in his classroom?
    A. he was   B. he's
    C. him   D. he is
72. Can you tell me _____ he did not turn off the light when he
    left the classroom?
    A. how   B. why
    C. what   D. whether
73. _____ do you think is brighter, Mike or Bob?

A. Whom B. Whoever
C. Who D. Whomever
74. Do you know _____ the meeting will last?
A. how soon B. how long
C. how often D. how far
75. — _____ do you think _____ to him?
— He must have lost his way in the forest, I think.
A. What, of happening B. How, happened
C. How, that has happened D. What, has happened
76. _____ was the first to confess the mistake?
A. Do you suppose who B. Do you suppose whom
C. Who do you suppose D. Who do you suppose that
77. A reward of 1,000 dollars will be given _____ can find the lost child.
A. to whoever B. to whomever
C. whomever D. whoever that
78. I want to know _____ the thief was caught on the spot.
A. which B. that
C. what D. whether
79. He looked behind to make _____ he was not being followed.
A. clear that B. it clear if
C. sure that D. sure whether
80. The kindly old man never _____ to help _____ he thinks is in trouble.
A. comes, who B. gets, whom
C. provided, whomever D. fails, whoever
81. The living conditions of people today are quite different from _____ they were ten years ago.
A. which B. the fact
C. conditions D. what
82. She was trying to think _____ there's a place to have a drink around here.
A. that B. of what
C. where D. of where

113

83. You can return the book to _____ in my office.
   A. whichever teacher
   B. no matter which teacher
   C. any teacher which you meet
   D. which teacher you meet
84. _____ do you think _____ the first prize?
   A. Which, that will win   B. Whom, will win
   C. Who, will win   D. Whom, that will win
85. The other day, my brother drove his car down the street at
   _____ I thought was a dangerous speed.
   A. as   B. what
   C. which   D. that

第十四讲 主语从句

1. _____ he referred to in his article was unknown to the general reader.
   A. That
   B. What
   C. Whether
   D. Where

2. _____ we are sure about is the need to prevent children from being spoiled.
   A. What
   B. Which
   C. Whether
   D. That

3. It has been proved _____ eating vegetables in childhood helps to protect you against serious illnesses in later life.
   A. if
   B. because
   C. when
   D. that

4. It is not immediately clear _____ the financial crisis will soon be over.
   A. since
   B. what
   C. when
   D. whether

5. — We've only got this small bookcase. Will that do?
   — No, _____ I am looking for is something much bigger and stronger.
   A. who
   B. that
   C. what
   D. which

6. _____ she was at the time of the murder was of major concern to the police that are investigating the case.
   A. When
   B. Why
   C. Whether
   D. Where

7. _____ surprised me most was the sudden change of his attitude.
   A. That
   B. Which
   C. What
   D. It

8. _____ follows is the list of goals for salt reduction for our typical

dieter.

    A. Who   B. When

    C. What   D. How

9. _____ he said at the meeting astonished everybody present.

    A. What   B. That

    C. The fact   D. The matter

10. _____ the boy said turned out to be true.

    A. Which   B. All that

    C. What   D. Where

11. _____ he had not locked the door before he left.

    A. That occurred to him   B. He occurred that

    C. To him it occurred   D. It occurred to him that

12. _____ deserves the award will certainly get it.

    A. Who we think   B. Whoever we think

    C. Who do you think   D. Whoever do we think

13. _____ hasn't been decided yet.

    A. When a meeting is taking place

    B. When a meeting will be taken place

    C. When will a meeting take place

    D. When a meeting will take place

14. _____ is necessary to us all is _____ we must know what we are fit for.

    A. It, what   B. As, what

    C. What, that   D. It, that

15. It is pretty well understood _____ controls the flow of carbon dioxide in and out the atmosphere today.

    A. that   B. when

    C. what   D. how

16. He feels sure that _____ wins the election will have the support of both parties.

    A. whoever   B. who

    C. anyone   D. those

17. _____ he couldn't understand was _____, as a teacher of Chinese, he was asked to teach English.

A. What, that   B. What, why

C. Which, why   D. That, what

18. _____ is that I have promised to make friends with the dishonest girl.

A. The only thing what I regret

B. All what I really regret most

C. What that I regret most

D. What I regret most

19. _____ gave you a present should be invited to the party.

A. Anyone   B. Who

C. No matter who   D. Whoever

20. After Yang Liwei succeeded in circling the earth, _____ our astronauts desire to do is walk in space.

A. where   B. what

C. that   D. how

21. _____ leaves the room last ought to turn off the lights.

A. Anyone   B. Those who

C. Whoever   D. Who

22. _____ our team lost the final was really a surprise to us. You can't imagine _____ disappointed we were.

A. That, how   B. That, what

C. /, that   D. What, that how

23. Although a lot of people say that any noise disturbs their concentration, _____ really influences their concentration is a change in the level of noise.

A. that   B. whatever

C. that what   D. what

24. In that mountainous primary school I found that _____ was required of a teacher never went beyond "reading, writing and adding".

A. it   B. what

C. whatever   D. anything

25. _____ we are doing has never been done before.

A. Whether   B. That

C. What   D. Which

26. It is doubtful _____ he knows it or not.
   A. whether   B. that
   C. if   D. what

27. _____ the hero had done and said _____ everyone present deeply.
   A. What, moved   B. That, to move
   C. What, moving   D. That, moved

28. _____ really matters at a debate is not what you say but the way you say it.
   A. What   B. That
   C. Whether   D. It

29. _____ comes will be welcome.
   A. Anyone   B. Whoever
   C. No matter who   D. The boy

30. _____ will attend the important meeting hasn't been decided yet.
   A. Who   B. Whoever
   C. Whomever   D. Those who

31. It doesn't matter _____ one says. _____ is important is the things _____ he does.
   A. that, What, which   B. what, That, that
   C. what, What, that   D. that, That, what

32. _____ we shall make the trip depends on _____ much money we have got.
   A. That, how   B. Whether, how
   C. When, so   D. If, how

33. Is it necessary _____ I should go there by plane?
   A. that   B. why
   C. how   D. when

34. _____ we are in need of money is quite clear to all.
   A. What   B. That
   C. If   D. Whatever

35. _____ he became a millionaire seemed a mystery.

A. How   B. What

C. Who   D. Which

36. Is _____ Mr. Black said at the meeting liked by all?

A. this   B. that

C. which   D. what

37. I am sure that _____ you said is wrong.

A. which   B. all

C. this   D. what

38. _____ she needs is a good rest.

A. That   B. What

C. The thing what   D. This job doing

39. What has _____ has been done!

A. been done   B. done

C. to be   D. to be done

40. _____ we will start the experiment depends on _____ we can get enough money.

A. If, whether   B. Whether, whether

C. Whether, that   D. If, that

41. _____ he made an important speech at yesterday's meeting was true.

A. That   B. Why

C. It was said   D. When

42. _____ she couldn't understand was _____ fewer and fewer students showed interest in her.

A. What, why   B. Why, that

C. What, because   D. That, that

43. _____ the hero and the heroine got married is not mentioned at the end of the story.

A. If   B. Whether

C. That   D. Which

44. It was the first time _____ I had met a man who held such a view.

A. when   B. that

C. in which   D. where

45. All the countries have agreed _____ bears the Red Cross must never be attacked.
    A. that whatever
    B. that
    C. that no matter what
    D. no matter what

46. It is a wonder _____ the boy, who had _____, could compose such beautiful music.
    A. of which, bad temper
    B. with which, a bad temper
    C. which, bad temper
    D. that, a bad temper

47. _____ a mother has a strong affection _____ her children.
    A. It is natural, to
    B. It is natural that, for
    C. As is known to all, to
    D. Natural, for

48. _____ wants to see the play can buy tickets in the office for students' union.
    A. Who
    B. Anyone
    C. Those who
    D. Whoever

49. _____ in the regulations that you should not tell other people the password of you e-mail account.
    A. What is required
    B. What requires
    C. It is required
    D. To require

50. Two little boys lost their way in a big city, and _____ made matters worse was that it began to rain heavily.
    A. it
    B. what
    C. which
    D. that

第十五讲　表语从句

1. One advantage of playing the guitar is _____ it can give you a great deal of pleasure.
   A. how B. why
   C. that D. when

2. The traditional view is _____ we sleep because our brain is "programmed" to make us do so.
   A. when B. why
   C. whether D. that

3. One reason for preference for city life is _____ she can have easy access to places like shops and restaurants.
   A. that B. how
   C. what D. why

4. Perseverance is a kind of quality — and that's _____ it takes to do anything well.
   A. what B. that
   C. which D. why

5. What the doctors really doubt is _____ my mother will recover from the serious disease soon.
   A. when B. how
   C. whether D. why

6. Go and get your coat. It's _____ you left it.
   A. there B. where
   C. there where D. where there

7. This is _____ the river was polluted.
   A. what B. how
   C. that D. whether

8. The reason why they are closing the factory is _____ they cannot get enough raw materials.
   A. for B. because

C. the fact   D. that

9. _____ all the inventions have in common is _____ they have succeeded.
   A. What, what   B. That, that
   C. What, that   D. That, what

10. Shanghai was _____ was once called as "the land for adventurers".
    A. that   B. what
    C. when   D. where

11. Some children like to eat food rich in fat and sugar. _____ they have weight problems and bad teeth.
    A. That's why   B. The fact is that
    C. There's the reason   D. It's how

12. To some people, the Sahara Desert is _____ "the sea of death".
    A. what we call   B. that we call
    C. we call it   D. which is called

13. I feel a bit disappointed as the new house isn't quite _____ it should be.
    A. that   B. what
    C. as   D. whatever

14. In movies, many things are not _____ they seem.
    A. as it   B. I like that
    C. as to what   D. what

15. The reason for his lateness is _____ he got up too late this morning.
    A. that   B. because
    C. for   D. why

16. The thing _____ I like to do is just _____ you want me to.
    A. what, what   B. that, that
    C. what, that   D. that, what

17. _____ surprised us all was _____ he did manage to stop smoking.
    A. That, that   B. What, what

  C. That, what   D. What, that

18. The problem is _____ or not we can find the right person to deal with the situation.
  A. why   B. how
  C. if   D. whether

19. The reason why he was late for class was _____ he got up too late.
  A. because   B. that
  C. how   D. so

20. The question for the new worker is _____ he can operate the machine correctly.
  A. whether   B. that
  C. if   D. because

21. Shanghai is no longer _____ it used to be twenty years ago.
  A. it   B. that
  C. what   D. which

22. _____ impressed the visitors deeply was _____ the workers made it with their hands.
  A. What, that   B. That, that
  C. What, what   D. That, what

23. The reason _____ he told me is _____ he was caught in the traffic jam.
  A. why, that   B. that, that
  C. what, why   D. /,/

24. The reason _____ he gave for his absence was _____ he had missed the bus.
  A. why, that   B. that, because
  C. why, because   D. which, that

25. The city is _____ we visited three years ago.
  A. where   B. the place where
  C. what   D. place which

第十六讲 同位语从句

1. Doris' success lies in the fact _____ she is co-operative and eager to learn from others.
   A. which
   B. that
   C. when
   D. why

2. The news _____ our athlete won another gold medal was reported in yesterday's newspaper.
   A. which
   B. whether
   C. what
   D. that

3. There is no obvious evidence _____ there is life on any other planet in the solar system.
   A. which
   B. that
   C. how
   D. where

4. There is clear evidence _____ the most difficult feeling of all to interpret is bodily pain.
   A. what
   B. if
   C. how
   D. that

5. Despite the fact _____ they lacked food, the explorers continued towards the goal.
   A. which
   B. that
   C. what
   D. whether

6. There is much truth in the idea _____ kindness is usually served by frankness.
   A. why
   B. which
   C. that
   D. whether

7. An idea has been repeatedly stressed _____ it is worthwhile for parents to participate in school activities together with their children.
   A. while
   B. as
   C. that
   D. why

8. The problem _____ the quality of the products is up to requirement has not been settled.
   A. if
   B. that
   C. what
   D. whether
9. I _____ the view _____ no one is able to fool all the people all the time.
   A. held, that
   B. held, which
   C. hold, that
   D. hold, which
10. _____, Walt Disney was born in Chicago in 1901.
    A. He was a great film maker
    B. A great film maker
    C. A great film maker who was
    D. Though a great film maker
11. It is no longer a question now _____ China is a strong country.
    A. that
    B. which
    C. whether
    D. what
12. We thought the idea _____ more computer lessons was a good one.
    A. that we should have
    B. having
    C. which we have
    D. about to have
13. The report is a clear sign _____ the city government is going to do something to make the river water clean again.
    A. in which
    B. that
    C. of which
    D. which
14. I have no idea _____.
    A. what does this sentence mean
    B. what the meaning of this sentence
    C. what this sentence means
    D. what's the meaning is this sentence
15. In the end the news came _____ all of them had been killed in the air crash, but we believed _____ things were not so bad.
    A. that, that
    B. /, /
    C. /, that
    D. that, which
16. I'll never forget the day _____ I joined the army.

125

A. that   B. which
C. in which   D. when

17. Steve had a wish _____ he would travel round the country
    after he retired.
    A. which   B. that
    C. what   D. in which

18. You have no idea _____ then.
    A. what a hard time we had   B. we had what a hard time
    C. what we had hard time   D. what hard time we had

19. Word came _____ the enemy officer had hanged himself.
    A. whether   B. if
    C. where   D. that

20. The fact has to be faced _____ few people like to work there
    with so little pay.
    A. what   B. how
    C. that   D. when

21. By the spring of 1945, there was no question in minds of Japan's
    leaders _____ their nation _____.
    A. how, had already been badly defeated
    B. that, was already defeated badly
    C. how, was already defeated badly
    D. that, had already been badly defeated

22. The scientist buried himself in his studies in the belief _____
    he could serve his country with his knowledge.
    A. when   B. that
    C. where   D. which

23. Along with the letter was his promise _____ he would visit me
    this coming Christmas.
    A. which   B. that
    C. what   D. whether

24. He pointed to the fact _____ they were not there.
    A. which   B. what
    C. that   D. /

25. A story goes _____ Elizabeth I of England liked nothing more

126

than being surrounded by clever and qualified noblemen at court.

A. when   B. where

C. what   D. that

26. His proposal _____ to see the art exhibition interested every one of us.

A. that we go   B. which we should go

C. that we would go   D. when we should go

27. The fact _____ English teaching had become business-driven is not surprising when considering the great number of learners of English throughout the world.

A. if   B. whether

C. that   D. why

28. There is a new problem involved in the popularity of private cars _____ road conditions need _____.

A. that, to be improved   B. which, to be improved

C. where, improving   D. when, improving

29. I don't know the day _____ John joined the club.

A. which   B. in which

C. when   D. what time

30. The reason _____ he went to Australia is for further study.

A. that   B. why

C. which   D. in which

第十七讲 状 语 从 句

1. _____ most of the earth's surface is covered by water, fresh water is very rare and precious.
   A. As   B. Once
   C. If   D. Although

2. A typhoon swept across this area with heavy rains and winds _____ strong as 113 miles per hour.
   A. too   B. very
   C. so   D. as

3. A dozen ideas were considered _____ the chief architect decided on the design of the building.
   A. because   B. before
   C. whether   D. unless

4. My parents were quarrelling about me _____ I could not quite tell why.
   A. since   B. though
   C. if   D. until

5. _____ there is a snowstorm or some other bad weather, the mail always comes on time.
   A. Because   B. If
   C. When   D. Unless

6. — Don't you know the school will provide us with everything, from bed sheets to drinking cups?
   — Yes. I am bringing this basin _____ I need it.
   A. for fear of   B. in case
   C. as long   D. so that

7. Pop music is such an important part of society _____ it has ever influenced our language.
   A. as   B. that
   C. which   D. where

8. Small sailboats can easily turn over in the winter _____ they are not managed carefully.
   A. though   B. before
   C. until   D. if

9. Please remind me of the meeting again tomorrow _____ I forget.
   A. though   B. so that
   C. in case   D. until

10. _____ this is only a small town, it's crowded with tourists who come here all year round.
   A. Since   B. Unless
   C. Once   D. Although

11. In my view, London's not as expensive in price as Tokyo but Tokyo is _____ in traffic.
   A. the most organized   B. more organized
   C. so organized as   D. as organized as

12. — Are you ready for Spain?
    — Yes, I want the girls to experience that _____ they are young.
   A. while   B. until
   C. if   D. before

13. The Great Wall is _____ tourist attraction that millions of people pour in every year.
   A. so a well-known   B. a so well-known
   C. such well-known a   D. such a well-known

14. You can't borrow books from the school library _____ you get your student card.
   A. before   B. if
   C. while   D. as

15. _____ some people come here for a short break, others have decided to stay forever.
   A. Because   B. If
   C. Once   D. While

16. _____ our manager objects to Tom's joining the club, we shall

accept him as a member.

A. Until   B. Unless

C. If   D. After

17. If a lot of people say a film is not good, I won't bother to see it or I'll wait _____ it comes out on DV D.

A. whether   B. after

C. though   D. until

18. The police officers in our city work hard _____ the rest of us can live a safe life.

A. in case   B. as if

C. in order that   D. only if

19. _____ you take a photo, you should always check the position of the sun.

A. Before   B. After

C. Because   D. Though

20. I have a tight budget for the trip, so I'm not going to fly _____ the airlines lower ticket prices.

A. once   B. if

C. after   D. unless

21. The map is one of the best tools a man has _____ he goes to a new place.

A. whenever   B. whatever

C. wherever   D. however

22. At a rough look, the new area of the city is about _____ the old one.

A. three times the size as   B. three times the size of

C. three times that is   D. three times what is

23. The businessman is very modest about his success. He says it's _____ the result of good luck as of his own diligence.

A. more than   B. so much

C. more   D. as much

24. Beijing was attacked by such a terrible sandstorm _____ few citizens had ever experienced.

A. which   B. that

C. as   D. when

25. The rich top-soil is easily washed away by floods _____ there are no trees.
    A. wherever   B. in any place
    C. in which   D. somewhere

26. _____ convincing an argument is, it needs support of evidence.
    A. No matter   B. Though
    C. However   D. As

27. _____ may point out our mistakes in the work, _____ he is.
    A. Whoever, anyone   B. Anyone, whoever
    C. One, whichever   D. Whenever, who

28. They are _____ little children that they can't have _____ much money.
    A. so, so   B. such, such
    C. such, so   D. so, such

29. The director gave me a better offer than _____.
    A. that of Dick's   B. Dick's
    C. he gave Dick   D. those of Dick

30. _____ your composition carefully, some spelling mistakes can be avoided.
    A. Having checked   B. Check
    C. If you check   D. To check

31. _____ everybody knows about it, I don't want to talk any more.
    A. For   B. Even
    C. Since   D. However

32. Paper produced every year is _____ the world's production of vehicles.
    A. the three times weight of
    B. three times the weight of
    C. as three times heavy as
    D. three times as heavier as

33. I thought her nice and honest _____ I met her.

A. first time   B. for the first time
C. the first time   D. by the first time

34. Jasmine was holidaying with her family in a wildlife park
_____ she was bitten on the leg by a lion.
 A. when   B. while
 C. since   D. once

35. We advertised for pupils last autumn, and got _____ 60.
 A. more than · B. more of
 C. as much as   D. so many as

36. It is _____ work of art that everyone wants to have a look at it.
 A. so unusual   B. such unusual
 C. such an unusual   D. so an unusual

37. _____ we do, we are bound to change the environment.
 A. What   B. Whatever
 C. Although   D. Even if

38. She found her calculator _____ she lost it.
 A. where   B. when
 C. in which   D. that

39. In summer people shut the doors and windows in the evening
_____ the insects can be kept out.
 A. unless   B. as long as
 C. in order that   D. while

40. Anyone can borrow books from the library _____ he has a
library card.
 A. so long as   B. since
 C. even though   D. unless

41. He was about to tell me the secret _____ someone patted him
on the shoulder.
 A. as   B. until
 C. while   D. when

42. It is six years _____ I came to this school.
 A. before   B. after
 C. when   D. since

43. You will succeed in the end _____ you give up halfway.

A. even if   B. as though
C. as long as   D. unless

44. _____ , Tom can never keek up with Jack in English study.
A. However he tried hard
B. No matter how hard he tries
C. No matter how he tries hard
D. As hard he tries

45. It worried her a bit _____ her hair was turning grey.
A. while   B. that
C. if   D. for

46. The foreigner spoke with signs _____ he could make listeners understand what he meant.
A. so that   B. if
C. because   D. as if

47. _____ the poem a second time, the meaning will become clearer to you.
A. Your having read   B. While reading
C. If reading   D. When you read

48. _____ much advice I gave him, he did exactly what he wanted to do.
A. How   B. Whatever
C. What   D. No matter how

49. She doesn't speak _____ her friend, but her written work is excellent.
A. as well as   B. so often as
C. so much as   D. as good as

50. — What was the party like?
— Wonderful. It's years _____ I enjoyed myself so much.
A. after   B. before
C. when   D. since

51. Sometimes the more you tell him, _____ .
A. less notice he will take   B. the little notice he takes
C. the less notice he takes   D. the least notice he will take

52. — How long has this bookshop been in business?

— _____ 1982.

    A. After   B. In

    C. From   D. Since

53. John plays football _____ , if not better than, David.

    A. as well   B. as well as

    C. so well   D. so well as

54. _____ Huggin had been fined $50 for careless driving he began to observe the traffic signs with more caution.

    A. That   B. Though

    C. Even if   D. After

55. Parents should take seriously their children's requests for sunglasses _____ eye protection is necessary in sunny weather.

    A. because   B. though

    C. unless   D. if

56. Sorry I didn't hear what you said just now _____ I was completely absorbed in my reading.

    A. so that   B. because

    C. now that   D. as if

57. I often spend weekends in Shanghai Library, _____ I can find a lot to read.

    A. where   B. as

    C. which   D. that

58. We had _____ hard time trying to work out the maths problem.

    A. so   B. a so

    C. such   D. such a

59. You are not supposed to park your bike _____ you are asked not to, for we don't have much parking space on our campus.

    A. which   B. where

    C. that   D. in which

60. Remember, science requires your whole life. _____ you had two lives to give, they would not be enough.

    A. Although   B. Though

    C. If only   D. Even if

61. The culture and customs of America are more like _____ of

134

English than of any other country.

    A. the one   B. the ones

    C. that   D. those

62. I'd like you to take my picture _____ stands the ancient tower.

    A. which   B. there

    C. that   D. where

63. You can no more swim than I can fly. The sentence means:

    _____.

    A. Both of us can't swim or fly

    B. You can never swim, which I am sure of

    C. Either you or I can fly

    D. You can swim as I can fly

64. Time passed quickly and three months went by _____ we knew it.

    A. after   B. till

    C. before   D. when

65. I am sure that Laura's latest play, _____ staged, will prove a great success.

    A. since   B. unless

    C. once   D. until

66. His handwriting is better than _____ in his class.

    A. anyone   B. anyone's

    C. anyone else   D. anyone else's

67. All animals, _____ their sizes are, breathe once for every four heartbeats.

    A. however   B. whatever

    C. no matter   D. in spite of

68. After the new technique was introduced, the factory produced _____ cars in 1999 as in the year before.

    A. as twice many   B. as many twice

    C. twice as many   D. twice as many as

69. Nothing _____ her more than _____ her son doing well at school.

    A. please, to hear   B. pleased, to hear

C. was pleased with, hearing   D. was pleased with, hearting

70. _____ , you have to do it for me.
    A. However you like it   B. No matter you like it
    C. Unless you like it   D. Whether you like it or not

71. The manager had declared the meeting open _____ we could make preparations for it.
    A. until   B. before
    C. unless   D. after

72. — The cake is delicious!
    — Well, at least it's _____ the one I baked last week.
    A. as worse as   B. no worse than
    C. no better than   D. as better than

73. Through long power lines electricity goes _____.
    A. to the place needed   B. there it is needed
    C. to the place it is needed   D. where it is needed

74. — Why don't you walk with me?
    — All right. I'll walk _____ the corner with you.
    A. at   B. until
    C. as far   D. as far as

75. The kind gentleman comforted the young boy who couldn't find his mother and promised that he would be with him _____ his mother came back.
    A. as soon as   B. while
    C. until   D. as

76. I'm afraid I won't have any influence on my husband _____ his mind is made up.
    A. the moment   B. once
    C. even   D. as soon as

77. Don't leave the sharp knife _____ our little Jane can get it.
    A. in which   B. to which
    C. that   D. where

78. It was three weeks _____ she realized that she was fooled by her friends.
    A. after   B. before

C. that   D. until
79. The newly-built Zhongshan Road is _____ before.
    A. as three times wide as   B. as wide as three times
    C. three times as wide as   D. as three times wider than
80. The sun had no sooner started to shine _____ it was clouded over again.
    A. than   B. when
    C. as   D. while
81. Everything will be all right _____ Tom is left to do the work in his own way.
    A. as far as   B. meanwhile
    C. so long as   D. in case
82. My new glasses cost me _____ the last pair that I bought.
    A. three times more than that
    B. three times as much as
    C. as much three times as
    D. as three times as much
83. How much _____, it will be worth it.
    A. does the watch cost   B. costs the watch
    C. the watch costs   D. the watch will cost
84. She wore clothes that were better than _____.
    A. the other girls   B. that of any other girl
    C. any other girl   D. those of any other girl
85. _____ I saw her, I remembered the task.
    A. While   B. The moment
    C. Suddenly   D. Soon as
86. The more Bill worked on the math problems, _____.
    A. he was much more confused
    B. and the much confused he was
    C. the more he was much confused
    D. the more confused he was
87. I was about to leave _____ someone knocked at my door.
    A. when   B. as soon as
    C. since   D. once

88. He is a warm-hearted man. _____ he does for the people, _____ he feels.
    A. The more, the happiest   B. The more, the happier
    C. The much, the happy   D. The many, the happier
89. Doctor Manatter wasn't set free _____ he was old and sick.
    A. when   B. since
    C. until   D. after
90. It is six years _____ his father came back from London.
    A. after   B. before
    C. since   D. until
91. Matches ought to be kept _____ children can't get them.
    A. from which   B. in which
    C. from where   D. where
92. It was midnight _____ we made up our minds to rescue the man stranded in the marsh straight away.
    A. that   B. until
    C. when   D. since
93. Don't turn to your dictionary _____ you come across a word that you don't know while reading.
    A. at the moment   B. when
    C. if   D. every time
94. _____ I know, middle school students are not accustomed to thinking in English when they are speaking to others.
    A. So far   B. As long as
    C. As far as   D. So long
95. Nearly a month had gone by _____ they gave up the price for which they had held out.
    A. until   B. while
    C. before   D. so that
96. — Dad, I've finished my assignment.
    — Good, and _____ you play or watch TV, you mustn't disturb me.
    A. whenever   B. whether
    C. whatever   D. no matter

97. Contrast may make something appear more beautiful than it is when _____ alone.
   A. it is seen   B. seeing
   C. to be seen   D. having been seen
98. Chinese are eating _____ eggs per person today as they did in the 1970s.
   A. more than twice   B. as twice
   C. twice more   D. more than twice as many
99. _____ to the top of the hill, the strength gave out.
   A. Getting   B. To get
   C. When they got   D. Having got
100. I haven't the slightest idea _____.
   A. where does he live   B. what he lives where
   C. where he lives   D. that where he lives
101. Send us a message _____ you have any difficulty.
   A. in case that   B. in case
   C. while   D. as
102. The purpose of the research had a more important meaning for them than _____.
   A. for ours   B. with us
   C. for ours it had   D. it did for us
103. There isn't such book in our library _____ I know.
   A. as soon as   B. as long as
   C. so far as   D. so much as
104. The money spent on social insurance last year was four times _____ ten years ago.
   A. that as much of   B. as much as of
   C. as much of that   D. as much as that of
105. Mr. Philips wanted to buy the ancient painting and told his wife _____ the painting cost, it would be _____ it.
   A. however, worth   B. whatever, worth
   C. how much, worthy   D. what, worthy of
106. It will be more than ten years _____ the city is rebuilt.
   A. after   B. before

C. when   D. that

107. *China Daily* is _____ a newspaper; it can also help us to improve our English.
    A. not more than   B. no more than
    C. more than   D. less than

108. _____ a bad habit is formed, it will not be easy to get rid of it.
    A. Since   B. Because
    C. Once   D. While

109. _____ I saw you I knew you were angry with me.
    A. A moment   B. In the moment
    C. The moment   D. At the moment

110. Watching a basketball match on TV is often _____ or even better than watching it in the gymnasium.
    A. as well   B. as good
    C. as well as   D. as good as

111. His father came home at night, and _____, he was drunk.
    A. as a result   B. that is to say
    C. what's more   D. sooner or later

112. Television is different from radio _____ it sends and receives pictures.
    A. in that   B. that
    C. in which   D. which

113. I'll get some beer in case Mike _____ this evening.
    A. came   B. comes
    C. would come   D. will come

114. _____ you dislike ancient monuments, Warrick Castle is worth a visit.
    A. Soon after   B. As soon as
    C. Even if   D. Now that

115. He has _____ little education _____ he is unable to find a job.
    A. such, that   B. so, and
    C. so, that   D. such, and

116. These stories expressed the same idea that all individuals, no matter how poor, were capable of becoming wealthy _____ they were hardworking and honest.
    A. if only   B. ever since
    C. in order that   D. so long as
117. Take your umbrella with you _____ it rains.
    A. since   B. because
    C. in case   D. for
118. There was _____ much water on the floor of the classroom _____ the students could not go in.
    A. such, that   B. no, and
    C. so, that   D. such, and
119. Not to waste time searching, Alex kept everything just _____ he could get his hands on it.
    A. where   B. as
    C. when   D. if
120. We deserve respect, _____ we are, if we behave in an honest and fair way.
    A. whether or not   B. who
    C. no matter who   D. how ever
121. Electricity flows through a wire _____ water flows through a pipe.
    A. while   B. just as
    C. much as   D. whenever
122. Some children are mad over video games. They just can't tear themselves away from them _____ they start.
    A. since   B. once
    C. even if   D. as
123. It's a terrible thing to work in a dirty place _____ you have been used to a clean environment.
    A. when   B. that
    C. as   D. where
124. The beauty of the West Lake is _____ I can describe.
    A. more than   B. no more than

C. not more than   D. rather than

125. _____ sick _____ well, she is always cheerful.

   A. Either, or   B. No matter, or
   C. Whether, or   D. Even, or

126. I'll discuss it with you any time _____.

   A. you are convenient   B. it is convenient to you
   C. of convenience for you   D. for your convenience

127. Young people are not ready to believe something just _____
their teachers or parents say so.

   A. that   B. like
   C. because   D. for

128. He has sold 100 copies of *the Evening Paper*, but I've sold
_____.

   A. twice as many   B. twice
   C. twice too many   D. twice the amount

129. Food shortage will long be a world problem, _____ much has
been done to supply enough for everyone.

   A. although   B. even
   C. no matter   D. since

130. _____, the doctors were sure of its success.

   A. However difficult the operation might be
   B. However the operation might be difficult
   C. Whatever difficult the operation might be
   D. Whether might the operation be difficult or not

131. I happened to be caught in a heavy rain, and it was just a couple
of minutes _____ I was wet through.

   A. when   B. that
   C. before   D. since

132. If Sam doesn't agree to have the part in the play, we can choose
another equally _____.

   A. as well   B. as good
   C. better   D. the best

133. _____ in a new environment, old habits may soon be forgotten.

   A. Once we settle   B. Settled

C. Settling   D. Having settled
134. His heart was filled with joy _____ of arriving home in a
couple of days.
A. when thinking   B. when he thought
C. having thought   D. to think
135. The new swimming pool is _____ the old one.
A. the two thirds size of   B. two thirds the size of
C. two thirds as much as   D. as two thirds big as
136. I had to buy _____ these books because I didn't know which
one was the best.
A. both   B. none
C. neither   D. all
137. The feature report, _____ long in length, still attracted
many readers, who couldn't stop once they started reading it.
A. though   B. thought which was
C. as it was   D. as though
138. A man will suffer brain injury if he gets no air for _____ four
or five minutes.
A. as long as   B. so long as
C. as much as   D. so far as
139. He was looking for his briefcase _____ he might have put it.
A. wherever he thought   B. where he thought that
C. as he thought   D. in the places he thought
140. The girl wasn't afraid _____ she had been with other people.
A. as long as   B. unless
C. except that   D. if only
141. _____ careless in a wild zoo where there are beasts around,
accidents are likely to happen.
A. Be   B. Being
C. If you are   D. To be
142. — That's a beautiful dress you gave my daughter for her
birthday.
— I hope it's big enough for her; _____, you can exchange
it.

A. not so　　　　　　　　B. not that
C. if not　　　　　　　　D. if no

143. — You are going to Shanghai with us, aren't you? I want to show everybody around my hometown.
— Yes. I certainly won't miss it, especially _____ the tour guide is a native in Shanghai.
A. that　　　　　　　　B. when
C. unless　　　　　　　D. while

144. Nowhere have I seen _____ untidy office than my friend James's.
A. a more　　　　　　　B. more an
C. the most　　　　　　D. a most

145. Leading a hard life is not always a bad thing. Sometimes, _____ life is, _____ it will do to young people.
A. the harder, the better　　B. the hardest, the best
C. harder, the better　　　　D. the harder, the more good

146. I _____ my place when I _____ a small coin a few feet away from my desk.
A. had just taken, noticed
B. just took, had noticed
C. was just taking, noticed
D. just took, was noticing

147. Time spent in a bookshop can be most enjoyable, _____ you are a booklover _____ go there to buy a book as a present.
A. whether, or　　　　　　B. even if, or else
C. both, and　　　　　　　D. however, or

148. You may have some difficulty in operating the machine at first. _____ , telephone us at once.
A. It being the case　　　　B. If so
C. If it is　　　　　　　　D. When possible

149. Don't touch those papers. Leave them _____ .
A. as they are　　　　　　B. wherever they are
C. where they do　　　　　D. when they have

150. Try _____ he might, Tom could not get out of the trouble.

144

A. as if   B. although
C. if   D. as

151. He speaks English well indeed, but of course not _____ a native speaker.
   A. as fluent as   B. more fluent than
   C. so fluently as   D. much fluently than

152. It was an exciting moment for the player, _____ for the first time he had entered the semi-final.
   A. that   B. while
   C. which   D. when

153. It was several days _____ the patient was able to sit up and eat himself.
   A. since   B. that
   C. when   D. before

154. _____ I admire that artist's work, I don't like him personally.
   A. While   B. As
   C. Until   D. As long as

155. Good eating habits mean eating breakfast. _____ you eat breakfast, you do not eat a proper meal from dinner the night before until lunch the next day.
   A. If   B. When
   C. As   D. Unless

156. It was reported that the enemy was _____ their army.
   A. twice as larger as   B. twice the size of
   C. the twice larger of   D. as twice large as

157. Meeting with difficulties, some see a hopeless end, _____ others see an endless hope.
   A. so   B. however
   C. while   D. otherwise

158. *A Tale of Two Cities* is _____ a novel. It helps us to understand the history of that time.
   A. not more than   B. no more than
   C. more than   D. less than

159. He has never seen _____ little worms in _____ big a hole.
    A. so, so
    B. such, such
    C. such, so
    D. so, such
160. I like watching TV _____ to the cinema.
    A. more than to go
    B. more than going
    C. than going
    D. rather than to go
161. My new computer works _____ the one I bought three years ago.
    A. ten times as fast as
    B. ten times faster
    C. ten times more than
    D. as ten times as
162. _____ you go on trying, you will succeed sooner or later.
    A. As soon as
    B. As far as
    C. As long as
    D. As well as
163. You may have some trouble in writing the article, _____, don't hesitate to ask me for help.
    A. if not
    B. if so
    C. if that
    D. if any
164. There has been little change in the patient's condition _____ he began to be treated.
    A. since
    B. after
    C. when
    D. as
165. At a rough estimate. Nigeria is _____ the Great Britain.
    A. three times the size as
    B. the size three times of
    C. three times as the size of
    D. three times the size of
166. We had heard about this new-type machine _____ we saw it.
    A. before long
    B. long before
    C. long ago
    D. before a long time
167. The crowd started cheering _____ he rose to speak.
    A. as
    B. since
    C. till
    D. where
168. Many people prefer to spend their weekends in Shanghai Library, _____ all kinds of books are available to them.
    A. where
    B. as
    C. which
    D. that

169. You can use _____ you need, but don't waste it.
    A. so much water that   B. much water just as
    C. water as much as   D. as much water as
170. It is already five years _____ we knew each other.
    A. since   B. after
    C. when   D. as
171. Don't leave here _____ your mother comes back.
    A. when   B. while
    C. after   D. until
172. The more she tried to listen to him, _____ she could understand.
    A. much   B. much more
    C. the less   D. the least
173. There are not _____ many students in their school _____ in our school.
    A. so, as   B. so, than
    C. such, as   D. too, than
174. No. 1 reading room is _____ No. 2 reading room.
    A. twice as big as   B. as big twice as
    C. as twice big as   D. as big as twice
175. I was not able to work out the problem _____ my teacher explained it.
    A. as   B. unless
    C. until   D. when
176. The programs were _____ than I had expected.
    A. very better   B. more better
    C. far better   D. very much better
177. It is nearly half a century _____ the first computer was invented.
    A. when   B. that
    C. since   D. until
178. We have only a sofa, a table and a bed in our new apartment. We need to buy _____ more furniture.
    A. any   B. many

      C. little   D. some

179. _____ the letter, a smile came to her face.

      A. Reading   B. Having read

      C. After reading   D. While she was reading

180. She looks young but she is _____ than her younger sister.

      A. three years younger   B. three younger years

      C. three years older   D. older three years

181. You've got to school _____ than he.

      A. earlier 20 minutes   B. 20 minutes earlier

      C. 20 minutes early   D. early 20 minutes

182. _____ the price is, they are ready to pay.

      A. However   B. Whichever

      C. Whenever   D. Whatever

183. To my surprise, the so-called cheap restaurant was _____ I expected.

      A. as expensive as twice   B. as twice expensive as

      C. expensive as twice as   D. twice as expensive as

184. If a person _____ doesn't eat or drink for a few days, he will not stay alive any longer.

      A. who   B. that

      C. /   D. he

185. I am sorry _____ I don't think it is the best way to solve the problem.

      A. and   B. as

      C. but   D. unless

186. _____ her son had come back, her face lit up.

      A. Hearing   B. Having heard

      C. While hearing   D. When she heard

187. How I wish I could have received her letter _____ I left!

      A. till   B. since

      C. before   D. until

188. Sometimes rain clouds and smoke caused by pollution look so much alike _____ one can hardly tell the difference between the two of them.

A. and   B. that
C. since   D. because

189. _____ whales are very large, they are no longer an even match for man.
A. Since   B. Because
C. Now that   D. Although

190. _____ coal is burned, the chemical energy is turned into heat energy.
A. When   B. Just as
C. Though   D. Now that

191. Children need education _____ they need air and water.
A. because   B. when
C. just as   D. since

192. All matter, _____ it is solid, liquid or gas, is made up of atoms.
A. if   B. no matter
C. even though   D. whether

193. You must do the experiment _____ the teacher told you.
A. as   B. since
C. so that   D. unless

194. _____ your daughter hasn't come back, let me take you to the Friendship Hospital.
A. When   B. Since
C. That   D. For

195. Stand _____ you are. Don't move.
A. where   B. wherever
C. as   D. if

196. Jane didn't know this news _____ I told it to her.
A. since   B. after
C. before   D. when

197. It was not long _____ the news spread out.
A. since   B. until
C. when   D. before

198. _____ Tom is not feeling well today, he has to stay at home.

A. Though   B. For
C. Finding   D. As

199. The teacher is explaining _____ sentence as _____ last period.

 A. the same difficult, he did it

 B. such a difficult, he did so

 C. as a difficult, he did

 D. as difficult a, he did

200. Take this suitcase and _____ you can find enough space.

 A. put it which   B. put it in which

 C. put it wherever   D. put where

第十八讲 定语从句

1. You can find whatever you need at the shopping centre, _____ is always busy at the weekend.
   A. that   B. where
   C. what   D. which

2. In an hour, we can travel to places _____ would have taken our ancestors days to reach.
   A. where   B. when
   C. which   D. what

3. The thought of going back home was _____ kept him happy while he was working abroad.
   A. that   B. all that
   C. all what   D. which

4. The mayor has offered a reward of $5,000 to _____ who can capture the tiger alive or dead.
   A. both   B. others
   C. anyone   D. another

5. His movie won several awards at the film festival, _____ was beyond his wildest dream.
   A. which   B. that
   C. where   D. it

6. Villagers here depend on the fishing industry, _____ there won't be much work.
   A. where   B. that
   C. by which   D. without which

7. We went through a period _____ communications were very difficult in the rural areas.
   A. which   B. whose
   C. in which   D. with which

8. Mozart's birthplace and the house _____ he composed *The*

Magic Flute are both museums now.

    A. where   B. when

    C. there   D. which

9. Samuel survived when the car _____ he was a passenger in turned off the road and hit a tree.

    A. where   B. which

    C. as   D. why

10. Wind power is an ancient source of energy _____ we may return in the near future.

    A. on which   B. by which

    C. to which   D. from which

11. You'll find taxis waiting at the bus station _____ you can hire to reach your lost family.

    A. which   B. where

    C. when   D. as

12. Sailing across the ocean alone was an achievement _____ took courage.

    A. what   B. who

    C. which   D. where

13. Have you sent thank-you notes to the relatives from _____ you received gifts?

    A. which   B. them

    C. that   D. whom

14. The flood overflowed the riverbanks, _____ frequently happened in that area.

    A. as it   B. which

    C. it   D. such

15. Edith has invented a device _____ can solve the problem of saving electricity.

    A. what she claims   B. she claims it

    C. as she claims   D. which she claims

16. The can opener is easy to handle, _____ is shown in the picture.

    A. as it   B. as

C. that   D. since

17. The more the young man practiced, the worse he played, for
_____ he played was improper.
A. the way   B. his way which
C. whose way that   D. a way

18. Detergents in composition depend on the cleaning task _____
intended.
A. which they   B. for which they are
C. they are   D. in which they

19. She's the girl _____ when you entered the office.
A. that we were talking
B. we were talking about
C. what we were talking about
D. which we were talking

20. _____ is known to everybody, the moon travels round the
earth once every month.
A. It   B. As
C. That   D. What

21. _____ is mentioned above, the number of the students in
senior high schools is increasing.
A. Which   B. As
C. That   D. It

22. He made another wonderful discovery, _____ of great
importance to science.
A. which I think is   B. which I think it is
C. which I think it   D. I think which is

23. He was very rude to the Customs officer, _____ of course
made things even worse.
A. who   B. whom
C. what   D. which

24. Mrs. Brown was much disappointed to see the washing machine
she had had _____ went wrong again.
A. it   B. it repaired
C. repaired   D. to be repaired

25. All of the flowers now raised here have developed from those _____ in the forest.
    A. once they grew   B. they grew once
    C. that once grew   D. once grew
26. Recently I bought an ancient Chinese vase, _____ was very reasonable.
    A. which price   B. the price of which
    C. its price   D. the price of whose
27. He's got himself into a dangerous situation _____ he is likely to lose control over the plane.
    A. where   B. which
    C. while   D. why
28. Alec asked the policeman _____ he worked to contact him whenever there was an accident.
    A. with him   B. who
    C. with whom   D. whom
29. I will never forget the days _____ we spent together in the village.
    A. /   B. when
    C. what   D. how
30. Have you seen the film *Titanic*, _____ leading actor is world famous?
    A. its   B. it's
    C. whose   D. which
31. Mr. Zhang gave the textbooks to all the pupils except _____ who had already taken them.
    A. the ones   B. ones
    C. some   D. the others
32. In the dark street, there wasn't a single person _____ she could turn for help.
    A. that   B. who
    C. from whom   D. to whom
33. A fast food restaurant is the place _____, just as the name suggests, eating is performed quickly.

A. which   B. where
C. there   D. what
34. In the office I never seem to have time until after 5:30 p. m.,
    _____ many people have gone home.
    A. whose time   B. that
    C. on which   D. by which time
35. We want such materials _____ can bear high temperature and
    pressure.
    A. that   B. as
    C. what   D. which
36. In Northwest China, there are some areas _____ are short of
    daily necessaries and material service.
    A. where   B. which
    C. in which   D. on which
37. I was late for school this morning because of the traffic jam
    _____ I was caught.
    A. which   B. where
    C. in which   D. when
38. They bought a good number of novels yesterday, _____ are
    those written by Charles Dickens.
    A. that   B. among them
    C. among which   D. such
39. There are 45 students in our class, _____ some are from
    Beijing.
    A. /   B. of them
    C. of whom   D. who
40. Has everything _____ can be done _____ done?
    A. /, /   B. /, been
    C. that, been   D. that, be
41. Have you ever _____ to the museum _____ we paid a visit
    last year?
    A. been, which   B. been, to which
    C. gone, which   D. gone, to which
42. All _____ is a continuous supply of the basic necessities of

life.
    A. is needed   B. for our need
    C. which is needed   D. that is needed

43. He showed us a photo of Mary, _____ was taken in Hong
    Kong in 1997.
    A. which   B. that
    C. who   D. what

44. Is this bike _____ you would like to _____?
    A. that, repair   B. the one that, have repaired
    C. that, be repaired   D. which, repair

45. He isn't the person who _____ to ask favors of _____.
    A. likely, other   B. likes, the others
    C. is likely, others   D. is likely, other

46. They must also make use of such open forms of struggle
    _____ permitted by law.
    A. as are   B. who are
    C. which is   D. that is

47. Can you find me something _____?
    A. to open the tin   B. that I can open the tin
    C. I can open the tin with   D. by which to open the tin

48. She was much disappointed to find the watch she _____ went
    wrong again.
    A. had it repaired   B. had had repaired
    C. would repair   D. repaired

49. The reporters have found the clerk _____ it was _____
    saved the drowning child last week.
    A. which, who   B. whoever, that
    C. who, that   D. whom, who

50. The director of the enterprise places hope on _____ have the
    open-up ideas.
    A. anyone   B. who
    C. those who   D. the young

51. The scientists and technicians overcame a lot of difficulties
    _____ the personal computer.

A. they had developing   B. having developing

C. they had developed   D. which has to develop

52. In the lonely village, there was not a single person _____ the poor girl could turn for help.

    A. from whom   B. by whom

    C. on whom   D. to whom

53. Water dissolves a part of nearly everything _____ it comes in contact.

    A. where   B. with which

    C. that   D. as soon as

54. There is no one _____ has a few faults in the world.

    A. who   B. that

    C. but   D. whom

55. _____, everyone should handle these glass instrument with care.

    A. As was mentioned just now

    B. As having mentioned just now

    C. Mentioned as just now

    D. As just now being mentioned

56. — Is this camera _____ you want to buy?

    — Yes, this is the _____ camera I have been hunting for.

    A. which, very   B. the one, very

    C. that, one   D. what, what

57. _____ is known _____ all, the earth is round, just like a ball.

    A. As, to   B. Which, for

    C. As, for   D. It, to

58. I sent invitations to 80 people, _____ have replied.

    A. of whom only 30 of these

    B. only 30 of these who

    C. of whom only 30

    D. only 30 who

59. Alf used to get _____ he gets now.

    A. five times the money

    B. as much five times money as

C. twice the money as much as

D. twice as much as the money

60. I have a house, _____ the south.

    A. that window opens

    B. the window of which opens to

    C. whose window open to

    D. the windows of which open to

61. The United States is made up of fifty states, one of _____ is separated from the others by the Pacific Ocean.

    A. them   B. those

    C. which   D. whose

62. We will discuss such problems _____ something to do with our own interests.

    A. which has   B. as have

    C. as has   D. that have

63. He is such an outstanding leader _____ is loved by the people throughout the country.

    A. as   B. that

    C. which   D. who

64. I can't think of many cases _____ students obviously knew a lot of English words and expressions to write a good essay.

    A. why   B. which

    C. as   D. where

65. The size of the audience, _____ we had expected, was well over five hundred.

    A. whom   B. that

    C. who   D. as

66. — Which book do you think is best?

    — The one _____.

    A. is your favourite   B. you found

    C. it is also your favourite   D. worth reading it

67. Do you know anything about the fire _____ in the neighbourhood yesterday?

    A. which broke out   B. breaking out

C. broken out   D. that was broke

68. For a long time scientists have been trying to use computers to copy _____ brain works.

    A. the way   B. the way how

    C. in the way   D. in the way how

69. Anderson is the tennis player _____ will win the final in the tennis season.

    A. who we expect   B. whom we expect

    C. who we expect that   D. we expect him

70. Computers, _____ have many uses, cannot completely take the place of humans.

    A. though   B. which

    C. in spite they   D. even if

71. The police questioned everyone _____ there, _____ to find who was the last person to leave the office.

    A. having been, trying   B. being, tried

    C. who had been, trying   D. to have been, to try

72. _____ we had hoped, Li Yang was admitted into Beijing University.

    A. Like   B. As

    C. Which   D. What

73. The shop assistant I spoke _____ nothing.

    A. to say   B. to said

    C. said   D. to tell

74. American women usually identify their best friend as someone _____ they can talk frequently.

    A. who   B. as

    C. about which   D. with whom

75. Next winter _____ you will spend in Harbin, I'm sure, will be another exciting holiday.

    A. which   B. when

    C. in which   D. where

76. _____ often happened, Miss Sullivan slowly spelt the word onto Hellen's hand again.

A. Like   B. As
C. It   D. When

77. Among the most harmful species of insects are _____ that spread diseases.
A. which   B. who
C. those   D. these

78. You have to return the watch to _____ lost it.
A. the man   B. the one who
C. whom   D. whose

79. Scientists do not always have the same idea. One thing _____ they cannot agree is the origin of the universe.
A. with which   B. where
C. that   D. on which

80. Advertising can increase product sales, _____ has long been proved.
A. it   B. as it
C. as   D. which it

81. Greenland, _____ island in the world, covers over two million square kilometres.
A. it is the largest   B. that is the largest
C. is the largest   D. which is the largest

82. The excitement of diving into the sea is hard to explain to _____ hasn't done it.
A. anyone   B. those who
C. whoever that   D. someone who

83. _____ confidence I had was gone when I heard nearly all my classmates failed the driving test.
A. A little   B. The little
C. Little   D. Little of

84. He was offered a choice of two jobs, and he decided to take _____ was nearer to his house.
A. whatever   B. one
C. that which   D. the one which

85. Morgan was the only opponent _____ defeat me in the next

few matches.

A. who I imagined could   B. I imagined he could
C. I imagined could   D. that I imagined to

86. — What do you want for dinner, David?

— _____ you pick is fine with me.

A. Something   B. Any other
C. Everyone   D. Anything

87. John, _____ the instructions before the experiment, failed to get the desired result.

A. had read   B. who had read
C. who having read   D. to have read

88. Mrs. Wilson never gives her children more money _____ necessary.

A. than it is   B. than is
C. than they are   D. if she is

89. _____ has been planned, we'll leave the next step to you.

A. It   B. What
C. As   D. Such

90. When the mid-term exam was over, I went fishing — _____ I hadn't done for weeks.

A. anything   B. everything
C. nothing   D. something

91. She spent a lot of time preparing for the interview, _____ was quite unnecessary.

A. which I thought   B. which I thought it
C. and I thought she   D. but which I thought

92. This is the question _____.

A. that we've had so much discussion
B. we've discussed about
C. we've had so much discussion about
D. of which we've discussed

93. Have you heard the news _____ reported from the flooded area?

A. that   B. that was
C. that it was   D. was

94. The house _____ were broken was empty.
   A. of which the windows   B. windows of which
   C. and its windows   D. and whose windows
95. The students should be encouraged to read such books _____
   good for them.
   A. that are   B. as they are
   C. as are   D. that they are
96. The curious boy didn't believe the fact _____.
   A. most of us thought to be true
   B. that most of us thought it were to be true
   C. what most of us thought was true
   D. as most of us thought true
97. This is the very dictionary _____ I want to buy.
   A. to which   B. that
   C. which   D. what
98. This is the only thing _____ now.
   A. what I can do   B. I can do
   C. I can do it   D. which I can do
99. Tom is _____ of the boy students who is often late for school.
   A. the only one   B. one
   C. a boy   D. one boy
100. This building is _____ the other one.
   A. as the same height as   B. high as
   C. as higher as   D. the same height as
101. John is one of the students _____ the exercise.
   A. whom have finished   B. who has finished
   C. whom has finished   D. who haven't finished
102. Mother is very pleased with _____ you have told her and all
   _____ you have given her.
   A. what, that   B. that, what
   C. all, what   D. what, which
103. Men and horses _____ were killed at the battle were difficult
   to count.
   A. who   B. what

C. which   D. that

104. _____ glitters is not gold.
   A. All that   B. What
   C. All which   D. Anything

105. They have three sons, all _____ are interested in art.
   A. of them   B. of which
   C. of whom   D. that

106. Galileo made a telescope _____ he could observe the sky.
   A. on which   B. at which
   C. through which   D. that

107. Robert is good at languages, _____ we all know.
   A. because   B. for
   C. as   D. since

108. He is interested in _____ I have told him.
   A. that   B. all that
   C. which   D. all what

109. Read the text a second time and you will probably know what the principle _____ a hovercraft works.
   A. is on that   B. has on which
   C. is on which   D. on which

110. Dried foods are invaluable to climbers, explorers and soldiers in battle, _____ little storage space.
   A. which have   B. which has
   C. who have   D. that has

111. The first doll _____ say "mama" was invented in 1830.
   A. that it could   B. could
   C. it could   D. that could

112. The growing speed of a plant is influenced by a number of factors, _____ are beyond our control.
   A. most of them   B. most of which
   C. most of what   D. most of that

113. He was wearing the same hat _____ he'd had _____ on the day before.
   A. as, it   B. /, /

C. which, /   D. which, it

114. Can you tell me something about the accident _____ this morning?
    A. that happened   B. which was happened
    C. that was happened   D. which had happened

115. Everything was quite all right _____ one day _____ ·she got into trouble.
    A. not until, when   B. until, before
    C. not until, before   D. until, when

116. All _____ is a large sum of money.
    A. what is needed   B. that is needed
    C. the thing needed   D. for their needs

117. The boys _____ talked to just now are from Nanjing.
    A. I   B. who
    C. whose I   D. what I

118. The girl won an Olympic gold medal, _____ made her mother very proud.
    A. it   B. which
    C. that   D. this

119. Who is the man _____?
    A. to whom you just talked
    B. you just talked
    C. that you just talked
    D. who you just talked

120. Tom refused to take my advice _____ he failed to win the game, _____ was expected by all of us.
    A. but, which   B. though, and
    C. so, as   D. until, though

121. We went to different places _____ you find people _____ language was hard to understand.
    A. that, which   B. where, which
    C. in where, of which   D. where, whose

122. She went to the town _____ she stayed for three months _____ the piano.

A. and, for teaching   B. where, teaching

C. so that, to teach   D. because, by teaching

123. She is the only one of his daughters _____ been abroad.

     A. which has   B. which have

     C. who has   D. who have

124. Is this the engineer _____ your teacher said saved the train as well as all the passengers?

     A. /   B. who

     C. whom   D. of whom

125. This is the best novel _____ we have read in recent years.

     A. which   B. that

     C. and   D. so

126. The teacher _____ has been regarded as the best one in our school.

     A. who you talked   B. about whom talked

     C. you talked about   D. that you talked

127. Of course you'll have to go back the same way _____ you came.

     A. where   B. that

     C. which   D. as

128. The lawyer showed the policeman the place _____ the man was murdered.

     A. that   B. which

     C. where   D. when

129. I'll tell you all _____ I have learned about the accident.

     A. what   B. which

     C. whom   D. /

130. Soon he got to London, _____, some days later, he started his business.

     A. when   B. where

     C. that   D. which

131. He showed us round the house _____ he paid quite a lot of money.

     A. which   B. that

C. for which   D. on which

132. I've got a book _____ will interest you.
 A. I'm sure   B. and which
 C. and I'm sure which   D. which I'm sure

133. Such a film _____ was shown in the cinema yesterday is not
 worth seeing.
 A. as   B. that
 C. which   D. it

134. The video tape will give you some idea of _____ an astronaut
 has to experience in space.
 A. how   B. all that
 C. that   D. all what

135. Tigers live in forests, _____ there are plenty of other
 animals for them to hunt for food.
 A. when   B. if
 C. as   D. where

136. He paid the boy $10 for cleaning the windows, most of
 _____ hadn't been cleaned for at least a year.
 A. these   B. those
 C. them   D. which

137. The books here, _____ have beautiful pictures in them, were
 written by famous writers.
 A. which   B. where
 C. all   D. that

138. Jenny smiled _____ her mother did when she was Jenny's age.
 A. what   B. as if
 C. the way   D. that

139. Upon graduation, I asked the roommate _____ I lived to
 keep in touch with me at any time.
 A. who   B. with them
 C. whom   D. with whom

140. That was said to be the worst traffic accident _____ on A20
 Highway.
 A. having been happened   B. being happened

C. that had happened   D. ever happened

141. Having changed a lot, our hometown isn't the same _____.
    A. as it used to be   B. as it used to
    C. like what it was   D. like it was

142. Do you know the house _____ Mr. Smith had once lived?
    A. which   B. that
    C. in that   D. in which

143. Engels, _____ native language was German, could read and write in several foreign languages.
    A. who   B. whose
    C. that   D. which

144. The two things _____ Marx wasn't sure were grammar and idioms.
    A. about which   B. about that
    C. in which   D. at which

145. The book _____ isn't in the library.
    A. what I need   B. that I need it
    C. which I need it   D. I need

146. Now we can fly to Tokyo. There was a time _____ we had to take a boat.
    A. how   B. what
    C. why   D. when

147. Is this interesting book _____ he read last night?
    A. that   B. the one
    C. which   D. one

148. Did you tell your brother all _____ you had seen on your way home?
    A. that   B. what
    C. why   D. how

149. The old type of car must be, _____ it seems to me, replaced by a new one.
    A. which   B. as
    C. what   D. that

150. She keeps her keys and money in the handbag, _____ she

takes with her everywhere.

    A. which   B. so

    C. therefore   D. when

151. I am going to buy the same bicycle _____ you are using now.

    A. that   B. which

    C. as   D. like

152. Most of the students in his class want to know the way _____ he learns English.

    A. in which   B. which

    C. by which   D. about which

153. Is that woman _____ wants to talk to me sometime?

    A. who   B. the who

    C. the one   D. the one who

154. The novels, _____ I read some, are intended to deal with our daily life.

    A. that   B. which

    C. of which   D. in which

155. The sun beats the earth, _____ is very important to living things.

    A. that   B. what

    C. which   D. where

156. The knife _____ we used to cut the bread is very sharp.

    A. with which   B. with it

    C. with that   D. which

157. The film I saw yesterday is the best one _____ I've ever seen.

    A. which   B. what

    C. of which   D. /

158. _____ in today's newspaper, all the schools will open on September 1.

    A. As it is announced   B. As are announced

    C. As is announced   D. As they are announced

159. Have you got anything _____?

    A. which belongs to you   B. that belong to you

C. that is belonged to you   D. that belongs to you

160. _____ is announced in today's paper, they have succeeded in solving many problems in accordance with the new theory.
   A. Which   B. As
   C. What   D. That

161. We have to consider _____ to do in situations _____ there are many people involved.
   A. how, when   B. what, when
   C. how, where   D. what, where

162. The mineral resources _____ modern industry depends are running out quickly.
   A. that   B. where
   C. which   D. on which

163. Yesterday I bought a Chinese painting _____ was very reasonable.
   A. which price   B. the price of which
   C. its price   D. the price of whose

164. Forty-year-old Maradona, _____ soccer career was disgraced by drug violations, played more active soccer in 2000 than Ronaldo — the best young player to appear during the 1990s.
   A. who   B. for whom
   C. whose   D. of whom

165. Oh, look! That is the very disc _____.
   A. that I am going to buy
   B. that I am going to buy it
   C. which I am going to buy
   D. for which I am going to pay it

166. His wife, _____ Mr. White has been married for ten years, is still childish.
   A. to whom   B. with whom
   C. who   D. /

167. Fewer people _____ we had expected were present at that meeting.
   A. whom   B. who

C. that   D. than

168. Who reported to the police the accident _____ in the nearby
     street last Sunday?
     A. happened   B. happening
     C. that happened   D. which had happened

169. It is in the very factory _____ we worked last year that we
     will work for two weeks next month.
     A. that   B. where
     C. which   D. when

170. He found no way _____ I think is of great value to the study
     of science.
     A. that   B. in which
     C. which   D. /

171. One of my neighbours, _____ son is a journalist, was found
     _____ yesterday morning.
     A. his, dying   B. whose, died
     C. his, death   D. whose, dead

172. That tree, the branches _____ are almost bare, is a very old
     one.
     A. whose   B. of which
     C. in which   D. on which

173. About two hundred people died in the accident, _____
     children.
     A. many of them were   B. many of them are
     C. many of whom were   D. whom of many were

174. Is this _____ you have heard?
     A. the reason   B. the reason why
     C. why   D. reason that

175. Don't let the child who is _____ swim in rivers.
     A. not old enough   B. too young to
     C. not old enough to   D. young enough to

176. The plane was delayed, _____ was that the weather was
     terrible.
     A. the reason why   B. the reason for it

C. the reason of it   D. the reason for which

177. Tom is the boy _____ I think won the 100-metre dash.
   A. who   B. about who
   C. about whom   D. whom

178. The price of the camera, _____ we had expected, was more than one thousand *yuan*.
   A. what   B. as
   C. that   D. which

179. Mary, _____ parents died early, had to take care of herself.
   A. who   B. which
   C. of which   D. whose

180. All the novels here _____ you gave me one, are very instructive.
   A. they   B. of which
   C. it   D. which

181. _____ it turned out, the badly wounded soldier was the old man's long lost son.
   A. As   B. When
   C. Because   D. So

182. Has all _____ taught _____ learned by heart?
   A. were, been   B. that was, been
   C. had, been   D. he, /

183. Delia's going to join us, _____ was agreed the day before yesterday.
   A. it   B. that
   C. what   D. as

184. I think you've got to the point _____ , a change is needed, otherwise you'll fail.
   A. when   B. that
   C. where   D. which

185. John is the very boy _____ the foolish thing.
   A. whom I think did   B. whom I think that did
   C. who I think that he did   D. who I think did

186. — How far apart do they live?

— _____, I know, they live in the same neighbourhood.

    A. As long as   B. As far as

    C. As well as   D. As often as

187. The village lies at the foot of the mountain, _____ the villagers draw much profit.

    A. from where   B. from which

    C. for it   D. for which

188. The old man is almost known to everyone, _____ is a famous woman scientist.

    A. whose a daughter   B. the daughter of whom

    C. of whom a daughter   D. whose the daughter

189. I sent invitation to 80 people, _____ have replied.

    A. of whom only 20 of these   B. only 20 of these who

    C. of whom only 20   D. only 20 who

190. There is nothing in the world _____ is influenced by the sun.

    A. which   B. that

    C. /   D. but

191. Children should not have more money _____ is needed.

    A. than   B. than that

    C. than which   D. than it

192. There is scarcely a child _____ likes candy.

    A. but   B. who

    C. who not   D. that

193. There are few of us _____ admire his eloquence.

    A. who not   B. but

    C. who   D. that

194. I have bought the same watch _____ you have.

    A. which   B. as

    C. that   D. but

195. This is the same watch _____ I lost.

    A. which   B. as

    C. that   D. but

第十九讲　非谓语动词(一)　分词和
　　　　　独立主格结构

1. In the dream Peter saw himself _____ by a fierce wolf, and he woke suddenly with a start.
    A. chased　　　　　　　　　B. to be chased
    C. be chased　　　　　　　　D. having been chased
2. Russ and Earl were auto mechanics _____ the same pay, but Earl had more ambition.
    A. to earn　　　　　　　　　B. to have earned
    C. earning　　　　　　　　　D. earned
3. _____ automatically, the e-mail will be received by all the club members.
    A. Mailed out　　　　　　　B. Mailing out
    C. To be mailed out　　　　　D. Having mailed out
4. She wants her paintings _____ in the gallery, but we don't think they would be very popular.
    A. display　　　　　　　　　B. to display
    C. displaying　　　　　　　　D. displayed
5. After a knock at the door, the child heard his mother's voice _____ him.
    A. calling　　　　　　　　　B. called
    C. being called　　　　　　　D. to call
6. The Town Hall _____ in the 1800s was the most distinguished building at that time.
    A. to be completed　　　　　　B. having been completed
    C. completed　　　　　　　　D. being completed
7. Throughout history, the language _____ by a powerful group spreads across a civilization.
    A. speaking　　　　　　　　B. spoken
    C. to speak　　　　　　　　D. to be spoken

8. If we have illegal immigrants _____ in, many local workers will lose their jobs.
   A. came   B. coming
   C. to come   D. having come
9. My sister, an inexperienced rider, was found sitting on the bicycle _____ to balance it.
   A. having tried   B. trying
   C. to try   D. tried
10. Ideally _____ for Broadway theatres and Fifth Avenue, the New York Park Hotel is a favourite with many guests.
    A. locating   B. being located
    C. having been located   D. located
11. A small plane crashed into a hillside five miles east of the city, _____ all four people on board.
    A. killed   B. killing
    C. kills   D. to kill
12. With the government's aid, those _____ by the earthquake have moved to the new settlements.
    A. affect   B. affecting
    C. affected   D. were affected
13. _____ by the growing interest in nature, more and more people enjoy outdoor sports.
    A. Influenced   B. Influencing
    C. Having influenced   D. To be influenced
14. The report indicated that 45% of students were in jobs not _____ specific qualifications.
    A. requiring   B. to be required
    C. being required   D. to have required
15. Lucy has a great sense of humour and always keeps her colleagues _____ with her stories.
    A. amused   B. amusing
    C. to amuse   D. to be amused
16. _____ the city centre, we saw a stone statue of about 10 metres in height.

174

A. Approaching   B. Approached
C. To approach   D. To be approached

17. The rare fish, _____ from the cooking pot, has been returned to the sea.
A. saved   B. saving
C. to be saved   D. having saved

18. Once _____, Jo devoted her life to looking after children and being a full-time homemaker.
A. having married   B. being married
C. marrying   D. married

19. Big companies usually have a lot of branch offices _____ in different parts of the world.
A. to have operated   B. be operated
C. operating   D. having operated

20. The club, _____ 25 years ago, is holding a party for past and present members.
A. founded   B. founding
C. being founded   D. to be founded

21. "Genius" is a complicated concept, _____ many different factors.
A. involved   B. involving
C. to involve   D. being involved

22. _____ in 1636, Harvard is one of the most famous universities in the United States.
A. Being founded   B. It was founded
C. Founded   D. Founding

23. The _____ boy was last seen _____ near the East Lake.
A. missing, playing   B. missing, play
C. missed, played   D. missed, to play

24. Tony was very unhappy for _____ to the party.
A. having not been invited   B. not having invited
C. having not invited   D. not having been invited

25. Finding her car stolen, _____.
A. a policeman was asked to help
B. the area was searched thoroughly

C. it was looked for everywhere

D. she hurried to a policeman for help

26. The bell _____ the end of the period rang, _____ our heated discussion.

    A. indicating, interrupting　　B. indicated, interrupting

    C. indicating, interrupted　　D. indicated, interrupted

27. Though _____ money, his parents managed to send him to university.

    A. lacked　　　　　　　　　B. lacking of

    C. lacking　　　　　　　　　D. lacked in

28. Don't use words, expressions, or phrases _____ only to people with specific knowledge.

    A. being known　　　　　　B. having been known

    C. to be known　　　　　　D. known

29. Would you please tell me if there is anything _____ in the paper?

    A. excited　　　　　　　　B. excitedly

    C. excitement　　　　　　D. exciting

30. When _____ why he was late, he said he had missed the first bus.

    A. asking　　　　　　　　B. asked

    C. to be asked　　　　　　D. to ask

31. _____ from heart trouble for years, Professor White has to take some medicine with him wherever he goes.

    A. Suffered　　　　　　　B. Suffering

    C. Having suffered　　　　D. Being suffered

32. _____ a reply, he decided to write again.

    A. Not receiving　　　　　B. Receiving not

    C. Not having received　　D. Having not received

33. "Can't you read?" Mary said _____ to the notice.

    A. angrily pointing　　　　B. and point angrily

    C. angrily pointed　　　　D. and angrily pointing

34. The computer centre, _____ last year, is very popular among the students in this school.

    A. open　　　　　　　　　B. opening

    C. having opened　　　　　D. opened

35. The man managed to make himself _____ with his _____ English.
    A. understood, breaking   B. understand, broken
    C. understand, breaking   D. understood, broken
36. The visiting Minister expressed his satisfaction with the talks, _____ that he had enjoyed his stay here.
    A. having added   B. to add
    C. adding   D. added
37. The first textbooks _____ for teaching English as a foreign language came out in the 16th century.
    A. having written   B. to be written
    C. being written   D. written
38. He hung up the phone, _____ with a smile on his face.
    A. having satisfied   B. to be satisfied
    C. satisfying   D. satisfied
39. The whole building _____, all the workers left the construction site for home.
    A. are completed   B. completing
    C. being completing   D. completed
40. It took the driver five minutes to get the bus _____ again.
    A. gone   B. going
    C. go   D. to going
41. A little boy, with two of his front teeth _____, disappeared among the crowd.
    A. missing   B. have been lost
    C. were missed   D. being lost
42. At the well-known research institute, they have a number of laboratories with each of their rooms _____ computers.
    A. equipping with   B. equipping
    C. equipped with   D. equipped
43. The instrument, _____ to the computer, will be very useful.
    A. once attaching   B. once attached
    C. once to be attached   D. once be attached
44. My brother, _____ where to find a job, had to depend on my

parents.

    A. not knowing   B. never to know

    C. not to know   D. didn't know

45. Every minute must be made full use _____ English.

    A. of studying   B. to study

    C. of being studied   D. of to study

46. With all the things he _____, he went home at once.

    A. needed buy   B. needed bought

    C. needed buying   D. need buy

47. The boy _____ on the ground _____ that he had _____ the money on the desk.

    A. lay, lied, lay   B. lying, lied, lain

    C. lies, laid, lain   D. lying, lied, laid

48. Emily Post's book *Eliquette*, _____ in 1922, was an immediate success.

    A. published   B. was published

    C. when it published   D. which published

49. _____, the amount left in the bank is hardly worth mentioning.

    A. Having paid my taxes

    B. Paying my taxes

    C. My taxes having been paid

    D. My taxes had been paid

50. I'm quite sure even if _____ he won't go to the celebration.

    A. invite.   B. to be invited

    C. being invited   D. invited

51. I'll get him _____ me with the box if it's too heavy.

    A. help   B. helping

    C. to help   D. helped

52. When led into the room, _____.

    A. it was too hot to stay in

    B. it was impossible for us to stay in such a hot room

    C. in which I would stay was too hot

    D. I found it too hot to stay in

53. There _____ nothing to discuss further, the chairman got to

his feet, and then left.
A. leaving   B. having
C. being   D. is

54. _____, she ran out of the room.
A. With a sudden turn, tearful eye
B. Having tears in her eyes and turned suddenly
C. Turning suddenly, with tears in her eyes
D. With tears in her eyes and a sudden turn

55. If _____, he promises that he will do his best to promote public welfare.
A. electing   B. elected
C. being elected   D. elect

56. After an interesting match, we have much _____ discussion, with every member of the family _____.
A. heat, participated   B. heat, participated in
C. heated, participating   D. heated, participating in

57. Until quite recently, most mothers in Britain did not take _____ work outside the home.
A. to   B. paying
C. paid   D. from

58. _____ by the policeman, his face went pale with fear.
A. For being tied   B. Having been tied
C. What he did was seen   D. His hands tied

59. You will get a cup of coffee I made if _____ my essay for me.
A. typed   B. type
C. being typed   D. typing

60. With _____ she needed _____, she left the marketplace.
A. something, to buy   B. anything, having bought
C. everything, bought   D. everything, buying

61. The two thieves walked out of the shop separately, _____ a bag.
A. each carrying   B. both carrying
C. each carried   D. both carried

62. _____, have you ever been to Macao?

A. To talk of trips
B. Talking of trips
C. Talk of trips
D. Having talked of trips

63. His duty fulfilled, John felt a great weight _____ his mind.
 A. to take off
 B. take off
 C. taking off
 D. taken off

64. _____, many patients will die of the disease before they reach middle age.
 A. When not treated
 B. Not been treated
 C. Having been without treatment
 D. If left untreated

65. The teacher could not make himself _____ attention to because the students were so noisy.
 A. pay
 B. paid
 C. to pay
 D. to be paid

66. Time _____, I'll go on a picnic with you this Sunday.
 A. permit
 B. to permit
 C. permitted
 D. permitting

67. The scientist _____ to _____ the secret of nature was praised by the government.
 A. devoted, expose
 B. devoted, exposing
 C. devoting, exposing
 D. was devoted, exposing

68. The flowers _____ sweet in the botanic garden attract the visitors to the beauty of nature.
 A. to smell
 B. smelling
 C. smelt
 D. to be smelt

69. The speaker walked out of the hall, _____ happily with the teacher and _____ by a group of students.
 A. talking, followed
 B. talking, following
 C. talked, followed
 D. talked, was followed

70. I searched the desk, and discovered the letter _____ under a pile of papers.
 A. hidden
 B. hiding
 C. being hidden
 D. having hidden

71. Don't stand there _____. Lend us a hand.
    A. to watch   B. and watching
    C. watching   D. watch
72. _____, the boy still made some serious mistakes.
    A. Having advised many times
    B. Having been advised many times
    C. Being advised for many times
    D. Advising many times
73. Tom was found _____ in _____ problems.
    A. interested, puzzling   B. interesting, puzzling
    C. interesting, puzzled   D. interested, puzzled
74. The discussion _____ over, we went on to play tennis.
    A. be   B. was
    C. to be   D. being
75. _____, the car driver tried to get away without _____.
    A. Knocked down by a car, being punished
    B. Having knocked down an old man, punishing
    C. Knocked down by a car, punishing
    D. Having knocked down an old man, being punished
76. I like to get up early so that I can get _____ work _____ before lunch.
    A. plenty of, done
    B. a great deal of, to do
    C. a large number of, to be done
    D. a large quantity of, being done
77. _____ in deep thought, the old woman scientist dressed in red almost ran into the car in front of her.
    A. Losing   B. Having been lost
    C. Lost   D. To lose
78. Each of the engineers and professors is working hard at their posts, _____ to accomplish the goal as soon as possible.
    A. wish   B. for wishing
    C. wishing   D. to wish
79. Our English teacher had us all _____ our names on a card.

A. written   B. to write
C. write   D. for writing

80. _____ a learned man, they all respect him.
    A. Mr. Palmer being   B. Mr. Palmer is
    C. Being   D. To be

81. _____ a bus stop so near our college is a great advantage.
    A. There being   B. There to be
    C. Being   D. There is

82. Helicopters play an important part in rescuing those _____ in places inaccessible by ordinary vehicles.
    A. having been stranded   B. to be stranded
    C. be stranded   D. stranded

83. The trees _____ last year _____ very well.
    A. planted, are growing   B. were planted, grow
    C. grown, are planted   D. grown, grow

84. _____ several times, he still doesn't know how to do it properly.
    A. Being shown   B. Having shown
    C. Having been shown   D. I've shown him

85. Is this the very way _____ to the valley?
    A. leads   B. led
    C. leading   D. which lead

86. The new comer is shy and never speaks until _____.
    A. asked   B. asking to
    C. speaking   D. spoken to

87. Some of the middle-aged people _____ to the meeting were famous professors.
    A. were invited   B. who invited
    C. inviting   D. invited

88. _____, her suggestion is of greater value than yours.
    A. All things considered B. All things considering
    C. Considering all things D. Considered all things

89. _____, the speaker entered the meeting-room.
    A. Bag in hand   B. Bags in hand
    C. Bag in his hand   D. With bag in his hand

90. The experiment _____, we went out to play tennis.
    A. was done   B. was being done
    C. be done   D. done
91. With problems _____ between cost and profit, they set about this job.
    A. settled   B. to be settling
    C. settling   D. being settled
92. When I stopped thinking, I found _____ in the classroom.
    A. myself seated   B. me seated
    C. myself sat   D. myself sit
93. In one of these rooms was a window _____ into the street, where an old man sat alone.
    A. looked   B. looking
    C. to look   D. being looked
94. Suddenly, a tall man driving a golden carriage _____ the girl and took her away, _____ into the woods.
    A. seizing, disappeared   B. seized, disappeared
    C. seized, disappearing   D. seizing, disappearing
95. If you are not greeted by the host or hostess when you come into a party, then you should ask for them and make yourself _____.
    A. known   B. knowing
    C. to know   D. be known
96. The policeman questioned the _____ workers on the scene about the _____ thief.
    A. retiring, escaping   B. retired, escaping
    C. retired, escaped   D. retiring, escaped
97. In darkness he ran into a huge vase, which fell, _____ in to pieces.
    A. broke   B. broken
    C. breaking   D. having broken
98. _____ in the open air, the long table was soon covered with dust.
    A. Having left   B. Left
    C. Leaving it   D. Leave it

99. _____ about the road accident, the traffic policemen rushed towards the scene in their cars.
    A. Having informed   B. Informed them
    C. Having been informed   D. After informing them
100. Almost all the doctors _____ in the hospital _____ blood for the wounded.
    A. work, having given   B. working, have given
    C. who worked, and gave   D. who working, have given
101. Sorry, I can't go out with all these dishes and plates _____.
    A. to be washed   B. washed
    C. washing   D. to have washed
102. Scientists find that some birds, _____ in daylight, use the sun for guidance.
    A. while flight   B. when flying
    C. for flight   D. during flying
103. The Japanese film about the fox's life is the best of its kind _____.
    A. ever being made   B. that ever made
    C. having ever made   D. ever made
104. The state leaders of some European countries were among the _____ to the opening ceremony of the World Cup.
    A. invited guests   B. guests invited
    C. inviting guests   D. guests to invite
105. I'm sure that the dictionary will sell well _____ printed.
    A. after   B. if once
    C. even if   D. when
106. The old man avoided touching the hands _____ out to help him as he stepped out of the boat.
    A. holding   B. having held
    C. held   D. having been held
107. The policemen searched the room thoroughly, _____ nothing _____.
    A. leaving, untouched   B. left, untouched
    C. to leave, untouching   D. left, to be untouched

184

108. During the day tigers usually lie _____ , _____ in the long grass.
    A. rested, hidden   B. rested, hiding
    C. resting, hidden   D. resting, hide
109. His new job as a school principal has kept him _____ .
    A. to be fully occupied   B. fully occupying
    C. being fully occupied   D. fully occupied
110. _____ with the old one, the new school library looks more modern.
    A. Comparing it   B. Compared
    C. Being compared   D. In comparing
111. _____ with the difficulties ahead, they were determined to make more efforts.
    A. Facing   B. Faced
    C. In face   D. In facing
112. With only a few hours a week _____ in class, how can a college student claim _____ busy?
    A. spent, to be   B. to spend, to be
    C. spent, being   D. to be spent, being
113. — Hey, John, you can't possibly work with that noise _____ on downstairs.
    — Yes, it is rather loud.
    A. is going   B. goes
    C. to be going   D. going
114. _____ of as intelligent, the student felt happy.
    A. Thinking   B. Thought
    C. Thinking himself   D. To be thought
115. I am often at a loss about starting a conversation with a stranger. Can you give me some advice on how to get a conversation _____ ?
    A. gone   B. go
    C. going   D. to be going
116. When I got back to my office, I saw a note _____ on my desk, _____ "Tomorrow's meeting is at 10 a. m. in Room 3."

185

A. left, reading   B. left, to read
C. leaving, read   D. having been left, reads

117. — Our bus was held up for nearly an hour on Baker Street.
    — That kind of thing is really _____.
    A. annoyed   B. annoying
    C. to annoy   D. to be annoying

118. For most New Zealand high school students, a few hours' part-time _____ work each week is necessary.
    A. paid   B. paying
    C. pay   D. being paid

119. Henry sat quietly in his office, his eyes _____.
    A. close   B. closed
    C. closing   D. to be closed

120. _____ of what had happened, we could only keep silent.
    A. Not having informed   B. Not having been informed
    C. Not having informed us D. Having not informed us

121. _____ the steering wheel, one can change the direction of a car.
    A. Using   B. To use
    C. Having used   D. Only to use

122. As Mrs. Brown could remember, her husband was last seen _____ in his swimming pool before he died suddenly.
    A. to swim   B. to be swimming
    C. swimming   D. having been swimming

123. _____ Lake Michigan, Chicago covers a large area of land.
    A. It is situated on   B. Lying in
    C. Situated on   D. Lied to

124. In college Edith received all the training _____ for her job in the future.
    A. which needed   B. would be needed
    C. that needed   D. needed

125. Sometimes the store tries to satisfy the customers who have asked for service not _____ there.
    A. to be given   B. given

C. being given   D. having been given

126. _____ proper training, I can do the job as well as anyone else.
    A. Give me   B. To be given
    C. Given   D. Given me

127. When I suggested _____ to a forest, most of my friends said that was a good idea.
    A. a trip organized   B. an organized trip
    C. a trip to be organized   D. an organizing trip

128. _____ in the next room, her voice is like _____ of a boy.
    A. Hearing, the sound   B. Heard, the ones
    C. Heard, that   D. Having been heard, those

129. _____ the old man was deep in thought.
    A. His eyes fixing   B. His eyes fix
    C. He fixed his eyes   D. With his eyes fixed

130. The three sons wanted to find some gold _____ underground.
    A. hidden   B. to hide
    C. hiding   D. hid

131. The _____ mountain climbing really made all of us very _____.
    A. tired, tired   B. tiring, tiring
    C. tiring, tired   D. tired, tiring

132. My boss was very _____ with my work, and it gave me much _____ to hear his praise.
    A. pleasing, pleasant   B. pleased, pleasure
    C. pleasant, pleasure   D. pleased, pleasant

133. — What are you doing?
    — I'm looking for my _____ letter.
    A. missed   B. missing
    C. being missed   D. miss

134. In class the American teacher spoke slowly and clearly in order to make himself _____.
    A. understand   B. understood
    C. understanding   D. to understand

135. People found the young man _____ in uniform like a soldier.
    A. dress   B. to dress
    C. dressing   D. dressed
136. Everything in the world keeps _____.
    A. change   B. changed
    C. changing   D. to change
137. Many things _____ impossible in the past have come into realities.
    A. to be considered   B. considered
    C. considering   D. being considered
138. _____ my twentieth birthday my parents took me to the photographer's to have a picture _____.
    A. On, taken   B. In, taking
    C. On, to take   D. For, took
139. The two impostors tried to take away the invention _____ Professor Hunter.
    A. belonging to   B. which belong to
    C. which was belonged to   D. belonged to
140. As she was getting off the bus, a sudden push from behind _____ her falling to the ground.
    A. sent   B. threw
    C. made   D. let
141. _____, we should begin our meeting.
    A. Everyone was present   B. Everyone present
    C. Everyone presenting   D. Everyone who is present
142. Listen to me carefully and keep your books _____.
    A. shut   B. close
    C. shutting   D. closing
143. _____, the film began.
    A. Having been seated
    B. All of us having taken the seats
    C. Having seated
    D. After we have sat down
144. Mr. Lopes was much disappointed to find the bike he had had

_____ went wrong again.

   A. it repaired   B. repaired

   C. repaired it   D. to be repaired

145. We are told that our baby is short of something _____ by vitamin pills.

   A. can be supplied   B. which supplied

   C. supplied   D. that can supplied

146. Any student _____ in chess can apply for membership.

   A. having a keen interest   B. has a keen interest

   C. with a keen interesting   D. is keenly interested

147. The man was seen _____ down and the driver dashing away.

   A. to be knocked   B. having knocked

   C. to knock   D. knocked

148. The baseball equipment is designed for the boys _____ from 4 or up.

   A. of age   B. aged

   C. whose age is   D. whom ages

149. I crossed the street to avoid meeting him, but he saw me and came _____ towards me.

   A. and ran   B. run

   C. to running   D. running

150. Though _____ by the heavy housework for a year, he still did well in his exams.

   A. having been troubled   B. being troubled

   C. troubled   D. having troubled

151. _____ his behaviour, he's a man with good education.

   A. Judging by   B. Judged from

   C. Having judged by   D. Being judged from

152. The _____ expression on his face is really _____ to all of us.

   A. puzzling, puzzled   B. puzzled, puzzling

   C. puzzling, puzzling   D. puzzled, puzzled

153. The prize winner stood on the platform, _____. He could hardly keep back his tears.

A. excited   B. excitedly

C. exciting   D. calmly

154. When the first English settlers arrived in the New World, the Indians _____ jewellery made of animal bones greeted them warmly.

   A. wearing   B. to wear

   C. worn   D. having worn

155. Jane looks _____ and _____. What's the matter with her?

   A. worried, tired   B. worried, tiring

   C. worriedly, tired   D. worrying, tiring

156. With the gold chain _____ up in her hand, Della sat on the corner of the table near the door, _____ for her husband.

   A. screwing, waiting   B. screwed, waiting

   C. screwing, waited   D. screwed, waited

157. _____, we hurried home.

   A. Night fill   B. Being night

   C. Night felt   D. Night falling

158. On returning from school, _____.

   A. I found a letter in the mailbox

   B. a letter was in the mailbox

   C. a letter was found in the mailbox

   D. the mailbox had a letter in it

159. All the things _____ to you are going to _____ you there.

   A. belong, reach   B. belonged, be reached by

   C. belonging, reach   D. that belong, reach for

160. I was very _____ to have heard my composition _____ on the radio.

   A. pleasing, reading   B. pleased, read

   C. pleasant, being read   D. pleased, having been read

161. _____ as a postman in the city for a long time, John knows all the streets well.

   A. Working   B. To work

   C. Having worked   D. Worked

162. People _____ sliver or white cars were 50% less likely to suffer serious injury in a crash, compared with drivers of dark color cars.
A. drive
B. to drive
C. driving
D. driven

163. If _____, I'll come to your help at once. Don't hesitate _____ me.
A. needed, to call
B. needing me, calling
C. necessary, for calling
D. you need, to call

164. Certain rare metals, when _____ to a very high temperature, will become sources of light.
A. having heated
B. heating
C. heated
D. to be heated

165. _____ by hunger and tiredness, the fisherman couldn't walk any longer.
A. Wore out
B. Wearing out
C. Worn out
D. To wear out

166. _____ there more than once, he offered to show us around the newly-built library.
A. Being
B. Been
C. Having been
D. To be

167. The old man walked in the street with his dog _____.
A. to follow
B. following
C. followed
D. to be followed

168. _____ by a cigarette end, the fire quickly spread and destroyed the whole house.
A. Starting
B. Started
C. To start
D. To be started

169. It's _____ cold today. Look at the _____ river. Now we can walk on it.
A. frozen, frozen
B. freezing, freezing
C. frozen, freezing
D. freezing, frozen

170. While _____ for the bus, I began _____ the magazines _____ from the library.

A. waiting, reading, borrowing

B. waited, reading, borrowed

C. waiting, reading, borrowed

D. waited, read, borrowed

171. _____ in the storm, the children felt _____.

    A. To catch, discouraging   B. Caught, discouraging

    C. Catching, discouraged   D. Caught, discouraged

172. The doctor _____ from Beijing is a famous specialist.

    A. sending for   B. having been sent for

    C. sent for   D. to send for

173. Reading the letter, _____.

    A. a smile appeared on her face

    B. she began to smile

    C. someone found her crying

    D. tears fell down her cheeks

174. _____ plenty of exercise, the brain will keep its power.

    A. Given   B. To be given

    C. Gave   D. Giving

175. If you keep a dog, you won't have your house _____ as easily as I did.

    A. break into   B. broken into

    C. being broken into   D. be broken into

176. _____ white, the house looks much better than before.

    A. Having painted   B. Painting

    C. Painted   D. To be painted

177. If you go to the lecture in the hall, don't forget to take a _____ chair with you.

    A. folded   B. folding

    C. fold   D. folds

178. At last we found ourselves in a pleasant park with trees providing shade and _____ down to eat our picnic lunch.

    A. sitting   B. having sat

    C. to sit   D. sat

179. A nod is a form of greeting _____ to a person you know only

slightly.

    A. given   B. to give

    C. giving   D. being given

180. For the sake of safety, you'd better keep the door _____ .

    A. close   B. closing

    C. closed   D. being closed

181. Don't worry. We'll have the car _____ for you outside till you are ready.

    A. to wait   B. waited

    C. will wait   D. waiting

182. The house _____ up two months ago is ready _____ .

    A. put, to paint   B. put, to paint it

    C. putting, to be painted   D. put, to be painted

183. He likes to sleep with the windows _____ and a candle _____ .

    A. closed, lighted   B. closing, lighting

    C. closed, lighting   D. closing, lit

184. _____ the wrong information, he failed to work out this problem.

    A. Having given   B. Being given

    C. To be given   D. Having been given

185. Though _____ the flood, the villagers did what they could to fight it.

    A. suffering   B. suffered

    C. suffering from   D. suffered from

186. The girl stood there still, not _____ a word.

    A. dare to say   B. daring to say

    C. dared to say   D. daring saying

187. _____ by doctors and nurses, his uncles soon got better.

    A. Look after   B. Looking after

    C. Looked after   D. Having looked after

188. _____ born in Chicago, the author is most famous for his stories about New York City.

    A. Although   B. Since

C. As   D. When
189. With his textbook _____ he had to get another one.
A. losing   B. had lost
C. lost   D. having lost
190. I heard them _____ in German.
A. to speak   B. speaking
C. speaks   D. spoken
191. He wants _____ as soon as possible.
A. that this job is done   B. this job done
C. this job to do   D. this job doing
192. I sat near the entrance for a long time _____ him, but he
didn't come.
A. expecting   B. attending
C. waiting   D. excepting
193. I found him _____ near the window.
A. being sat   B. sitted
C. seated   D. seating
194. With everything he _____, he had to turn to his parents.
A. used to stealing   B. used to steal
C. used stolen   D. used to be stolen
195. It was very cold in the open. They had to have the fire _____
all night long.
A. burns   B. to burn
C. burning   D. burned
196. Time _____, we'll go over the test paper once more. The
sentence means, "If time _____, we'll go over the test paper
once more. "
A. permitted, permitted   B. permitting, permits
C. permits, permits   D. to permit, permitting
197. Suddenly they found a dog _____ on the grass, _____.
A. lay, dead   B. lying, died
C. lay, died   D. lying, dead
198. _____ into use in April 2000, the hotline was meant for
residents reporting water and heating supply breakdowns.

A. Put   B. Putting

C. Having put   D. Being put

199. The young man managed to make himself _____ with his _____ English.

A. understood, breaking

B. understand, broken

C. understanding, breaking

D. understood, broken

200. Once _____, the clock will go half a month and keep good time.

A. start   B. to start

C. started   D. starting

第二十讲　非谓语动词(二)　动名词

1. The parents suggested _____ in the hotel room but their kids were anxious to camp out during the trip.
   A. sleep
   B. to sleep
   C. sleeping
   D. having slept

2. There are hundreds of visitors _____ in front of the Art Gallery to have a look at Van Gogh's paintings.
   A. waited
   B. to wait
   C. waiting
   D. wait

3. Eugene's never willing to alter any of his opinions. It is no use _____ with him.
   A. to argue
   B. arguing
   C. argued
   D. having argued

4. All staff in our company are considering _____ to the city centre for the fashion show.
   A. to go
   B. going
   C. to have gone
   D. having gone

5. As a new driver, I have to practice _____ the car in my small garage again and again.
   A. parking
   B. to park
   C. parked
   D. park

6. Something as simple as _____ some cold water may clear your mind and relieve pressure.
   A. to drink
   B. drinking
   C. to be drinking
   D. drink

7. Bill suggested _____ a meeting on what to do for the program during the vacation.
   A. having held
   B. to hold
   C. holding
   D. hold

8. _____ well in an interview will be an important part of getting

a place at university.

    A. Do   B. Doing

    C. Done   D. Being done

9. I had great difficulty _____ the suitable food on the menu in the restaurant.

    A. find   B. found

    C. to find   D. finding

10. It's no use _____ without taking any action.

    A. complain   B. complaining

    C. being complained   D. to be complained

11. At one point I made up my mind to talk to Uncle Sam. Then I changed my mind _____ that he could do nothing to help.

    A. to realize   B. realized

    C. realizing   D. being realized

12. _____ a wet football can hurt you foot if you are not careful.

    A. Kicking   B. Kicked

    C. Having kicked   D. Kick

13. When Peter speaks in public, he always has trouble _____ the right things to say.

    A. thinking of   B. to think of

    C. thought of   D. think of

14. Many people are crazy at Mo Yan's _____ in winning the Nobel Prize for Literature.

    A. success   B. successful

    C. succeeding   D. succeeded

15. — Let me tell you something about the journalists.

    — Don't you remember _____ me the story yesterday?

    A. told   B. telling

    C. to tell   D. to have told

16. Please excuse _____ you.

    A. me to delay   B. for me to delay

    C. for my delaying   D. my delaying

17. — What do you think made Mary so upset?

    — _____ her new bicycle.

A. As she lost   B. Lost
C. Losing   D. Because of losing

18. These football players had no strict _____ until they joined our club.
    A. practise   B. education
    C. train   D. training

19. Just after putting away the dishes, _____.
    A. the doorbell rang loud
    B. Nancy heard the doorbell ring
    C. someone knocked at the door
    D. the doorbell was rung

20. I really appreciate _____ to relax with you on this nice island.
    A. to have had time   B. having time
    C. to have time   D. to having time

21. _____ to sunlight for too much time will do harm to one's skin.
    A. Exposed   B. Having exposed
    C. Being exposed   D. After being exposed

22. I don't think the play is worth _____.
    A. to see   B. seeing
    C. to be seen   D. being seen

23. Mr. Reed made up his mind to devote all he had to _____ some schools for poor children.
    A. set up   B. setting up
    C. have set up   D. having set up

24. — I usually go there by train.
    — Why not _____ by boat for a change?
    A. to try going   B. trying to go
    C. to try and go   D. try going

25. I would appreciate _____ back this afternoon.
    A. you to call   B. you call
    C. your calling   D. you're calling

26. While shopping, people sometimes can't help _____ into buying something they don't really need.
    A. to persuade   B. persuading

C. being persuaded   D. be persuaded
27. How about the two of us _____ a walk down the garden?
    A. to take   B. take
    C. taking   D. to be taking
28. — I must apologize for _____ ahead of time.
    — That's all right.
    A. letting you not know   B. not letting you know
    C. letting you know not   D. letting not you know
29. She looks forward every spring to _____ the flower-lined garden.
    A. visit   B. paying a visit
    C. walk in   D. walking in
30. Once your business becomes international, _____ constantly will be part of your life.
    A. you fly   B. your flight
    C. flight   D. flying
31. — The old lady has been sad since her husband died.
    — Yes, she needs _____.
    A. being comforted   B. comforting
    C. be comforted   D. to comfort
32. They didn't like him at first, but they ended up _____ the praises of him.
    A. to sing   B. singing
    C. and sang   D. sung
33. Some movie stars are always wearing sunglasses, afraid of _____.
    A. recognizing some fans   B. being recognized
    C. having been recognized   D. having recognized
34. You can hardly imagine Bob _____ the housework by himself.
    A. do   B. have done
    C. to do   D. doing
35. The new computer leads to _____ a lot of people and labour. It is a _____ machine.
    A. save, labour-saving   B. saving, labour-saved

C. saving, labour-saving   D. save, labour-saved

36. What made me puzzled was _____ to Shanghai Jiao Tong University.
    A. her being not admitted   B. being her not admitted
    C. her not being admitted   D. having not been admitted

37. What about _____ to the Summer Palace _____ the weekend?
    A. to go, for   B. to go, at
    C. going, for   D. going at

38. Can you imagine the best boy in the class _____ in the examination?
    A. cheating   B. to cheat
    C. cheat   D. to have cheated

39. They say _____ is no use _____ over spilt milk.
    A. that, to cry   B. it, to cry
    C. that, crying   D. it, crying

40. Do you remember _____ to Professor Smith during your last visit?
    A. to be introduced   B. being introduced
    C. having introduced   D. to have introduced

41. The manager of the company said they should have prevented such silly mistakes _____.
    A. occurring   B. being occurred
    C. to occur   D. from being occurred

42. _____ is worth doing at all is worth doing well.
    A. That   B. Which
    C. Whatever   D. If

43. We were delighted to find the trees planted a year before _____ very tall.
    A. grown   B. being grown
    C. to have been growing   D. growing

44. She didn't mind _____ all her spare time to _____ the sick old woman.
    A. to give, help   B. to give, helping
    C. giving, help   D. giving, helping

45. Your door needs _____. Would you like me to do it for you?
   A. to paint   B. painting
   C. paint   D. to be painting
46. It's no use _____ me at the office this week because I'm _____.
   A. to ring, on my leave   B. to ring, at leave
   C. ringing, in holidays   D. ringing, on holiday
47. On hearing the _____ result, all the teachers of Class Six couldn't help _____.
   A. satisfied, to jump   B. satisfactory, to jump
   C. satisfied, jumping   D. satisfactory, jumping
48. What I really mean is the noise of _____.
   A. the desks being opened and shut
   B. the desks' being opened and shut
   C. the desks opening and shutting
   D. the desks' opening and shutting
49. Why not try _____ in more sugar — that might make the soup taste a bit better?
   A. put   B. to put
   C. putting   D. being put
50. The farmer who admitted _____ the tiger was severely punished.
   A. to kill   B. killing
   C. killed   D. to have killed
51. _____ the sad news, she burst out _____.
   A. On, crying   B. At, crying
   C. At, tears   D. On, tears
52. His hesitation means _____ the chance.
   A. to give up   B. giving up
   C. to give in   D. giving in
53. _____ president for so long, it was an unpleasant thought that he would have to take a back seat.
   A. After being   B. Being
   C. To have been   D. Not being

201

54. Do you remember _____ to Mr. Green during your last visit?
   A. to be introduced   B. being introduced
   C. to introduce   D. having introduced
55. I realized we should do something to avoid _____ to death.
   A. freezing   B. to freeze
   C. to be frozen   D. being frozen
56. You may have been right when you said I didn't have to help him. But I don't regret _____ what I thought was right.
   A. having to do   B. being done
   C. to do   D. to have done
57. According to a recent U. S. survey, children spend up to 25 hours a week _____ TV.
   A. to watch   B. to watching
   C. watching   D. watch
58. Excuse _____ you, but I have an important message for you.
   A. me to interrupt   B. for my being interrupted
   C. my interrupting   D. me of interrupting
59. She used to _____ a girl used to _____ jokes.
   A. be, make   B. be, making
   C. being, making   D. being, tell
60. No one likes _____ at in public.
   A. a laughing   B. to laugh
   C. laughed   D. being laughed
61. Mike doesn't regret _____ even if it might have upset her.
   A. to tell her what he thought
   B. to tell her that he thought
   C. telling her what he thought
   D. telling her that he thought
62. Do you think his hesitation means _____ an underwater tunnel here?
   A. giving up building   B. to give up building
   C. giving up to build   D. to give up to build
63. There is no risk _____ when your boat is upset if you learn to swim.

A. of your being drowned   B. for you to be drowned
C. that you will be drowned   D. at you being drowned

64. The idea of fighting a noise _____ more noise sounds strange,
    but that's exactly what some scientists are doing.
    A. to make   B. for making
    C. only to make   D. by making

65. Doctors say that _____ to sunlight for a long time is harmful
    to one's skin.
    A. exposed   B. exposing
    C. being exposed   D. to expose

66. A man can never accomplish if he always puts off _____ a
    decision.
    A. to make   B. making
    C. in making   D. till making

67. I regretted _____ my son for the mistake, for I later found
    that it was my own fault.
    A. to blame   B. blaming
    C. blamed   D. being to blame

68. The whole family objected _____ a Japanese.
    A. Jane to marry   B. that Jane should marry
    C. to Jane's marrying   D. Jane from marrying

69. Having lived in France for many years, they still enjoyed the
    foods _____ in their homeland.
    A. which were used to having
    B. they were used to having
    C. which used to have
    D. they were used to have

70. _____ the next morning upset his parents very much.
    A. His being operated on
    B. He would be operated on
    C. Him to be operated on
    D. The fact that he be operated on

71. They couldn't stand _____ by the host at the party.
    A. to be neglected   B. being neglected

C. neglected　　　　　　　　　D. that they were neglected

72. A heavy smoker is usually unaware of the damage _____ to his body while he continues to smoke.
    A. having been done　　　　　B. to have been done
    C. to be doing　　　　　　　　D. being done

73. I can hardly imagine Kate _____ so difficult a job in three days.
    A. doing　　　　　　　　　　B. to do
    C. to have done　　　　　　　D. has done

74. The news of victory _____ in.
    A. keep pouring　　　　　　　B. keep to pour
    C. keeps pouring　　　　　　　D. keeps poured

75. He _____ to bed early, but now he _____ to bed late.
    A. used to go, is used to going
    B. used to go, is used to go
    C. uses to go, is used to go
    D. uses to go, is used to going

76. It is no use _____ a lot without doing anything.
    A. talk　　　　　　　　　　　B. talking
    C. to talk　　　　　　　　　　D. to talking

77. I can hardly imagine Victor _____ across the Atlantic Ocean in five days.
    A. sail　　　　　　　　　　　B. to sail
    C. sailing　　　　　　　　　　D. to have sailed

78. They dare not tell the truth, for they are afraid _____.
    A. to be laughed　　　　　　　B. of laughing at
    C. of being laughed at　　　　　D. being laughed at

79. Only _____ students in Senior Three can _____ so much time travelling.
    A. very few, take　　　　　　　B. a few, spare
    C. few, find　　　　　　　　　D. few, spend

80. The rocks brought from the moon are _____.
    A. worth to study　　　　　　　B. worthy of being studied
    C. worthy of studying　　　　　D. worth being studied

81. I need _____ a cleaner. The room needs _____.
    A. to get, to clean   B. get, cleaned
    C. getting, cleaning   D. to get, cleaning
82. Don't you still remember _____ him once when you were in Paris?
    A. having met   B. to have met
    C. to meet   D. had met
83. My uncle _____ live in the north, but he _____ the hot weather in the south now.
    A. used to, is used to   B. used to, used to
    C. was used to, is used to   D. was used to, used to
84. His stomach began to _____ because of the bad food he had eaten.
    A. pain   B. ache
    C. be hurt   D. go bad
85. — What made his mother angry?
    — _____.
    A. Because he had lost the ticket
    B. Because of his having lost the ticket
    C. As he had lost the ticket
    D. Having lost the ticket
86. He kept _____ how things were going on in the earthquake areas.
    A. informed us of   B. informing us of
    C. us informing of   D. informing on
87. That's one of those questions that really don't need _____.
    A. to answer   B. answer
    C. answering   D. being answered
88. Victor apologized for _____ to inform me of the change in the plan.
    A. his being not able   B. him not to be able
    C. his not being able   D. him to be not able
89. Without _____, the boy was hit by a third bullet and fell from the tree, dead.

A. able to finish his words

B. abling to finish his words

C. being able to finish his words

D. being able finished his words

90. The children are fond of _____ to the New Year party, and they don't mind _____ there till midnight.

    A. inviting, keeping   B. invite, keep

    C. be invited, stay   D. being invited, being kept

91. Accustomed to _____ the steep mountains, he had no difficulty reaching the top.

    A. climbing   B. climb

    C. having climbed   D. have climbed

92. Did you have difficulty _____ the professor's house in the dark?

    A. to find   B. finding

    C. by finding   D. to have found

93. It is no use _____ any more since you have made the decision.

    A. to discuss   B. to be discussed

    C. discussing   D. for discussion

94. Trying without success is better than _____ at all.

    A. not to try   B. to not try

    C. not trying   D. trying not

95. The milk is too cold. It requires _____.

    A. to heat   B. heating

    C. to be hot   D. being heated

96. _____ the work in that way would cost much more time and money.

    A. If doing   B. Do

    C. To be doing   D. Doing

97. Do you object _____ Japanese as a second foreign language?

    A. to my choosing   B. for me to choose

    C. that I choose   D. that I should choose

98. Anyone who does a crime won't _____.

    A. escape to be punished   B. be escaped punishing

    C. be escaped to punish   D. escape being punished

99. _____ as the top student on her campus made her parents very happy.
   A. Jane was chosen   B. Jane's being chosen
   C. Jane chosen   D. Jane to be chosen

100. The murderer was sentenced to death even though he had admitted _____ the small boy.
   A. killing   B. to have killed
   C. to kill   D. by having killing

101. We are looking forward to _____ you at our party, but we wouldn't mind _____ soon if you have to.
   A. have, you to leave   B. having, your leaving
   C. have, your leaving   D. having, your being left

102. We don't allow _____ in the school.
   A. smoking   B. to smoke
   C. they smoking   D. anyone smoked

103. Bethune never stopped _____ to save our wounded soldiers _____ he died at his post on November 12, 1939.
   A. working, until   B. to work, until
   C. working, not until   D. to work, not until

104. He set about _____ the experiment last month and succeeded _____ a good result.
   A. doing, in getting   B. doing, to get
   C. to do, in getting   D. to do, to get

105. He got well-prepared for the job interview, for he couldn't risk _____ the good opportunity.
   A. to lose   B. losing
   C. to be lost   D. being lost

106. What about _____ a drink in that inn?
   A. having   B. to have
   C. have   D. to having

107. They went on _____ football all afternoon.
   A. plays   B. played
   C. play   D. playing

108. He was busy _____ his lessons.

A. prepare   B. to prepare

C. preparing   D. prepared

109. He is _____ an artist.

    A. on the way to become   B. on the way to becoming

    C. on way to become   D. on the way become

110. He succeeded _____ everyone laugh.

    A. in making   B. to make

    C. for making   D. in make

111. Your window wants _____. You'd better have it _____ this week.

    A. cleaning, do   B. to be cleaned, do

    C. cleaning, done   D. being cleaned, done

112. I'll never forget _____ you for the first time.

    A. to meet   B. meeting

    C. to have met   D. having to be meeting

113. Tired of the cold weather in New England, Mr. and Mrs. Smith are considering _____ to the south.

    A. to move   B. moving

    C. move   D. to be moving

114. _____ the Victoria Line with other lines of ten caused great problems.

    A. Connect   B. Connecting

    C. Connected   D. Connection

115. The _____ video games all day made his mother very angry.

    A. child's playing   B. child playing

    C. child's play   D. child play

116. These days he is busy _____ a job but no job _____ him.

    A. finding, suit   B. look for, suit

    C. finding, is suitable to   D. looking for, suits

117. The old nurse devoted herself _____ the patients.

    A. to look after   B. to looking after

    C. in looking after   D. for looking after

118. The house needs _____ before we move in.

    A. to clean   B. being cleaned

C. cleaned   D. cleaning
119. If you miss _____ for a couple of hours, no harm _____ to you.
   A. sleeping, will do   B. to sleep, will be done
   C. to sleep, will do   D. sleeping, will be done
120. Ms Nancy didn't mind at all _____ to ceremony.
   A. being not invited   B. not inviting
   C. not to be invited   D. not being invited
121. How much time does he spend _____ piano every day?
   A. practicing playing   B. to practice playing the
   C. practicing playing the   D. to practice playing
122. I am sure all of us have had experience of _____ when we are worried about something.
   A. staying waking   B. remaining wakening
   C. staying awake   D. remaining awakened
123. I meant to have a look at books in stock, but at last I _____ a number of reference books.
   A. ended up buying   B. finished with
   C. ended with getting up   D. finished off
124. — What is it that made Obama happy?
    — _____ the US President.
   A. To elect   B. Electing
   C. Being elected   D. Having elected
125. He suggested _____ to Beijing by plane and _____ without a word.
   A. going, left   B. to go, to leave
   C. going, leaving   D. go, left
126. He walked into the library on tiptoe, afraid _____ the others.
   A. of disturbing   B. to disturb
   C. for disturbing   D. about disturbing
127. Scanning before you read means _____ quickly and thoroughly.
   A. to look a passage   B. looking a passage
   C. to look over a passage   D. looking over a passage

128. Last night the policemen caught a thief _____ Wang's car.
    A. when stealing   B. that he stole
    C. when stolen   D. stealing
129. The discovery of new evidence led to _____.
    A. the thief having caught   B. catch the thief
    C. the thief being caught   D. the thief to be caught
130. At that time she was so angry that she felt like _____ something at him.
    A. to throw   B. throwing
    C. to have thrown   D. having thrown
131. _____ the meeting himself gave them a great deal of encouragement.
    A. The mayor will attend   B. The mayor to attend
    C. The mayor is attending   D. The mayor's attending
132. Mark often attempts to escape _____ whenever he breaks traffic regulations.
    A. having been fined   B. to fined
    C. to have been fined   D. being fined
133. The old man caught a thief _____ Mike's bike.
    A. to steal   B. stealing
    C. steeling   D. steal
134. Wind can send a junk (帆船) _____.
    A. sailing   B. to sail
    C. sail   D. sailed
135. Fancy his _____ like that.
    A. talking   B. to talk
    C. talk   D. talked

第二十一讲 非谓语动词(三) 动词不定式

1. _____ the employees' working efficiency, the supervisor will allow them to have a coffee break.
   A. Improving   B. To improve
   C. Having improved   D. Improved

2. China has promised to revise its existing regulations and _____ new policies according to WTO requirements.
   A. forming   B. to form
   C. to be forming   D. have formed

3. Energy drinks are not allowed _____ in Australia but are brought in from New Zealand.
   A. to make   B. to be made
   C. to have been made   D. to be making

4. The mother felt herself _____ cold and her hands trembled as she read the letter from the battlefield.
   A. grow   B. grown
   C. to grow   D. to have grown

5. _____ the safety of gas, the government has checked the city's gas supply system thoroughly.
   A. To ensure   B. Ensuring
   C. Having ensured   D. To have ensured

6. There is nothing more I can try _____ you to stay, so I wish you good luck.
   A. being persuaded   B. persuading
   C. to be persuaded   D. to persuade

7. Due to the heavy rain and flooding, ten million people have been forced _____ their homes.
   A. leaving   B. to leave
   C. to be left   D. being left

8. If there's a lot of work _____, I'm happy to just keep on until it is finished.
   A. to do   B. to be doing
   C. done   D. doing

9. David threatened _____ his neighbour to the police if the damages were not paid.
   A. to be reported   B. reporting
   C. to report   D. having reported

10. _____ as an Olympic event, a sport must be played in at least 75 countries on at least four continents.
    A. To accept   B. Having accepted
    C. To be accepted   D. Accepting

11. That is the only way we can imagine _____ the overuse of water in the students' bathroom.
    A. reducing   B. to reduce
    C. reduced   D. reduce

12. Today we have chat rooms, text messaging, e-mail... but we seem _____ the art of communication face-to-face.
    A. losing   B. to be losing
    C. to be lost   D. having lost

13. People have learnt the importance of keeping a balanced diet _____ their nutritional needs.
    A. satisfy   B. satisfied
    C. to satisfy   D. having satisfied

14. As Jack left his membership card at home, he wasn't allowed _____ into the sports club.
    A. going   B. to go
    C. go   D. gone

15. — I'd like a bicycle for my daughter. Would you show me the latest model?
    — All right. We have several new models _____.
    A. of your choice   B. for you to choose
    C. for your choosing   D. for you to choose from

16. The boy wanted to ride his bicycle in the street, but his mother

told him _____.

  A. not to   B. not to do

  C. not did it   D. don't to

17. Such a comment on Jerry, whom we know _____ so kind and thoughtful, is unfair.

  A. as   B. being

  C. to be   D. for

18. — I'd love _____ with you on your trip in Greece. You must have had a good time.

  — Yes, I really enjoyed my trip very much.

  A. to be   B. to have been

  C. being   D. having been

19. — I regret _____ you again, Jimmy.

  — I'll be glad to be of any help.

  A. having troubled   B. to have to trouble

  C. to have troubled   D. having to trouble

20. A clever student will try _____ mistakes.

  A. to learn by   B. to learn from

  C. learning through   D. learning

21. The two leaders have agreed on the principles, but the details _____ out later.

  A. are worked   B. being worked

  C. to be worked   D. are to be worked

22. The police concluded that the bosses themselves were as much _____ as anybody for the accident.

  A. blame   B. to be blamed

  C. blaming   D. to blame

23. Have you ever responded to someone's question about the weather by saying it was warm, only _____ out the person thought it was cold?

  A. finding   B. found

  C. to find   D. to have found

24. I am busy preparing for the mid-term examination, so I can't help _____ housework at home.

A. doing   B. to do
C. being done   D. to be done

25. There are so many ties _____, but I really don't know which
one suits me best.
A. to choose   B. to be chosen
C. to choose from   D. for choosing

26. In Europe some people hold that the more conservative (守旧的)
the world becomes, the smarter _____ have old furniture, old
houses and old paintings.
A. is to   B. it is to
C. is it to   D. is one to

27. I can't write anything because I have got neither a pen nor a
pencil _____.
A. for writing   B. to write
C. for me to write   D. to write with

28. _____ away from the noise in the living-room, Sally went to
the garden behind the house.
A. To be   B. Being
C. Having been   D. For being

29. There are five pairs _____. But I'm at a loss which to buy.
A. to be chosen   B. to choose from
C. to choose   D. for choosing

30. — Mum, why do you always make me eat an egg every day?
— _____ enough protein and nutrition as you are growing up.
A. Get   B. Getting
C. To get   D. To be getting

31. A computer does only what thinking people _____.
A. have it do   B. have it done
C. have done it   D. having it done

32. — Does your brother intend to study German?
— Yes, he intends _____.
A. /   B. to
C. so   D. that

33. He claimed _____ in the supermarket when he was doing

shopping yesterday.
  A. being badly treated   B. treating badly
  C. to be treated badly   D. to have been badly treated
34. To fetch water before breakfast seemed to me a rule _____.
  A. to never break   B. never to be broken
  C. never to have broken   D. never to be breaking
35. She can't help _____ the house because she's busy making a cake.
  A. to clean   B. cleaning
  C. cleaned   D. being cleaned
36. Do let your mother know all the truth. She appears _____ everything.
  A. to tell   B. to be told
  C. to be telling   D. to have been told
37. In such dry weather, the flowers will have to be watered if they _____.
  A. have survived   B. are to survive
  C. would survive   D. will survive
38. I feel it is your husband who _____ for the spoiled child.
  A. is to blame   B. is going to blame
  C. is to be blamed   D. should blame
39. In order to gain a bigger share in the international market, many state-run companies are striving _____ their products more competitive.
  A. to make   B. making
  C. to have made   D. having made
40. Quite a few people used to believe that disaster _____ if a mirror was broken.
  A. was sure of striking   B. was sure of having struck
  C. was sure to be struck   D. was sure to strike
41. Don't forget _____ your map next time you come to school.
  A. to take   B. bringing
  C. to bring   D. taking
42. Sandy could do nothing but _____ to his teacher that he was

wrong.
A. admit   B. admitted
C. admitting   D. to admit

43. In order to improve English, _____.
A. Jenny's father bought her a lot of tapes
B. Jenny bought a lot of tapes for herself
C. a lot of tapes were bought by Jenny
D. a lot of tapes were bought by Jenny's father

44. Little Jim should love _____ to the theatre this evening.
A. to be taken   B. to take
C. being taken   D. taking

45. The daughter asked her father whether he had any clothes
_____ because she was doing so.
A. would be washed   B. being washed
C. washed   D. to be washed

46. There're so many kinds of tape-recorders on sale that I can't
make up my mind _____ to buy.
A. what   B. which
C. how   D. where

47. When the streets are full of melting snow, people can't help
_____ their shoes wet.
A. get   B. but get
C. but getting   D. but to get

48. Charles Babbage is generally considered _____ the first computer.
A. to invent   B. inventing
C. to have invented   D. having invented

49. Why does the lady look so worried? She seems _____
something.
A. to lose   B. to have lost
C. to be losing   D. having lost

50. His method has proved _____ very effective and it is worthy
of _____.
A. to be, adopting   B. being, being adopted
C. to be, being adopted   D. being, adopting

51. I don't want you _____ your brains about such problems.
    A. being always bothered   B. always to be bothered
    C. to be always bothering   D. to be always bothered
52. You have to consider _____ these old letters.
    A. what to do with   B. how to do with
    C. doing what with   D. how doing with
53. Everybody said the problem was very difficult _____ him to
    _____.
    A. for, work out   B. to, work it out
    C. for, work it out   D. to, work out
54. To succeed in passing the exam, _____.
    A. one needs to be diligent   C. one needs be a diligent person
    B. diligence is needed   D. diligence is what one needs
55. My God! You were _____ tell lies to the police.
    A. very foolish as to   B. so foolish as to
    C. too foolish as to   D. rather foolish as to
56. I'll be _____ from you.
    A. much glad to hear   B. only too glad to hear
    C. too glad only to hear   D. too only glad to hear
57. The old gentleman has relied on his daughter _____ house in
    the past five years.
    A. keeping   B. to keep
    C. to have kept   D. keep
58. _____ long, one must eat healthy food and do some exercise.
    A. To live   B. Living
    C. Having lived   D. Live
59. There was nothing left to do but _____.
    A. staying   B. to stay
    C. stay   D. stayed
60. This kind of machine is believed _____ in a few years.
    A. to have been made   B. to be made
    C. should be made   D. to make
61. The first computer is universally thought _____ by Charles
    Babbage.

217

A. to invent   B. to have been invented
C. to have invented   D. having been invented

62. There is no need _____ too anxious about the result of the exam.
    A. to become   B. become
    C. becoming   D. to be become

63. We thought it a pity _____ him to the tea party.
    A. being not invited   B. not to have invited
    C. to not have invited   D. not to have been invited

64. The young officer left home, _____.
    A. never returned   B. never to return
    C. never returning   D. never having returned

65. I seated myself in the front row so as to make myself _____ the speaker.
    A. understand   B. understood
    C. understanding   D. to understand

66. Would you be _____ to help me with my English?
    A. so kind as   B. enough kind
    C. so kind   D. as kind as

67. In 1938 Pearl Buck became the first American woman _____ the Nobel Prize for literature.
    A. to receive   B. she receive
    C. receive   D. received

68. It is good _____ you to have half an hour for sports every day.
    A: of   B. for
    C. to   D. at

69. I think that this problem is hard _____.
    A. to deal   B. to deal with
    C. to be dealt   D. to be dealt with

70. I went to see William, _____ that he had left two days before.
    A. only to learn   B. learning
    C. to learn   D. learned

71. Alexander Graham Bell is believed _____ the telephone.
    A. to invent   B. inventing

218

C. to have invented   D. having invented

72. — I'd like to buy a colour TV set.
    — Well, we have several models _____.
    A. to choose from   B. to be chosen
    C. of choice   D. for choosing

73. We should do as we are required _____.
    A. doing   B. to
    C. so   D. to be done

74. My aunt decided not to make a trip to Singapore _____ where she was.
    A. but remained   B. so she remained
    C. but to remain   D. instead of remaining

75. The movie star _____ with your sister, didn't he?
    A. was used to dance   B. used to dancing
    C. used to dance   D. was used to dancing

76. She told us that she had written _____ being elected to be head of the office.
    A. to congratulate her friend on
    B. to congratulate on her friend
    C. to congratulate her friend's
    D. to congratulate on her friend's

77. Listen! The students of Class Four seem _____ some important matters in the classroom.
    A. to be discussing   B. to have discussed
    C. that they are discussing   D. to have been discussing

78. — I wish you had brought your wife and daughter with you.
    — I'll get them _____ on the next trip.
    A. coming along with me   B. come along with me
    C. to come along with me   D. to be coming along with me

79. Amily was admitted into a senior high school which happened _____ in her neighbourhood.
    A. to locate   B. to have located
    C. to have ben located   D. to be located

80. — Why did he write to the mayor's office?

— _____ about the poor taxi service of the city.

A. He complained   B. To complain

C. Complaining   D. For complaining

81. With nothing left _____ the fire became weak and finally died out.

A. to burn   B. burning

C. burnt   D. burn

82. Wilma wasn't chosen to do the job as she _____ experience.

A. considered lacking

B. was considered to lack

C. was considered that she lacked

D. considered that she lacked

83. We went in on tiptoe _____ not to disturb the readers.

A. as if   B. so as

C. if only   D. as for

84. Thousands of houses were said _____ damaged during the severe flood.

A. to have been   B. to be

C. that had been   D. that were

85. Because of the acid rain, the entire hardwood forest in Canada _____ with extinction.

A. believes to be threatened   B. is believed to be threatened

C. believes in threatening   D. is believed to threaten

86. His work was so good _____ him internationally famous.

A. only to make   B. having made

C. as to make   D. that made

87. The computer is useful in watering trees as it can correctly decide the right quantity of water _____.

A. to use   B. to be used

C. of using   D. of being used

88. It seemed _____ windy. The leaves were being blown about.

A. to get   B. to be getting

C. to have got   D. getting

89. Have you ever considered _____ after graduation from

220

university?
- A. what to do
- B. what doing
- C. which to do
- D. which doing

90. We had great hopes of his success only _____ later.
- A. to be disappointed
- B. being disappointed
- C. having disappointed
- D. to have disappointed

91. The man is _____ to carry the heavy box _____ books.
- A. too strong, filled with
- B. strong enough, filled of
- C. so strong as, full of
- D. so strong enough, filled with

92. James walked round the museum, and stopped _____ only the works of art that he found especially attractive.
- A. studying
- B. to study
- C. in studying
- D. to have studied

93. The front door is shut. Why not _____ at the back door _____ in?
- A. to try to knock, for getting
- B. to try knocking, getting
- C. try knocking, to get
- D. try to knock, to get

94. The musician felt it an honour _____ to play the composition at the concert.
- A. asking
- B. to ask
- C. being asked
- D. to be asked

95. I never expected the shoes _____ so soon.
- A. wearing out
- B. to be worn out
- C. to have worn out
- D. being worn out

96. They appear _____ in the accident.
- A. to injure
- B. to be injured
- C. to have been injured
- D. being injured

97. I hurried to Professor Wang's house only _____ he was out.
- A. finding
- B. find
- C. to find
- D. found

98. This company was the first _____ portable radios as well as cassette tape recorders in the world.
    A. producing   B. to produce
    C. having produced   D. produced
99. This semester I am very busy. I have six subjects _____.
    A. to major in   B. to be majored in
    C. to major   D. to have majored in
100. Here are the papers _____ by Mr. Wilson when he returns from his holidays.
    A. signed   B. to be signed
    C. being signed   D. having been signed
101. The sick old man had someone _____ after him from Monday to Friday, but not at weekends, so Jia Ming came to his help.
    A. looked   B. to look
    C. looking   D. look
102. Once _____, he threw himself into his work.
    A. recovering   B. his recovering
    C. recovered   D. he has recovered
103. Mary tried for the post of secretary, but was too late _____ for it.
    A. to consider   B. to be considered
    C. to have been considered   D. to be considering
104. To make greater progress, _____.
    A. one must work hard
    B. working hard is important
    C. it is important to work hard
    D. to work hard is necessary
105. We're going to visit the Great Wall. Everybody says this is _____ chance _____.
    A. a too good, for being lost
    B. too good a, to be lost
    C. a too good for being missed
    D. too good a, to missing
106. We have a nice restaurant _____.

A. to eat

C. to eat at

B. eating at

D. for eating

107. There is no need _____ the door of the meeting room tonight.

A. to lock

C. to be locked

B. to be locking

D. locked

108. We should do _____ we should _____ others when we know they are in trouble.

A. what, to help

C. what, help

B. all what, to help

D. all, help

109. I prefer _____ at home rather than go out in such bad weather.

A. to stay

C. staying

B. stay

D. stayed

110. Would you be _____ to lend me a hand?

A. as kind as

C. so kind as

B. as kind so

D. very kind to

111. He ordered the room _____ at once.

A. to swept

C. to be swept

B. swept

D. sweeping

112. I'm going to the supermarket this afternoon. Do you have anything _____?

A. to be buying

C. for buying

B. to buy

D. bought

113. — What did John ask you?

— He asked me _____ him some money.

A. for borrowing

C. to lend

B. to borrow

D. that I lend

114. It was unbelievable that the fans waited outside the gym for three hours just _____ a look at the sports stars.

A. had

C. to have

B. having

D. have

115. The last man _____ the office is always Mr. Zhu.

A. left

B. to be leaving

223

C. to leave D. leaves
116. I would like _____ me what happened the day before yesterday.
    A. you tell B. you telling
    C. that you tell D. you to tell
117. The doctors in this hospital are _____ provide the patients with their requirements.
    A. very ready to B. far ready to
    C. only too ready to D. so much as ready as to
118. The beautiful is _____ the evil in the end.
    A. to be supposed to win B. believed to overcome
    C. thought of to overcome D. considered winning
119. You have spoiled your child. You _____ and not your wife.
    A. are blamed for it B. are to blame
    C. blame for it D. are to be blamed
120. His words reminded me _____.
    A. in when kept silent B. that when to keep silent
    C. when to keep silent D. of when keeping silent
121. To learn English well, _____.
    A. it must be spoken regularly
    B. much practice is needed
    C. it is necessary to do much practice
    D. one must do much practice
122. When Alice first came to China, she couldn't use the chopsticks _____.
    A. to eat B. eating
    C. for eating D. to eat with
123. Two years ago I didn't know _____ the new equipment and now I have learned _____ it.
    A. what to do with, how to deal with
    B. how to do with, what to deal with
    C. what to do with, what to deal with
    D. how to do with, how to deal with
124. It was not the tools he uses but _____ the tools that _____ him successful.

A. to use, makes B. to use, make
C. how to use, makes D. how to use, make

125. He can't help _____ the bike because he is busy doing the homework.
A. to repair B. repairing
C. repaired D. being repaired

126. _____ frank, I'd rather you were not involved in the case.
A. To be B. Having been
C. Being D. By being

127. _____ Mrs. Johnson on my way to the supermarket.
A. It happened to me that I met
B. I happened that I meet
C. I happened to meet
D. It happened for me to meet

128. The experiment is not _____ until everything is ready.
A. to do B. to be done
C. doing D. done

129. She had saved only $1.87, _____ for Jim.
A. was not enough to buy a present
B. to buy a present was not enough
C. not enough to buy a present
D. to buy a present not enough

130. He asked me if I had decided which hotel _____.
A. I to stay B. is to stay at
C. to stay at D. is for staying

131. The young worker who saw the car _____ into the river telephoned the police station.
A. plunged B. plunge
C. was plunging D. to plunge

132. The purpose of new technology is to make life easier, _____ it more difficult.
A. not making B. not make
C. not to make D. nor to make

133. She spoke in a whisper _____ the children, but only

225

_____ a lot of misunderstanding.

A. not frightening, causing

B. not to frighten, to cause

C. not frightened, caused

D. not to frightened, to cause

134. Would you be so kind _____ me a favour?

    A. to do   B. of doing

    C. for doing   D. as to do

135. _____ such a good chance, she tried hard and _____ good preparations.

A. Not missing, make

B. Not to miss, made

C. Having not missed, made

D. Not having missed, make

136. If you think there's something wrong with the machine, I'll have Jack _____ over and _____ it for you. I'll have it _____ soon.

A. come, check, repaired

B. coming, checking, repaired

C. come, checked, repaired

D. coming, check, repaired

137. The problem _____ tomorrow will be of great importance to our company, and I'm pretty sure there will be a _____ discussion then.

    A. to discuss, heating   B. to be discussed, heated

    C. for discussing, heated   D. for discussion, heating

138. Sam made the cards himself _____ to his friends _____ money.

    A. send, so as to save   B. to send, in order to save

    C. to send, for saving   D. send, for saving

139. It's most kind of you _____ me the beautiful vase. I'll do something _____ you.

    A. to give, to repay   B. giving, repaying

    C. given, repaid   D. to have given, for repaying

140. All the guests have been invited here to the celebration _____ tomorrow.
    A. holding   B. held
    C. to hold   D. to be held

141. We must get her _____ the doctor. We can have someone _____ her to the hospital.
    A. to see, take   B. see, taken
    C. seeing, taking   D. see, to take

142. You had better not _____. I'll teach you _____ electricity from water power.
    A. to worry, to get   B. worry, getting
    C. worry, how to get   D. to worry, how getting

143. Having broken the vase, the boy stood still without _____ his head.
    A. daring raise   B. dare raising
    C. being able to rise   D. daring to raise

144. We feel it a great honour _____ to visit this beautiful city.
    A. to invite   B. inviting
    C. having invited   D. to be invited

145. Have you got anything interesting _____ in the holiday?
    A. to read   B. reading
    C. for reading   D. to read it

146. I think he should get a permanent job, but you can't force him _____.
    A. /   B. to
    C. do   D. so

147. I need some paper _____.
    A. for writing a report   B. to write a report
    C. for writing a report on   D. to write a report on

148. Having stood for a long time, I was eager to find a chair _____.
    A. for sitting   B. so as to sit
    C. to sit   D. to sit in

149. All the printing mistakes are said to _____.
    A. be correct   B. have been corrected

C. have corrected　　　　　　D. have been correct

150. More and more trees in the area are found _____ from the effect of polluted air.

    A. died　　　　　　　　　B. to be dying

    C. having died　　　　　　D. to be dead

151. He was just _____ up when he felt something moving near his feet.

    A. to jump　　　　　　　B. about to jump

    C. jumping　　　　　　　D. jumped

152. If you drive in England, you'll have _____ on the left side of the road.

    A. to get used to driving　　B. used to drive

    C. to be used to drive　　　D. used to driving

153. I need that book badly. If you go to the bookshop this afternoon, please remember _____ a copy for me.

    A. to buy　　　　　　　B. buying

    C. having bought　　　　D. to have bought

154. Mr. Brown isn't in at the moment. I'll _____ you as soon as he's back in the office.

    A. have him calling　　　　B. have him call

    C. tell him call　　　　　　D. ask him calling

155. Don't _____ the door when you leave the room.

    A. remember to lock　　　B. remember locking

    C. forget to lock　　　　　D. forget locking

156. I'm very sorry _____ for such a long time.

    A. keeping you wait　　　　B. to keep you to wait

    C. for keeping you to wait　　D. to have kept you waiting

157. What you have to do right now is _____.

    A. having the dishes wash

    B. to have the dishes washed

    C. to have the dishes washing

    D. having the dishes to wash

158. The students went to the spare-time school _____ their English.

    A. for improving   B. to improve
    C. by improving   D. so that improve

159. I did not want to do harm to you. I meant _____ you.
    A. to help   B. helping
    C. having helped   D. for helping

160. Some of the stars are so far away that it is impossible _____ in miles.
    A. that we measure it   B. to us to measure
    C. for us to measure them   D. that measures them

161. The flu is believed _____ by viruses that like to reproduce in the cells inside the human nose and throat.
    A. causing   B. being caused
    C. to be caused   D. to have caused

162. We sat up late to _____ our lessons for the examination.
    A. prepare   B. doing
    C. preparing   D. does

163. He knows _____ his books.
    A. how use   B. how to use
    C. how using   D. how used

164. Don't make the little baby _____.
    A. cries   B. is crying
    C. cry   D. cried

165. It took me a long time _____ what he meant.
    A. taking in   B. take in
    C. to take in   D. in taking out

166. Let's not _____ tonight. There's a good film on TV.
    A. to go somewhere   B. go to some where
    C. go nowhere   D. go anywhere

167. Many parents allow their children _____ own decisions.
    A. to make their   B. to make the
    C. making their   D. making the

168. The first thing a dog needs to learn in order to be trained is _____.
    A. to attack   B. to obey

C. to stay still   D. to run

169. My books seemed _____.
     A. so heavy to carry   B. so heavy to be carried
     C. so heavily to carry   D. so heavily carrying

170. He begged his father _____ him.
     A. excusing   B. excused
     C. to excuse   D. excuse

171. _____ the text?
     A. Whose turn is it reciting
     B. Whose turn is it to recite
     C. Whose is it turn to recite
     D. Whose is it turn reciting

172. The policeman observed the man _____.
     A. leave   B. to leave
     C. left   D. is leaving

173. You look pale. You'd better _____ the doctor _____ you
     a check-up.
     A. have, to give   B. have, given
     C. get, give   D. get, to give

174. Having taken the medicine, I felt my cough seemed _____ a
     lot.
     A. to go out   B. to disappear
     C. to have been relieved D. to be well

175. Whom would you rather _____ with you to Hangzhou?
     A. have to go   B. to go
     C. have go   D. have gone

176. Students are often too busy _____ their lessons _____
     outdoor sports.
     A. doing, to take part in   B. to do, taking part in
     C. doing, taking part in   D. to do, to take part in

177. They have been determined _____ for Mary to come back.
     A. having been waiting   B. to have waited
     C. to wait   D. waiting

178. It would be better _____ to George about the bad news

instead of phoning.

A. write   B. to write

C. writing   D. to have written

179. In 2000, Mary Pierce became the first French woman _____
the French Open since Fancoise Durr in 1967.

A. winning   B. to win

C. won   D. having won

180. Pudong International Airport is said _____ already.

A. to build   B. to be built

C. to being built   D. to have been built

181. The problem is believed _____ at the meeting two weeks ago.

A. to have been discussed   B. to discuss

C. to be discussing   D. to have discussed

182. It is better for you to go to bed than _____ watching TV.

A. staying up   B. stay up

C. to stay up   D. to get up

183. We look forward only _____ a narrow path _____ to the
top of the mountain.

A. to seeing, leading   B. to see, leading

C. to seeing, lead   D. to see, led

184. — What's the matter with John?

— He didn't pass the test but he still _____.

A. hopes so   B. hopes it

C. hopes that   D. hopes to

185. I would love _____ to the party last night but I had to work
extra hours to finish a report.

A. to go   B. going

C. to have gone   D. having gone

186. People are not allowed _____ the garden to prevent the
flowers _____.

A. entering, being destroyed

B. to enter, to destroy

C. to enter, being destroyed

D. entering, destroying

187. It looks like rain. It _____ go out and watch TV at home.
  A. is better not to   B. had better not
  C. isn't better to   D. had no better

188. With the watch _____, he could do nothing but _____ a new one.
  A. stolen, to buy   B. stolen, buy
  C. stealing, buy   D. being stolen, buying

189. He made up his mind _____ playing volleyball.
  A. to be devoted to   B. to devote to
  C. to devote himself for   D. devoting his life to

190. One of the books you have bought is hard _____.
  A. to be read   B. to read it
  C. to read   D. to have read

191. There are many ways for people _____ what is going on at home and abroad.
  A. to inform of   B. to inform about
  C. to be informed about   D. informing of

192. It is said that the best way to learn a language is _____ the people who speak it.
  A. communicate with   B. communicating about
  C. to communicate with   D. communicated about

193. Does the doctor think it difficult _____ the baby?
  A. to treat   B. treating
  C. in treating   D. for treating

194. I am sorry _____ so rude to your guest last Sunday.
  A. having been   B. to have been
  C. to be   D. being

195. Every minute is made full use of _____ the test.
  A. to prepare for   B. preparing
  C. preparing for   D. being prepared for

第二十二讲　直接引语和间接引语

1. He said to me,"I used to watch TV every evening."
   Which sentence is correct?
   A. He said to me I used to watch TV every evening.
   B. He told me he used to watch TV every evening.
   C. He told me I used to watch TV every evening.
   D. He said to me he used to watch TV every evening.

2. Abraham Lincoln told his people,"The living must finish the work of the dead, and they must fight for freedom for all — Negroes and whites and America must strengthen government of the people, by the people and for the people."
   Which sentence is correct?
   A. Abraham Lincoln told his people that the living must finish the work of the dead, and they must fight for freedom for all — Negroes and whites and America must strengthen government of the people, by the people and for the people.
   B. Abraham Lincoln told his people that the living must finish the work of the dead, that they must fight for freedom for all — Negroes and whites and America must strengthen government of the people, by the people and for the people.
   C. Abraham Lincoln told his people that the living must finish the work of the dead, that they must fight for freedom for all — Negroes and whites and that America must strengthen government of the people, by the people and for the people.
   D. Abraham Lincoln told his people the living must finish the work of the dead, and they must fight for freedom for all — Negroes and whites and America must strengthen government of the people, by the people and for the people.

3. The headmaster said to me,"What is your name?" This sentence means _____.

A. The headmaster said to me what your name was

B. The headmaster asked me what was your name

C. The headmaster asked me what my name was

D. The headmaster said to me what was your name

4. The teacher asked, "What is the matter with you, Tom?" The sentence means _____.

A. The teacher asked Tom what the matter was with him

B. The teacher asked Tom what was the matter with him

C. The teacher asked what the matter is with Tom

D. The teacher asked what is the matter with Tom

5. He asked, "May I leave if she doesn't come?" Which sentence is correct?

A. He asked me if he might leave if she didn't come.

B. He asked me whether he might leave whether she didn't come.

C. He asked me if he might leave whether she didn't come.

D. He asked me that he might leave if she didn't come.

6. Mr. Li said to me, "Are you tired out or not?" Which sentence is correct?

A. Mr. Li asked me whether I was tired out or not.

B. Mr. Li asked me whether you were tired out or not.

C. Mr. Li asked me if I was tired out or not.

D. Mr. Li asked me if you were tired out or not.

7. Mary told me, "What an interesting novel it was ten years ago!" Which sentence is correct?

A. Mary told me how interesting a novel it was ten years ago.

B. Mary told me what an interesting novel it had been before ten years.

C. Mary told me what an interesting novel it was ten years ago.

D. Mary told me what an interesting novel it had been ten years before.

8. Father said to us, "How funny it is to swim in summer!" Which sentence is right?

A. Father told us how fun it was to swim in summer.

B. Father told us what fun it was to swim in summer.

C. Father told us what a fun it was to swim in summer.

D. Father told us how a funny thing it was to swim in summer.

9. He said that I could go home.

This sentence means _____.

A. He agreed to go home.

B. He allowed me go home.

C. He made me to go home.

D. He let me go home.

10. He said,"Go there to fetch me a magazine, boy."

Which sentence is right?

A. He told the boy to go there to fetch a magazine to me.

B. He told the boy go there to fetch a magazine for me.

C. He told a boy to go there to fetch a magazine to him.

D. He told the boy to go there to fetch a magazine for him.

第二十三讲 "IT" 的用法

1. Harold's Snack Bar enjoyed good business, and _____ daily sale added up to as much as $1,000.
   A. his　　　　　　　　B. it's
   C. its　　　　　　　　D. a

2. Don't _____ that all those who get good grades in the entrance examination will prove to be most successful.
   A. take as granted　　　B. take this for granted
   C. take that for granted　D. take it for granted

3. Someone is ringing the doorbell. Go and see _____.
   A. who is he　　　　　B. who he is
   C. who is it　　　　　D. who it is

4. In fact _____ is a hard job for the police to keep order in an important football match.
   A. this　　　　　　　B. that
   C. there　　　　　　　D. it

5. Our club is open to adults only. _____ your children have entered without permission.
   A. There seems that　　B. It seems to be
   C. There seems to be　　D. It seems that

6. Tom doesn't sit on the chair. _____ lost one of _____ legs.
   A. It is, its　　　　　B. It's, its
   C. Its, it's　　　　　D. It has, whose

7. Do you like _____ when someone greets you without looking at you?
   A. that　　　　　　　B. it
   C. him　　　　　　　D. those

8. He made _____ clear that the number of the supermarkets should be increased.

236

A. /   B. it
C. this   D. that

9. The wet weather has lasted for three weeks now; _____ rained every day.
   A. there has   B. there was
   C. it has   D. it was

10. We find _____ to finish so much work in such a short period of time.
    A. that is impossible   B. it impossible
    C. that impossible   D. impossible

11. Does _____ matter if she can't finish typing the paper by tomorrow?
    A. this   B. that
    C. it   D. she

12. His good idea _____ to produce electric cookers in great numbers.
    A. made us possible   B. made possible
    C. made it possibly   D. made it possible

13. _____ possible to arrange for us to take the 10:00 train for Boston?
    A. Are you   B. Is that
    C. Is it   D. Is now

14. After _____ seemed a long time, an iceberg was in sight in the distance.
    A. it   B. there
    C. what   D. that

15. To what extent will future scientific discoveries _____ the lengthening of the human life?
    A. be made possible   B. make it possible
    C. be made it possible   D. make possible

16. _____ require a great effort to give up smoking?
    A. Does one   B. Does it
    C. Is there   D. Is it to

17. — What is the date today?

237

— _____ September 1.

    A. This is   B. That is

    C. It's   D. Its

18. — What is the distance from Shanghai to Tianjin?

    — _____ over one thousand kilometres.

    A. This is   B. That is

    C. It's   D. Its

19. — What day is tomorrow?

    — _____ Wednesday.

    A. This is   B. That is

    C. It's   D. Its

20. I think _____.

    A. it important eight hours' sleep a day

    B. eight hours' sleep a day important

    C. it important eight hours of sleep a day

    D. it unimportant eight hours' sleep a day

第二十四讲　强调句

1. David said that it was because of his strong interest in literature _____ he chose the course.
   A. that
   B. what
   C. why
   D. how
2. It is imagination _____ makes the world colourful, full of vigour and vitality.
   A. where
   B. what
   C. that
   D. when
3. It was by making great efforts _____ she caught up with other students.
   A. how
   B. when
   C. what
   D. that
4. It was not until 1920 _____ American women had the chance to vote in national elections.
   A. when
   B. that
   C. where
   D. which
5. — Was it by cutting down staff _____ she saved the firm?
   — No, it was by improving work efficiency.
   A. when
   B. what
   C. how
   D. that
6. It was not _____ she took off her dark glasses _____ I realized she was a famous film star.
   A. when, that
   B. until, that
   C. until, when
   D. when, then
7. Was _____ that I saw last night at the concert?
   A. it you
   B. not you
   C. you
   D. that yourself
8. It was the training that he had as a young man _____ made him such a good engineer.

A. that   B. has
C. what   D. later

9. It was _____ the telephone rang.
    A. when Tom was about to go to bed when
    B. that Tom was about to go to bed when
    C. when Tom was about to go to bed that
    D. that Tom was about to bed then

10. It is your body that is continually at work _____ has a
    wonderful way of repairing itself.
    A. that   B. which
    C. why   D. of which

11. It was the university _____ he was studying _____ sent
    him abroad.
    A. which, that   B. where, that
    C. that, which   D. that, had

12. — Who played for keeps?
    — _____ .
    A. John and Bill does   B. It was John and Bill
    C. They were John and Bill   D. John and Bill were

13. Where was _____ the traffic accident happened last night?
    A. it   B. the place that
    C. the place   D. it that

14. It was at middle school _____ I learned something _____
    Madam Curie and her great discovery of radium.
    A. where, from   B. that, about
    C. that, from   D. where, about

15. The laboratory was built two years ago, but it was _____ it
    came into use.
    A. until last month that   B. not until last month
    C. last month when   D. not until last month that

16. Is it _____ we played football _____ you found the key to
    the bike?
    A. that, that   B. that, where
    C. where, that   D. where, in which

17. It was at that moment _____ he realized _____ serious trouble he had got in.
   A. when, what   B. then, how
   C. before, that   D. that, what
18. — Can you guess who these flowers are from?
   — I expect _____ one of our friends who wants to give us a nice surprise.
   A. it to be   B. there is
   C. they are   D. it is
19. Was it for the sake of his family _____ the retired teacher took up teaching again in an evening school?
   A. that   B. why
   C. so   D. so that
20. Where _____ you got that painting at such a low price?
   A. was it that   B. it was until
   C. was it before   D. it was since
21. It is only by what one has done _____ we judge one.
   A. that   B. for
   C. until   D. which
22. It was at yesterday's meeting _____ I came to know your principal.
   A. when   B. that
   C. where   D. since
23. It was in the hall _____ we have dinner _____ we had a dancing party.
   A. where, that   B. that, where
   C. where, which   D. which, where
24. It is not until the bill was looked through that _____ the money.
   A. would he pay   B. did he pay
   C. he would pay   D. he paid
25. _____ he arrived _____ we learned about the death of the hero.
   A. Not until, that   B. It was not until, had
   C. Not until, then   D. It was not until, that
26. It was only with the help of the local guide _____.

A. was the mountain climber rescued

B. that the mountain climber was rescued

C. when the mountain climber was rescued

D. then the mountain climber was rescued

27. Who is it _____ is waiting outside the room?
    A. who   B. whom
    C. which   D. that

28. _____ months later that the matter was cleared up.
    A. Not until   B. It was until
    C. It was not until   D. Until

29. It was in a cave _____ he found the old sick goat.
    A. where   B. which
    C. that   D. in that

30. _____ the footprint _____ Crusoe saw in the sand.
    A. It is, which   B. It is, that
    C. It was, which   D. It was, that

31. It was in that old shabby laboratory _____ Madam Curie discovered radium.
    A. where   B. which
    C. that   D. there

32. It is I who _____ next.
    A. am   B. be
    C. is   D. are

33. Where _____ the next Olympic Games will take place?
    A. is it that   B. is it
    C. was it   D. was it that

34. This is the commonest dress _____ she has ever bought.
    A. which   B. that
    C. who   D. it

35. It was by taxi _____ I got here.
    A. how   B. when
    C. that   D. in which

36. It was _____ he refused to obey the policeman _____ he was fined.

242

A. because, that   B. that, so

C. because, so   D. reason that

37. Why! I have nothing to confess. _____ you want me to say?

A. What is it that   B. What it is that

C. How is it that   D. How it is that

38. It was _____ the old clock that the old man spent the whole morning at home.

A. repaired   B. repairing

C. to repair   D. in repair

39. It is these poisonous products _____ can cause the symptoms of the flu, such as headache and aching muscles.

A. who   B. that

C. how   D. what

40. It was the dog _____ frightened my daughter _____ the young man caught.

A. who, so   B. that, so

C. that, that   D. which, which

41. It was a long time _____ that his father joined the Party.

A. since   B. before

C. during   D. ago

42. It was in the hotel _____ I stayed a few weeks ago _____ we had a meeting.

A. which, that   B. that, which

C. where, that   D. that, when

43. Why _____ took me five days to look for my lost ring?

A. was it that it   B. was it that that

C. was that it that   D. was that that that

44. _____ polite to others.

A. To do   B. Being

C. Do be   D. Be do

45. It was after the invention of printing _____ to publish large numbers of books and pictures.

A. were people able   B. that people were able

C. when were people able D. people were able

第二十五讲　词类(一)　名词

1. _____ has just taken his first step into _____.
   - A. Man, space
   - B. The man, space
   - C. Man, the space
   - D. Men, a space
2. He never admitted that his life was _____.
   - A. failed
   - B. failure
   - C. a failure
   - D. failing
3. Though our home was right in the centre of the tornado, there was _____ fortunately.
   - A. few damages
   - B. few of damages
   - C. little damage
   - D. little of damage
4. The _____ is just around the corner and you won't miss it.
   - A. bicycle's shop
   - B. bicycle shop
   - C. bicycles shop
   - D. bicycles' shop
5. He dropped the _____ and broke it.
   - A. cup of coffee
   - B. coffee's cup
   - C. cup for coffee
   - D. coffee cup
6. We waited _____ for the bus.
   - A. long time
   - B. a long time
   - C. the long time
   - D. some long time
7. He went to the front a soldier and came back _____.
   - A. to be a general
   - B. becoming a general
   - C. a general
   - D. being a general
8. _____ food and equipment was kept in that cave during the war time.
   - A. Quite a few
   - B. Large quantities
   - C. A great deal of
   - D. A large number of
9. He is used to _____.
   - A. work hard
   - B. hard work
   - C. work hardly
   - D. hard-working

10. To reach the top of the building, you have to climb 18 _____
    of _____.
    A. flight, stairs   B. flights, stairs
    C. flight, stair   D. flights, stair
11. It's really _____ to play computer games. But remember not
    to play too much.
    A. funs   B. fun
    C. funny   D. a fun
12. He is very tired. He needs _____.
    A. a night rest   B. a rest night
    C. a night's rest   D. a rest of night
13. The child is looking forward to _____ the Great Wall.
    A. visiting to   B. a visit to
    C. visit   D. be visited
14. Despite the moving story and the wonderful acting, the _____
    film could not attract the foreign audience.
    A. three-hour's   B. three-hours'
    C. three-hour   D. three-hours
15. — Did your father give you courage?
    — Yes, but I spoke from my own thought and certainly not
    _____.

    A. him   B. his
    C. from him   D. from his
16. _____ the gold ring made Fred worried.
    A. Lost   B. Loss
    C. Lose   D. The loss of
17. What a _____ that your mother is ill again!
    A. pain   B. sorrow
    C. sadness   D. pity
18. If the shoes are too small, buy a bigger _____.
    A. one   B. pair
    C. copy   D. set
19. There was a small _____ of sugar in the bowl.
    A. number   B. amount

C. part   D. size

20. David is writing home. _____ will soon be finished and posted.
    A. It   B. He
    C. That   D. The letter

21. It took us quite a long time to get to the amusement park. It was _____ journey.
    A. three hour   B. a three-hours
    C. a three-hour   D. three hours

22. The _____ reading room is quite close to the computer room in the library.
    A. students   B. student's
    C. student   D. students'

23. How can you go to the cinema since you have so _____ to do?
    A. many homeworks   B. much homework
    C. few homeworks   D. so little homework

24. Mother bought her some white trousers, and she went out to buy _____.
    A. another   B. one more
    C. others   D. another pair

25. It is good _____ to thank the person who has done you a favour.
    A. manner   B. manners
    C. action   D. actions

26. We need _____ in our new laboratory.
    A. a good deal of equipment   B. a great many equipments
    C. a large number of equipments   D. a plenty of equipment

27. Mary told the children to play outdoors because they made _____ in the room.
    A. a good deal noise   B. so loud noise
    C. too much noise   D. such lots of noise

28. The village is far away from here indeed. It's _____ walk.
    A. a four hour   B. a four hour's
    C. a four-hours   D. a four hours'

29. The young dancers looked so charming in their beautiful clothes that we took _____ pictures of them.
   A. many of   B. masses of
   C. the number of   D. a large amount of
30. Go and have _____ before we set out.
   A. sleep   B. a good sleep
   C. the sleep   D. some good sleep
31. Let me give you _____.
   A. some advice   B. advices
   C. an advice   D. the advice
32. The information in my _____ is obviously wrong.
   A. idea   B. possession
   C. hand   D. mouth
33. We pulled out the telescope _____.
   A. to full length   B. to full long
   C. to its full length   D. to its full long
34. Now, many people use the word Ms. instead of Miss or Mrs., for example, before the names of _____ in business letters.
   A. woman manager   B. women manager
   C. woman managers   D. women managers
35. Mr. Brown wasn't in his car; he was driving _____ car.
   A. someone's else   B. someone else
   C. someone else's   D. someone's else's
36. — The test itself may also make students too nervous to perform well.
   — Especially on their second try, _____ confidence may have prevented the students from thinking clearly enough to produce correct answers.
   A. lack of   B. lacking of
   C. lack   D. lack for
37. Let's take _____ to sing songs to make our party more active.
   A. turn   B. turns
   C. a turn   D. our turn
38. My birthday is _____. Which answer is wrong?

A. in two weeks   B. in two weeks' time
C. two weeks away   D. in two weeks' time away

39. My pronunciation of English is better than _____ in my class.
A. any other student's   B. any other student
C. any student's   D. any students

40. There are _____ in your composition.
A. too many but's   B. too many but
C. many too buts   D. many too but

第二十六讲 词类(二) 代词

1. Both sides have accused _____ of breaking the contract.
   A. another   B. the other
   C. neither   D. each
2. I made so many changes in my composition that only I could read it. To _____ else, it is hard to make out.
   A. none   B. everyone
   C. someone   D. anyone
3. Treat _____ to a glass of wine to help you relax at the end of the day.
   A. one   B. oneself
   C. you   D. yourself
4. Many fast-growing countries are less concerned with protecting _____ against climate change.
   A. one   B. oneself
   C. them   D. themselves
5. — Do you want tea or coffee?
   — _____. I really don't mind.
   A. None   B. Neither
   C. either   D. All
6. — Wow! You've got so many clothes.
   — But _____ of them are in fashion now.
   A. all   B. both
   C. neither   D. none
7. It is said that two man-made structures are clearly visible from space. One is the Great Wall of China and _____ is Japan's Kansai International Airport.
   A. another   B. other
   C. the other   D. either
8. If our parents do everything for us children, we won't learn to

249

depend on _____.

    A. themselves   B. them

    C. us   D. ourselves

9. To stay awake, he finished a cup of coffee and ordered _____.

    A. the other   B. other

    C. the others   D. another

10. They don't come to the book club any more, for _____ reason or other.

    A. some   B. all

    C. either   D. both

11. When he took his gloves off, I noticed that _____ one had his name written inside.

    A. each   B. every

    C. other   D. another

12. I wanted to have some more coffee, but there was _____ left in the coffee pot.

    A. nothing   B. none

    C. not anything   D. no one

13. Knowledge began to increase as soon as one individual communicates his ideas to _____ by means of speech.

    A. other   B. another

    C. the other   D. some other

14. The children who do best in examinations are not always _____ with the best brains.

    A. who   B. ones

    C. them   D. the ones

15. The Martins joined the volunteer team to help others, especially those older and weaker than _____.

    A. himself   B. them

    C. him   D. themselves

16. I can see most of the children waiting in the room. But where are _____ children who are to take part in the dance?

    A. the few other   B. the other few

    C. a few other   D. another few

17. In this company, the clerks could start working at _____ time during the first three hours when their office was open.
    A. any   B. any other
    C. any of   D. whatever
18. The house _____ is beautiful, but the surroundings are rather unpleasant.
    A. by itself   B. itself
    C. for itself   D. of itself
19. I don't think _____ should overwork _____.
    A. one, oneself   B. someone, oneself
    C. one, one's self   D. anyone, self
20. Harding and his wife want to move to their native town, but _____ of their children wants to.
    A. no one   B. not anyone
    C. nobody   D. no one else
21. My family are wonderful. They do all they can for me. I don't know _____ family who would do so much.
    A. some other   B. any other
    C. some more   D. any more
22. I'd like to undertake _____ job so long as it will provide useful experience.
    A. any   B. some
    C. every   D. any one
23. — Could I have a single room with a bath?
    — Sorry, sir, all the single rooms are occupied at the moment. Can you try _____ hotel?
    A. other   B. the other
    C. another   D. other's
24. _____ student with a little common sense should be able to answer the question.
    A. Each   B. Any
    C. Either   D. One
25. If you don't care for the design of the furniture, I can show you _____.

A. another B. some
C. some other D. other

26. Both teams were in hard training; _____ was willing to lose the game.
    A. either B. neither
    C. another D. the other

27. Don't lose heart. Have _____ try.
    A. another B. other
    C. the other D. another one

28. — Would you like some wine?
    — Yes. Just _____.
    A. little B. very little
    C. a little D. little bit

29. — Is your camera like Bill's and Ann's?
    — No, but it's almost the same as _____.
    A. her B. yours
    C. them D. their

30. Everyone was surprised when Mr. Wang chose _____ for his assistants.
    A. both she and I B. both I and she
    C. both her and me D. both me and her

31. Some friends tried to settle the quarrel between Mr. and Mrs. Smith without hurting the feeling of _____, but failed.
    A. none B. either
    C. all D. neither

32. All of my classmates went to see the play. I didn't like it at all. In fact, _____ of us did.
    A. either B. neither
    C. none D. any

33. _____ who laughs last laughs best.
    A. He B. She
    C. That D. Those

34. We had a party last month, and it was a lot of fun, so let's have _____ one this month.

A. another   B. more
C. the other   D. other

35. Tom felt he knew everybody's business better than they knew
    _____.
    A. themselves   B. oneself
    C. itself   D. himself

36. — Is there any old equipment on sale in this second-hand store?
    — Yes, _____.
    A. there are many old ones   B. there are quite a lot
    C. there is quite a lot   D. there is good deal

37. If that pen is not hers, _____ can it be?
    A. who else   B. whose else's
    C. who else's   D. who's else

38. Grammar _____ is not the language, but a helping hand to our
    language learning.
    A. by itself   B. itself
    C. for itself   D. of itself

39. Uncle Sam's fast food restaurant enjoys good business and
    _____ daily sales can add up to 4,000 dollars.
    A. whose   B. who's
    C. its   D. his

40. This journal may not be suitable for you because _____ article
    in it is not written in plain English.
    A. all   B. each
    C. every one   D. every

41. You should close your _____ eye while I'm having a checkup
    on the eyesight of one eye.
    A. another   B. other
    C. the other   D. some other

42. Charlie offered me twenty dollars for my jacket, but it was not
    worth half _____.
    A. that many   B. that much
    C. so much   D. such a lot

43. Until he found a stranger looking at him, he thought _____ of

the terrible scene in the film.

A. everything   B. nothing

C. anything   D. something

44. You'd better go back and see to _____ that all the medicine bottles are under lock and key.

A. /   B. the fact

C. it   D. all

45. — Do you know that girl with long hair?

— I don't think so, although she reminds me of _____ I know.

A. someone   B. one

C. that   D. anyone

46. Life gets noisier every day and very few people can be free from noise of _____ sort or _____.

A. some, other   B. one, the other

C. a, others   D. some, another

47. — Lovely weather, isn't it?

— Yes, I hope tomorrow will be _____ nice day.

A. the other   B. some

C. another   D. some other

48. Some of the stamps belong to me, while the rest are _____.

A. him and her   B. his and hers

C. his and her   D. him and hers

49. In nature some animals depend on each other so much that one or _____ would die without _____ help.

A. two, another   B. both, other's

C. both, the other's D. another, someone's

50. In my opinion, the sentence _____ is wrong.

A. himself   B. herself

C. it   D. itself

51. Reading is _____ thing while speaking is quite _____.

A. a, the other   B. one, the other

C. one, another   D. a, another

52. The girl is old enough to dress _____.

A. her   B. herself

C. her clothes   D. in

53. Her spoken English is better than _____ in our class.
    A. anyone's else   B. anyone else's
    C. anyone else   D. anyone's else's

54. You must improve _____ in English.
    A. yours   B. your
    C. you   D. yourself

55. There are flowers and trees on _____ side of this street.
    A. both   B. all
    C. every   D. each

56. _____ of them was greatly moved by his words.
    A. All   B. Everyone
    C. Both   D. Every one

57. _____ many people have tried, but _____ have succeeded.
    A. Such, few   B. Such, a few
    C. So, a few   D. So, few

58. He always says _____ but does much.
    A. a little   B. a few
    C. little   D. few

59. The apples on the table belong to us, but the _____ on the floor belong to Mary.
    A. thing   B. one
    C. ones   D. one's

60. _____ of them promised to tell the truth.
    A. Every one   B. Everyone
    C. Every body   D. Everybody

61. _____ has gone to the meeting; _____ is absent today.
    A. Nobody, somebody   B. Either, none
    C. Everyone, no one   D. Each, either

62. People like different colours. _____ like red, and _____ like green.
    A. One, others   B. Some, the others
    C. Some, others   D. All, none

63. Together with Dickens' novels were a number of less famous

_____.
A. some   B. ones
C. book   D. others

64. Order, please. _____ will have a chance by turn. Please come in _____ after _____.
  A. One, one, another
  B. All, each, another
  C. Everyone, one, the other
  D. Each, one, other

65. If we don't have any other questions to ask, let's go on to _____.
  A. next   B. a next
  C. the next   D. other one

66. The doctor advised Vera strongly that she should take a holiday, but _____ didn't help.
  A. it   B. she
  C. which   D. he

67. The chicken tastes wonderful. Please give me _____.
  A. no more   B. something else
  C. some more   D. little more

68. You don't have to give me _____ of her books. I've read _____ of them.
  A. any, all   B. none, none
  C. any, some   D. all, any

69. He can talk _____ in English or French.
  A. either   B. neither
  C. or   D. also

70. When I try to understand _____ that prevents so many students from being as happy as one might expect, it seems to me that there are two causes.
  A. why it does   B. what it does
  C. what it is   D. why it is

71. She took _____ chance she could find to practice her spoken English.
  A. every   B. all

C. each   D. every one

72. He couldn't see the stranger clearly until he was only _____ yards from her.
    A. few   B. few of
    C. the few   D. a few

73. _____ student with a knowledge of geography should know that India is a country with a large population.
    A. One   B. Any one
    C. Any   D. Each

74. This metre is not sensitive enough. Please give me _____.
    A. one   B. other
    C. anyone   D. another

75. _____ who enjoys sports likes to take part in them.
    A. None   B. Not everyone
    C. No everybody   D. Not anyone

76. I interviewed them one by one, and _____ told me about his or her working experiences.
    A. each   B. every
    C. all   D. any

77. Not _____ has been arranged yet. You will have to wait.
    A. something   B. nothing
    C. everything   D. anything

78. In the future, robots will do more and more work for man. _____ people will have to work long hours.
    A. The few   B. A few
    C. Few of   D. Few

79. Oh, it's not my umbrella. I've taken _____.
    A. somebody else   B. somebody's else
    C. somebody else's   D. some other's

80. — Captain, can you tell us something about ships?
    — OK, I'll just talk about hovercrafts like _____ over there.
    A. ones   B. those
    C. them   D. these

81. I don't know which of the two countries began the war. It must

257

have been _____ or _____.

    A. one, another   B. this, other

    C. one, the other   D. some, other

82. The couple worked day and night just to buy _____.

    A. a house of their own   B. the house of theirs

    C. a house of themselves   D. the house of them

83. You are thirsty, I suppose. Please help _____ to the drinks in the icebox.

    A. me   B. you

    C. yours   D. yourself

84. To our relief, the drowning boy came to _____ at last.

    A. himself   B. him

    C. live   D. his life

85. I glanced at my watch, and _____ was earlier than I had thought.

    A. it   B. time

    C. which   D. that

86. Peter took up collecting coins as hobby, _____ surprised his family.

    A. and which   B. and it

    C. that   D. who

87. Betty's hair is longer than _____ in her class.

    A. any girl's   B. any others

    C. that of any girl   D. any other girl's

88. Does a nation's literature reflect _____ manners and morals?

    A. its   B. it's

    C. his   D. their

89. Shanghai is really a fascinating city and we decided to stay for _____ two weeks.

    A. another   B. other

    C. the other   D. other's

90. _____ of the boys has got a pencil and some paper.

    A. All   B. Every

    C. Everyone   D. Each

91. Sorry that I've got _____ money about me. Could you do me a

favour to lend me _____?

  A. some, some   B. any, any

  C. no, any   D. no, some

92. Peter is always ready to help _____. He studies at school for five days every week, and during _____ days he is always busy serving the old and sick people.

  A. each other, other   B. others, the other two

  C. other ones, other two   D. other people, others

93. These CDs are not _____, and so you are not in the position to deal with them on _____ own.

  A. yours, yours   B. your, your

  C. yours, your   D. your, yours

94. You can take _____ half of the turkey. They are of the same weight and price.

  A. both   B. either

  C. neither   D. any

95. I'll get _____ friends here to give you _____ help.

  A. a little, a little   B. few, a little

  C. a few, little   D. a few, a little

96. I don't think we've met before. You are confusing me with _____.

  A. some other   B. someone else

  C. other person   D. one other

97. I don't think I can introduce you to all the other guests, because I know only _____ of them.

  A. few   B. a few

  C. little   D. a little

98. He asked three men — Bob, Joe and _____ to be ready.

  A. I   B. herself

  C. me   D. himself

99. No progress was made in the trade talk as neither side would accept the conditions of _____.

  A. others   B. the other

  C. either   D. another

100. Your brother is good at maths and so is _____.
   A. her
   B. my
   C. mine
   D. you

101. There are two lifts going up. You may take _____ of them.
   A. both
   B. neither
   C. either
   D. each

102. I have four dictionaries. One is French, _____ in English and _____ in Chinese.
   A. one, the other two
   B. another, the other two
   C. one, two
   D. another, others

103. The dictionary doesn't belong to your brother _____, but it belongs to me.
   A. and me
   B. or yours
   C. or mine
   D. and yours

104. — It won't be long before you go to college.
   — Yes, we have _____ over two months.
   A. only a little
   B. only a few
   C. not a little
   D. not a few

105. The police _____ the thieves in the building but they found _____.
   A. searched, none
   B. searched for, nothing
   C. searched, no one
   D. searched for, none

106. Some people dream more, _____ less.
   A. others
   B. the others
   C. the other
   D. another

107. I need some blue ink badly, but there is _____ at hand.
   A. not
   B. little
   C. none
   D. nothing

108. — I love you more than her, child?
   — You mean more than _____ love her or more than she loves _____?
   A. you, me
   B. I, you
   C. you, you
   D. I, me

109. Can you tell _____ students in your class that Professor Li is

coming to give us a lecture tomorrow?

    A. another   B. the other

    C. others   D. the others

110. The number of the books in their school is larger than _____.

    A. that in ours   B. those in ours

    C. that in ours'   D. those in ours'

111. Believe _____ or not, they will surely be good doctors.

    A. you   B. it

    C. them   D. me

112. Maybe she is sick today, but she usually eats quite _____ and sleeps _____.

    A. little, little   B. a lot, a few

    C. a little, a lot   D. lot, a lot

113. Mary couldn't resist _____ bar of chocolate though she had said that she was slimming.

    A. other   B. some other

    C. another   D. more

114. Jack looked _____ to look for his girl friend, Mary.

    A. around himself   B. about himself

    C. about her   D. around him

115. My daughter often makes a schedule to get _____ reminded of what she is to do in the day.

    A. herself   B. her

    C. she   D. hers

116. There are trees on _____ side of the street.

    A. none   B. either

    C. both   D. all

117. This typewriter isn't good. I want _____ typewriter.

    A. some other   B. another

    C. other   D. any other

118. These three boys will help _____ to finish the experiment.

    A. one another   B. each and other

    C. one and other   D. one and the other

119. Almost _____ knew the boy's name.
   A. every   B. anybody
   C. somebody   D. nobody
120. Two people had met the General before, but _____ recognized him.
   A. either   B. any
   C. neither   D. some
121. You may write to me or come to see me. _____ way will do.
   A. All   B. Both
   C. One   D. Either
122. The scientist was doing his experiment attentively; he was _____ but lonely.
   A. anything   B. nothing
   C. something   D. everything
123. The girl sang well, and therefore she was _____ a singer.
   A. something of   B. anything of
   C. everything of   D. nothing of
124. The man standing over there is _____ I am looking for. Which is wrong?
   A. none other than the man
   B. no other than the man
   C. the very man
   D. no another than the man
125. — Are there any instruments in the laboratory?
   — _____.
   A. Nothing   B. None
   C. Not anything   D. No

第二十七讲 词类(三)
形容词和副词

1. Some experts think that language learning is much _____ for children as their tongues are more flexible.
   A. easy
   B. easier
   C. easily
   D. more easily

2. Nowadays the roles of husband and wife are not as _____ defined as before, especially when both partners work and earn money for family.
   A. clear
   B. clearer
   C. clearly
   D. more clearly

3. Those who have _____ money than sense may sometimes act foolishly.
   A. much
   B. more
   C. most
   D. many

4. Ernest visited the South Pole because he wanted to see one of the _____ regions in the world.
   A. colder
   B. coldest
   C. more coldly
   D. most coldly

5. In ancient times, people rarely travelled long distances and most farmers only travel _____ the local market.
   A. longer than
   B. more than
   C. as much as
   D. as far as

6. When Mon looked back on the early days of their marriage, she wondered how they had managed with _____ money.
   A. so few
   B. such few
   C. so little
   D. such little

7. After the accident, we are _____ concerned with the safety of school buses than we used to be.
   A. little
   B. less

C. much   D. more

8. Come _____, boys! Let's go over and bring those chairs here in case it rains.
   A. up   B. to
   C. along   D. across

9. The house is not big enough for us, and _____, it's too far from the town.
   A. therefore   B. however
   C. furthermore   D. yet

10. What we are talking about is that we should do as much as we can with _____ possible money.
   A. less   B. the least
   C. the little   D. little

11. I can't open the lock. There must be _____ key that will open it.
   A. some   B. other
   C. certain   D. some other

12. Some passengers seemed to have sensed the danger of their flight. They didn't say anything about it, _____.
   A. but   B. therefore
   C. either   D. though

13. — Could I speak to Mrs. Bragg?
    — Please _____ a minute. I'll try to connect you.
   A. hold up   B. hold out
   C. hold on   D. hold in

14. Having visited the Palace Museum, Mr. Boyd said that he had never been to a palace that interested him _____.
   A. most   B. more
   C. much   D. too much

15. The watch I bought at the second-hand shop is almost new. _____, it keeps very good time.
   A. Furthermore   B. Actually
   C. Therefore   D. However

16. He refused _____ medical treatment as he didn't think he was seriously ill.

A. farther   B. further
C. farthest   D. furthest

17. Many elderly people have to live on the money they set _____ when they were young.
 A. up   B. back
 C. aside   D. about

18. Bob, thank you so much. Your party couldn't have been _____ delightful. We had a wonderful time.
 A. most   B. less
 C. least   D. more

19. He was well prepared for the interview; _____, he couldn't help stammering before the examiner.
 A. therefore   B. on the other hand
 C. what's worse   D. nevertheless

20. Historians disagreed about how far the festival went _____.
 A. up   B. forward
 C. back   D. over

21. — Jimmy wants to stay up and watch an old movie on TV.
 — Ten o'clock is _____ for a boy of his age to stay up.
 A. a too late hour   B. very much late an hour
 C. too late an hour   D. a so late hour

22. The results of this experiment were _____ similar to those of the former experiments.
 A. efficiently   B. eventually
 C. gradually   D. essentially

23. Doctors hope to find _____ cases of cancer early when they can still be cured easily.
 A. any more   B. many more
 C. much more   D. too many

24. His explanation was so clear that everyone could understand it with the _____ possible effort.
 A. less   B. fewer
 C. least   D. fewest

25. What surprised me most was to find _____ little boys could

make _____ much progress in _____ a short time.

A. such, so, so   B. such, so, such

C. so, so, such   D. so, such, such

26. To fulfil the task ahead of time, we need _____.

A. more much money   B. more many workers

C. much more money   D. much more workers

27. Drivers can't be _____ while they are driving cars.

A. too careless   B. very careless

C. very careful   D. too careful

28. — How come you've been coming to our club _____ than you
used to?

— Oh, I've been busy writing a new book.

A. less   B. fewer

C. less often   D. much less

29. Which of the two pictures do you think is _____?

A. much more beautiful   B. the less beautiful

C. a most beautiful   D. the least beautiful

30. _____ to take this adventure course will certainly learn a lot of
useful skills.

A. Brave enough students   B. Enough brave students

C. Students brave enough   D. Students enough brave

31. This hat is too small for me. I want one _____.

A. two size bigger   B. bigger than three sizes

C. two size as big   D. big by three sizes

32. I don't think they will come tonight, and it's _____ impossible.

A. very   B. quite

C. much   D. probably

33. Their cheerful voices showed that they were having a _____
discussion.

A. noisy   B. serious

C. complete   D. friendly

34. Last night I had a terrible cold and ached all _____.

A. the way   B. over

C. at once   D. the worst

35. What he has done is far from _____ .
    A. satisfactory   B. satisfied
    C. satisfaction   D. satisfy
36. You're standing too near the camera. Can you move _____ ?
    A. a bit far   B. a little farther
    C. a bit of farther   D. a little far
37. Many foreigners like to eat traditional Chinese food because of its _____ smell.
    A. interesting   B. charming
    C. inviting   D. demanding
38. I think reading at home is _____ more comfortable.
    A. very   B. much
    C. so   D. too
39. He started running _____ in the last five minutes and became the champion.
    A. the fastest   B. the faster
    C. fast and fast   D. faster and faster
40. John was so sleepy that he could hardly keep his eyes _____ .
    A. open   B. to be opened
    C. to open   D. opening
41. Readers can _____ quite well without knowing the exact meaning of each word.
    A. get over   B. get in
    C. get along   D. get through
42. If there were no examinations, we should have _____ at school.
    A. the happiest time   B. a more happier time
    C. much happiest time   D. a much happier time
43. If the manager had to choose between the two, he would say John was _____ choice.
    A. good   B. the best
    C. better   D. the better
44. It was _____ late to catch a bus after the party, therefore we called a taxi.
    A. too very   B. much too

C. too much   D. far

45. John seems a nice person. _____, I don't trust him.
    A. Even though   B. Even so
    C. Therefore   D. Thus

46. You cannot be _____ careful when you drive a car.
    A. very   B. so
    C. too   D. enough

47. Alan is not a careful driver, _____ he wouldn't have had that accident.
    A. nevertheless   B. however
    C. otherwise   D. although

48. I think the Chinese team will win the final game; it's _____ that they will.
    A. rather possibly   B. almost surely
    C. very likely   D. quite certainly

49. Of all the students in the class, our monitor made the _____ mistakes in the dictation exercise.
    A. less   B. least
    C. fewer   D. fewest

50. I won't pay 800 *yuan* for the coat; it is not worth _____.
    A. all that much   B. that all much
    C. much that all   D. that much all

51. I don't know why my father preferred _____ of the two houses.
    A. more isolated one   B. the one more isolated
    C. the more isolated one   D. the most isolated one

52. The students are _____ young people from the northeast.
    A. most   B. mostly
    C. almost   D. at most

53. We have _____ more questions _____ these to ask you.
    A. much, besides   B. many, besides
    C. many, except   D. much, beside

54. Jack Thompson has written a number of short stories, but he is _____ known for his plays.
    A. more   B. the most

C. the best   D. better

55. _____, some famous scientists have the qualities of being both
careful and careless.
   A. Strangely enough   B. Enough strangely
   C. Strange enough   D. Enough strange

56. The opera, a _____ fascinating one, attracts a large audience
consisting _____ of women as _____ of the singers are
females.
   A. most, most, mostly   B. mostly, mostly, most
   C. most, mostly, most   D. mostly, most, mostly

57. — Are you going to the concert?
   — No. The tickets are _____ expensive for me.
   A. very much   B. so much
   C. far too   D. highly

58. The professor told his class that a good way to practice English is
to write _____.
   A. constant letters   B. letters constant
   C. letters constantly   D. constantly letters

59. This is _____ river.
   A. China's the second longest
   B. Chinese second longest
   C. China's second longer
   D. China's second longest

60. The food she has prepared for the party is not enough, for there
are _____ more people than she expected.
   A. much   B. many
   C. too   D. so

61. We cannot be _____ careful in performing the experiment as it
is such a critical link in the whole project.
   A. very   B. too
   C. quite   D. so

62. It's _____ a long time since I rode a bicycle.
   A. much   B. quite
   C. fairly   D. pretty

63. Strangely _____, although she's a famous actress, people rarely recognize her in the street.
    A. also   B. but
    C. enough   D. so
64. The _____ of his daughters is prettier.
    A. young   B. young one
    C. younger   D. youngest
65. Your cigarette ash is very long, and please knock it _____ before it falls onto the floor.
    A. out   B. in
    C. off   D. away
66. I don't _____ like the idea of walking home in the rain.
    A. so   B. very
    C. much   D. fairly
67. The girl lay _____ on the ground, thinking about something good.
    A. quite   B. quiet
    C. quitely   D. quietly
68. Jim didn't get the job because he wasn't _____.
    A. enough experience   B. enough experienced
    C. experience enough   D. experienced enough
69. The big earthquake is still on. _____ clothing is _____ needed in the mountain village.
    A. Many, much   B. Much, badly
    C. A good many of, badly   D. A great deal of, very
70. — What a nice fire you have in your fireplace!
    — During the winter I like my house _____.
    A. warmly and comfortably   B. warm and comfortable
    C. warm and comfortably   D. warmly and comfortable
71. Some of our dissatisfaction might come from expecting _____ of ourselves.
    A. much too   B. too much
    C. much more   D. such much
72. To my surprise, Palmer had _____ income to support his

family.
- A. a such small
- B. a too small
- C. too small an
- D. such small a

73. How beautiful the Grand Theatre is! I have never seen _____.
- A. a good one
- B. the best one
- C. the better one
- D. a better one

74. The fridge I bought at the second-hand shop is almost new; _____, it works very well.
- A. instead
- B. furthermore
- C. though
- D. nevertheless

75. He made _____ progress in his English studies as he had _____ knowledge of the language.
- A. little, a little
- B. little, little
- C. a little, little
- D. the little, a little

76. In some primary schools, the length of the average class period has been reduced to _____ 30 minutes.
- A. as much as
- B. so long as
- C. as far as
- D. less than

77. A teacher must remember that a child's mind must be developed _____ with his body.
- A. along
- B. alongside
- C. the same
- D. down

78. Though smoking is known to be harmful to one's health, many countries see _____ change in the number of smokers.
- A. only little
- B. quite a little
- C. little
- D. the little

79. Before they go to university, most senior high school graduates have _____ idea of what college life is like.
- A. no less
- B. no least
- C. not less
- D. not the least

80. _____ people prefer their dishes _____ salty.
- A. Most, less
- B. The most, less
- C. Most the, little
- C. Mostly, least

81. It costs _____ postage to send a letter by ordinary mail than

271

by airmail.

    A. even fewer   B. lot least

    C. very little   D. much less

82. He said that he had lost the game, and _____, that there was no hope of winning it again.

    A. yet   B. thus

    C. then   D. further

83. The six-hour walk was _____ for the old woman, who was _____ weak to walk alone.

    A. too much, much too   B. too much, too much

    C. much too, much too   D. much too, too much

84. This dictionary is the _____ useful of all.

    A. less   B. more

    C. fewer   D. most

85. There is still _____ ink in the bottle.

    A. a few   B. few

    C. a little   D. little

86. Buses are _____ cars.

    A. not same as   B. so different to

    C. different from   D. not as same as

87. There are _____ hotels and restaurants in Shanghai than in other cities.

    A. much more   B. many more

    C. a large more   D. a lot more

88. You got to the school _____ than he, but I got there _____.

    A. a little earlier, earliest   B. more early, the earliest

    C. much early, earliest   D. a little early, earlier

89. He had a curious _____ of making his lessons _____.

    A. method, alive   B. way, lively

    C. method, vividly   D. way, lovely

90. Tom's English is _____. He speaks English _____.

    A. poorly, poor   B. poor, poorly

    C. poorly, poorly   D. poor, poor

91. Don't worry! We'll reach the station _____.
    A. fast enough   B. quick enough
    C. quickly enough   D. soon enough
92. Peter and Bob both did well, but Peter is _____ of the two.
    A. the more talented   B. more talented
    C. the most talented   D. most talented
93. Slow _____ your steps. I can't keep _____ you.
    A. down, up with   B. down, on with
    C. off, up with   D. off, on with
94. I'm sorry. I can't _____ your handwriting.
    A. make up   B. make for
    C. make out   D. make off
95. The man-made trees look so _____ that all the guests mistook them for real ones.
    A. similar   B. natural
    C. beautiful   D. artificial
96. These winners from that key school are wise and diligent. Actually there are _____ students in that school.
    A. many such   B. such many
    C. so many   D. many so
97. It is a _____ experiment even though it will turn out to be a failure.
    A. worthless   B. worthwhile
    C. worth   D. worth while
98. After the Gulf War, the American soldiers returned _____.
    A. safe but tired   B. safely but tiringly
    C. safely and tired   D. safe and tiring
99. How beautifully she sings! I've never heard _____.
    A. to better voice   B. a good voice
    C. the best voice   D. a better voice
100. _____ friends I had made there were _____ from the United States.
    A. Few of, most   B. Few, the most
    C. The few, mostly   D. A few, the mostly

101. The museum is _____ worth visiting more than once.
    A. very   B. well
    C. far   D. very much
102. Now I have _____ classes every day, but I have _____ time for playing than ever before.
    A. more, less   B. fewer, less
    C. fewer, more   D. more, more
103. These national parks are very important for preserving many animals, which would _____ run the risk of becoming extinct.
    A. otherwise   B. therefore
    C. nevertheless   D. however
104. Hurry up. There is not _____ time left.
    A. more   B. many
    C. much   D. plenty
105. I have worked with him for some time and have found that he is _____ than John.
    A. more efficiently a worker   B. a more efficient worker
    C. more an efficient worker   D. a worker more efficiently
106. Iron is _____ of all the metals on the earth.
    A. very useful   B. most useful
    C. quite useful   D. the most useful
107. Susan is _____ girl. She never stops working.
    A. the most diligent   B. most diligent
    C. a more diligent   D. a most diligent
108. It's _____ price to pay for the piano lessons.
    A. a so high   B. so a high
    C. so high a   D. a such high
109. To tell the truth, I have never been to _____ city all my life.
    A. a dirtier   B. the dirtier
    C. the dirtiest   D. a such dirty
110. My job is becoming boring. _____, it doesn't offer much chance of advancement.
    A. However   B. Furthermore

C. Though D. Therefore
111. The book I bought yesterday is expensive. _____, it is not very useful.
    A. Still B. Besides
    C. Yet D. As a result
112. The cake is just wonderful. I'd like to have _____.
    A. some more B. the other
    C. others D. other
113. It is my _____ that your illness is caused by something _____ than overwork.
    A. belief, less serious B. thought, less seriously
    C. belief, more serious D. thought, more seriously
114. Peter spends _____ time studying than his cousin but has made _____ progress.
    A. little, great B. less, greater
    C. much, great D. more, greater
115. The salesman showed her several bags and chose _____ as she didn't want to spend too much money on it.
    A. the less expensive B. less expensive
    C. the least expensive D. least expensive
116. Li did _____ in the English exam. I did even _____.
    A. worse, worst B. badly, also worse
    C. bad, more badly D. badly, worse
117. It's a _____ longer sentence than any other one in the passage, so it's not _____ easy to understand.
    A. very, very B. so, so
    C. much, such D. far, so
118. As I didn't have a lot of money, I could only choose the _____ expensive goods and save the _____ possible amount of money.
    A. less, most B. least, more
    C. most, most D. more, much
119. Having lost the game, the players sat, quite _____.
    A. having upset B. upset

C. to be upset   D. upsetting

120. The master _____ satisfied with his students' progress that he praised them in class.
    A. was so   B. was so that
    C. was such   D. is such a

121. The cars are running _____.
    A. today   B. badly
    C. at once   D. to and fro

122. English is one of the _____ important languages in the world.
    A. much   B. more
    C. less   D. most

123. If you want to telephone him you will have to _____ the number in the book.
    A. look at   B. look to
    C. look through   D. look up

124. I have got _____ twenty *yuan* on me, so I can't afford to buy this dictionary.
    A. more than   B. no less than
    C. no more than   D. not less than

125. I am the _____ of the two children in our family.
    A. tallest   B. taller
    C. tall   D. most tallest

126. In Scotland the last day of the year is the most important holiday for the winter, _____ Christmas.
    A. as important as   B. less important than
    C. much important than D. more important than

127. I've got a severe headache, which kept me _____ the whole night.
    A. waking   B. wake
    C. woken   D. awake

128. Try and set _____ time _____ some mending jobs.
    A. out, doing   B. about, of doing
    C. aside, to do   D. down, doing

129. This is _____ the better of the two.
    A. by far
    B. much
    C. many
    D. both A and B
130. — Let's have dinner in the hotel dining-room.
    — Oh, I'm afraid it may be _____ expensive.
    A. too much
    B. much too
    C. greatly
    D. very great
131. Children are _____ to deal with.
    A. much too tired
    B. much too tiring
    C. tired
    D. too much tiring
132. Thousands of passengers were trapped in the tunnel till the fire

    _____.
    A. was put up
    B. was put off
    C. was put out
    D. was put down
133. _____ for him, his stepmother was so kind to him.
    A. Happily
    B. Happy
    C. Lucky
    D. Fortunate
134. The old man lived _____, but he didn't feel _____.
    A. alone, lonely
    B. lonely, alone
    C. alone, alone
    D. lonely, lonely
135. They arrived in Britain _____.
    A. safely
    B. safety
    C. safe
    D. safeness

第二十八讲 词类(四) 数词

1. 64,768,691 reads _____.
   A. sixty four millions seven hundreds and sixty eight thousands six hundreds and ninety one
   B. sixty-four millions seven hundred and sixty-eight thousand six hundreds and ninety-one
   C. sixty-four million seven hundred and sixty-eight thousand six hundred and ninety-one
   D. sixty four million seven hundred and sixty eight thousand six hundred and ninety one

2. That will be a _____ trip around the city.
   A. four-hour   B. four-hour's
   C. four-hours'   D. four-hours

3. _____ people in the world are sending information by e-mail every day.
   A. Several million   B. Many millions
   C. Several millions   D. Many million

4. Shortly after the accident, two _____ police were sent to the spot to keep order.
   A. dozen of   B. dozens
   C. dozen   D. dozens of

5. Don't all speak at once! _____, please.
   A. Each at one time   B. One by one time
   C. One for each time   D. One at a time

6. He works in a building of _____.
   A. two storeys   B. two storeies
   C. two-story   D. two-stories

7. Several of the apples are bad, and _____ have worm holes.
   A. more several   B. several more
   C. several others   D. several another

8. I have finished reading _____ chapters of the novel.
   A. the first four   B. first four
   C. one fourth   D. fourth
9. The teacher asked his students to answer his questions _____.
   A. each at on time   B. one by a time
   C. one at a time   D. one for each time
10. Why must you leave tomorrow? Can't you stay with us _____?
    A. for few more days   B. for a few days more
    C. for much more days   D. for a few more days
11. She is an English teacher, _____ ordinary teachers in our school.
    A. one of whom   B. one of which
    C. and one of many   D. one of many
12. _____ of the workers in this school _____ in _____.
    A. Three-fifth, are, twenties
    B. Three-five, is, twenty
    C. Three-fifths, are, their twenties
    D. Three-fives, is, twenties
13. He served in the army in _____ when he was in _____.
    A. 1970's, his twenties   B. 1970's, the twenties
    C. the 1970s, his twenties   D. the 1970's, the twenties
14. The new building is to be _____ high.
    A. six storeys   B. six storey
    C. six-storeys   D. six-storied
15. — What's the date today?
    — It's _____.
    A. Sunday   B. August the nineth
    C. the first of May   D. October fifth
16. — Do you think the chairs are enough?
    — No, I think we still need about _____ 20 ones.
    A. other   B. the other
    C. another   D. some other
17. The parking lot was so large that all our cars and buses occupied only _____ its space.

A. the third   B. one third of
C. third   D. the third of

18. Thanksgiving Day, which is _____ Thursday in November, is observed in America every year.
    A. fourth   B. the four
    C. a fourth   D. the fourth

19. The movement took place in _____.
    A. the 1940s'   B. 1940s
    C. 1940's   D. the 1940s

20. Mother went to the supermarket and bought _____ eggs.
    A. two dozens   B. two dozen of
    C. two dozen   D. two dozens of

21. The People's Republic of China was founded on _____, 1949.
    A. October the first   B. first of the October
    C. first October   D. the first of the October

22. We are asked to write a _____ composition about the traffic in Shanghai.
    A. five-hundreds-words   B. five-hundred-words
    C. five-hundreds-word   D. five-hundred-word

23. The weight of the moon is only about _____ of that of the earth.
    A. one of eighty   B. one eightieth
    C. one of eighties   D. one the eightieth

24. We were asked to write _____ composition in one hour.
    A. an 800-word   B. an 800-words
    C. a 800-word   D. a 800-words

25. Unfortunately, the bus slid into a snowdrift _____.
    A. four feet high   B. four-feet high
    C. four feet deep   D. four-feet deep

26. The doctor visited the patient every _____ day.
    A. a second   B. other
    C. two   D. another

27. _____ broke out in 1914.
    A. The World War First   B. First World War

C. The First World War   D. World War First

28. When Joe was _____ he went to the United States and became a worker.
 A. in his twenty   B. over his twenties
 C. in his twenties   D. more than twenties

29. — Is it eleven forty-five?
 — Yes, it's _____.
 A. fifteen to twelve   B. fifteen from twelve
 C. a quarter past eleven   D. a quarter to twelve

30. Though he speaks English well, he thinks it necessary to learn _____ foreign language.
 A. two   B. second
 C. a second   D. the second

31. Shortly after the accident, three _____ policemen were sent to the spot to keep order.
 A. score of   B. scores
 C. score   D. scores of

32. Cars moved very slowly in the _____.
 A. 1920   B. 1920s'
 C. 1920 year   D. 1920s

33. The suspension bridge is _____ between the two towers.
 A. 4,200 feet long   B. 4,200-foot-long
 C. 4,200-foot in length   D. 4,200 foot long

34. Mrs. Faulkner is _____ guest the hotel has ever received.
 A. a million   B. a millionth
 C. million of   D. the millionth

35. It is _____ that I've taken the driving test. I hope I will pass it this time.
 A. ten times   B. the tenth time
 C. a tenth time   D. for the tenth time

36. Most of their teachers are in their _____.
 A. thirty   B. thirties
 C. thirty years   D. thirty years of age

37. We were in Nanjing just for a short stay, only _____ to be

exact.
    A. two and a half days   B. two and a half day
    C. two days and half   D. half a day and two
38. The boy was born on _____.
    A. June 5, 1990   B. 1990 June 5
    C. 1990, 5 June   D. June 5 1990
39. We take an observation _____ day.
    A. every three   B. each three
    C. every third   D. each third
40. We'll stay in the hotel _____.
    A. for three other days   B. for three another days
    C. for another three days   D. for other three days
41. The war broke out in _____ of _____ century.
    A. the thirties, eighteenth
    B. thirties, the eighteenth
    C. the thirties, the eighteenth
    D. thirties, eighteenth
42. _____ students are gathering in the playground.
    A. Tens of hundreds of   B. Tens and hundreds
    C. Ten of hundreds   D. Ten and hundreds
43. _____ is equal to eighty-one.
    A. Nine plus nine   B. Nine minus nine
    C. Nine divided by nine   D. Nine times nine
44. The area of China is _____ square kilometres.
    A. nine hundred and sixty millions
    B. nine hundred, sixty million
    C. nine hundreds and sixty million
    D. nine million six hundred thousand
45. I have sent _____ eggs to the patient.
    A. dozens of   B. tens of
    C. score of   D. dozen of
46. Africa is _____ continent in the world.
    A. the second largest   B. the second larger
    C. a second largest   D. a second larger

47. He used to see me _____. Which answer of the following is wrong?
   A. every another day   B. every other day
   C. every second day   D. every two days
48. Pass me the bricks, _____.
   A. three one time   B. three every time
   C. three at a time   D. three times
49. That is a _____ letter.
   A. five hundred word's   B. five-hundred-words
   C. five hundred words'   D. five hundred word
50. He is a _____ boy. That is to say, he is _____.
   A. five-year-old, five-year-old
   B. five-year-old, five years old
   C. five years old, five years old
   D. five years old, five-year-old

第二十九讲 词类(五) 冠词

1. I was attracted by _____ most unusual picture made of
   _____ bits of coloured plastic.
   A. a, /   B. /, /
   C. a, the   D. the, the

2. The Curies, who had discovered _____ radium, were awarded
   _____ Nobel Prize for Physics.
   A. /, the   B. /, a
   C. the, the   D. the, a

3. His daughter is just starting to talk; she has got _____
   vocabulary of about 10 words.
   A. a   B. the
   C. /   D. some

4. _____ few weeks I spent in college were happiest in my life.
   A. A   B. The
   C. /   D. Quite

5. National leaders everywhere are focusing their attention on
   _____ education of _____ young.
   A. the, the   B. /, /
   C. an, the   D. /, the

6. This drug is occasionally useful in _____ treatment of
   _____ cold.
   A. /, /   B. the, a
   C. /, the   D. a, the

7. — Why not open the windows to let _____ cold air in?
   — I'd rather you didn't. _____ air in our town is quite
   polluted.
   A. the, The   B. /, /
   C. /, The   D. the, /

8. — The problem isn't so easy as it appears.

—Yes, it is easier for _____ teacher than for _____ student.

A. the, the
B. a, the
C. the, a
D. /, /

9. In Europe, children begin to study a second language in primary school and must begin _____ by seventh grade.

A. the third
B. a third
C. third
D. thirdly

10. — Who did you spend last weekend with?

— _____.

A. Palmer's
B. The Palmers'
C. The Palmers
D. The Palmer's

11. _____ friends Betty had made there were all invited to her birthday party.

A. Few of
B. Few
C. The few
D. A few

12. A bullet hit the soldier and he was wounded in _____ leg.

A. a
B. one
C. the
D. his

13. One way to understand thousands of new words is to gain _____ good knowledge of basic word formation.

A. /
B. the
C. a
D. one

14. Tom is _____ honest boy. Everyone in our class likes him.

A. the
B. a
C. an
D. /

15. Some of the wheat is from Canada. What about _____?

A. another
B. the other
C. others
D. the rest

16. His daughter is always shy in _____ and she never dares to make a speech to _____.

A. the public, the public
B. public, the public
C. the public, public
D. public, public

17. — Where is Jack?

285

— I think he's still in _____ bed, but he might just be in _____ bathroom.

A. /, /　　　　　　　　　　B. the, the

C. the, /　　　　　　　　　D. /, the

18. Many people are still in _____ habit of writing silly things in _____ public places.

A. the, the　　　　　　　　B. /, /

C. the, /　　　　　　　　　D. /, the

19. She is _____ newcomer to _____ chemistry but she has already made some important discoveries.

A. the, the　　　　　　　　B. the, /

C. a, /　　　　　　　　　　D. a, the

20. We all know _____ young are fond of _____ football.

A. the, the　　　　　　　　B. the, /

C. a, a　　　　　　　　　　D. /, /

21. A thief is a danger to _____ society.

A. the　　　　　　　　　　B. /

C. a　　　　　　　　　　　D. an

22. He got hurt in a traffic accident _____ other day. Now he has been in _____ hospital for a week.

A. the, /　　　　　　　　　B. the, the

C. /, /　　　　　　　　　　D. /, the

23. I have read it once. I have no idea _____ I shall read it for _____ second time.

A. that, the　　　　　　　　B. that, a

C. whether, the　　　　　　　D. whether, a

24. Biology is _____.

A. science of life　　　　　　B. science of the life

C. the science of the life　　　D. the science of life

25. _____ asked you to take _____ under the desk out to him.

A. The monitor, basketball　　B. Monitor, the basketball

C. Monitor, basketball　　　　D. The monitor, the basketball

26. They elected Lincoln _____ President of the United States.

A. the　　　　　　　　　　B. a

286

C. /　　　　　　　　　　　　D. his

27. We are raising money to buy a guide dog for _____ blind.
    A. a　　　　　　　　　　　B. the
    C. most　　　　　　　　　　D. all

28. After he got along with Mrs. Smith several years, he began to consider her _____.
    A. poet and novelist　　　　B. a poet and a novelist
    C. a poet and novelist　　　D. the poet and novelist

29. Many people agree that _____ good knowledge of English is a must in _____ international trade today.
    A. a, /　　　　　　　　　　B. the, an
    C. the, the　　　　　　　　D. /, the

30. Most animals have little connection with _____ animals of _____ different kind unless they kill them for food.
    A. the, a　　　　　　　　　B. /, a
    C. the, the　　　　　　　　D. /, the

31. In China, _____ tea has long established itself as _____ national drink of this country.
    A. /, the　　　　　　　　　B. a, the
    C. the, /　　　　　　　　　D. the, the

32. — Have you seen _____ pen? I left it here this morning.
    — Is it _____ black one? I think I saw it somewhere.
    A. a, the　　　　　　　　　B. the, the
    C. the, a　　　　　　　　　D. a, a

33. _____ beauty of _____ picture does not depend only on its subject but on its style.
    A. The, a　　　　　　　　　B. /, the
    C. The, the　　　　　　　　D. /, a

34. The flight to Antarctica was delayed by _____ absence of _____ information about the weather conditions there.
    A. /, /　　　　　　　　　　B. the, /
    C. /, the　　　　　　　　　D. the, the

35. Can you spare a few minutes? I want to _____ you.
    A. have words with　　　　B. have a few words for

C. have a word with   D. have word with

36. To our relief, _____ single case of cancer was found in the X-ray studies.
    A. no   B. not
    C. none   D. not a

37. The scientists disagreed about _____ kind of _____ weather the greenhouse effect would bring in the future.
    A. the, /   B. a, /
    C. /, /   D. the, the

38. A Christmas card is _____ gift before Christmas Day comes.
    A. a most welcome   B. the most welcome
    C. a most welcomed   D. the most welcomed

39. Timmy was at _____ table in the dining room, so I had to wait in _____ living room.
    A. the, the   B. /, the
    C. a, a   D. the, a

40. After visiting several areas, he realized that _____ hunger was not _____ only problem in that country.
    A. the, the   B. /, the
    C. the, an   D. /, /

41. Four years ago his sister was _____ university student of _____ physics.
    A. a, the   B. an, the
    C. an, /   D. a, /

42. Our country is separated from _____ America by _____ Pacific.
    A. the, /   B. /, the
    C. the, the   D. /, /

43. She likes playing _____ piano and _____ tennis.
    A. /, the   B. the, /
    C. /, /   D. the, the

44. _____ singer and _____ dancer has got the first prize.
    A. A, a   B. The, the
    C. The, a   D. The, /

45. Be _____ honest boy. Don't tell _____ lie.
    A. an, a   B. the, /
    C. an, the   D. /, the

46. _____ girl in blue is _____ translator.
    A. A, a   B. The, a
    C. A, the   D. The, the

47. "Prof" is the short form of "professor". You've dropped _____ "f" here.
    A. /   B. a
    C. the   D. an

48. _____ Yellow River is _____ second longest river in our country.
    A. The, the   B. /, the
    C. /, /   D. The, /

49. He is interested in _____ history, especially _____ history of _____ Tang dynasty.
    A. the, the, the   B. /, /, the
    C. /, the, the   D. /, /, /

50. We Chinese often have _____ rice for _____ lunch.
    A. /, a   B. a, /
    C. /, /   D. the, a

51. _____ old and _____ sick are taken good care of in our country.
    A. The, a   B. An, a
    C. The, the   D. An, the

52. _____ students in our class are mostly from _____ south.
    A. The, the   B. /, the
    C. The, /   D. /, /

53. Usually it takes us _____ hour and _____ half to finish writing _____ composition.
    A. an, a, a   B. one, a, the
    C. one, one, a   D. the, a, the

54. Taiwan is _____ island belonging to China.
    A. a   B. the

C. /   D. an

55. _____ one who leaves _____ room last, please don't forget
    to shut _____ door.
    A. Any, a, the   B. The, a, a
    C. Any, the, a   D. The, the, the

56. After studying chemistry for more than ten years I can only say I
    have _____ general knowledge of this subject.
    A. /   B. a little
    C. a   D. some

57. I spent last weekend with _____.
    A. the Evans   B. the Evans'
    C. the Evanses   D. the Evanses'

58. Terry is the _____ of the two sisters.
    A. young   B. younger
    C. youngest   D. old

59. _____ Smiths often eat in a good restaurant on Sunday.
    A. /   B. The
    C. Any   D. A

60. John was made _____ captain of the city football team last
    week.
    A. a   B. the
    C. an   D. /

61. The aeroplane flew across _____ Pacific Ocean and very soon
    we got to the U. S. A.
    A. /   B. the
    C. a   D. another

62. Not _____ single person was frightened when the house was
    on _____ fire.
    A. /, /   B. a, /
    C. a, a   D. /, a

63. Which mountain is _____ highest in _____ world?
    A. /, the   B. /, /
    C. the, the   D. the, a

64. I'd like to have _____ word with you. Can you do me

_____ favour?

A. a, a   B. the, the

C. /, a   D. a, /

65. She didn't tell _____ truth. On _____ contrary, she told _____ lie.

A. the, the, the   B. the, the, a

C. a, the, a   D. the, a, the

66. I enjoy _____ folk music, but _____ folk music he is playing now is unpleasant.

A. /, the   B. the, the

C. /, /   D. the, /

67. Of all _____ forms of energy now being used, _____ electricity is the most important.

A. /, the   B. /, /

C. the, the   D. the, /

68. There are nice restaurants and snack bars on both sides of _____ Fifth Avenue.

A. /   B. the

C. a   D. some

69. While he was making _____ fire, the pile of dry wood suddenly caught _____ fire.

A. a, the   B. a, /

C. /, a   D. the, the

70. He will prove to be _____ suitable person here to hold the post.

A. the most   B. a most

C. the more   D. a more

71. _____ number of boys were swimming in the lake, but I didn't know _____ exact number of them.

A. A, the   B. The, an

C. The, the   D. A, an

72. I earn 10 dollars _____ hour as _____ supermarket cashier on Saturday.

A. a, an   B. the, a

C. an, a   D. an, the

73. — What musical instrument do you play?

    — _____.

    A. Violin   B. A violin
    C. Violins   D. The violin

74. They say Charlie is the poorest man in _____.
    A. the town   B. a town
    C. town   D. towns

75. The pollution had _____ bad effect on people that quite a few young babies died.
    A. so   B. very
    C. a such   D. such a

76. On the wall of Hua Ting Sheraton Hotel, there is _____ "S", which stands for Sheraton Group.
    A. a   B. an
    C. the   D. /

77. As a rule, domestic servants doing odd jobs are paid _____.
    A. by the hour   B. by hour
    C. by an hour   D. by hours

78. English is _____ useful tool.
    A. an   B. a
    C. the   D. /

79. John Smith is _____ honest man.
    A. one   B. an
    C. the   D. a

80. My brother told me he was soon going to visit _____.
    A. the United State   B. the United States
    C. United States   D. United State

81. They failed five times. However, they have made up their minds to try _____.
    A. six times   B. the six time
    C. the sixth time   D. sixth time

82. You will find _____ girl in blue. She is _____ translator.
    A. a, the   B. the, a

C. a, a   D. the, the
83. He took the old worker by _____ hand.
    A. the   B. a
    C. his   D. an
84. Tom's brother hit Bob in _____ face.
    A. his   B. the
    C. its   D. a
85. Can you play _____?
    A. the piano   B. a piano
    C. piano   D. one piano
86. She is a Polish scientist. She comes from _____.
    A. Pole   B. Poland
    C. Polish   D. the Pole
87. Prepositions _____ in the structure of English.
    A. play the great part   B. play great part
    C. play a large part   D. play many parts
88. Early in the morning _____ word came that Mr. Li had been
    elected _____ Chairman of our Students' Union.
    A. a, /   B. the, /
    C. /, /   D. /, a
89. On _____ Spring Festival _____ most Chinese people like
    to watch TV programmes at home.
    A. the, /   B. /, /
    C. the, the   D. a, the
90. _____ like watching TV in China.
    A. Old and the young   B. The old and young
    C. The old and the young   D. Old and young
91. I took _____ advantage of the moment to leave the room.
    A. /   B. an
    C. the   D. my
92. _____ Taiwan Island is separated from _____ Province of
    _____ Fujian by _____ Taiwan Straits.
    A. The, the, /, the   B. /, the, /, the
    C. /, /, the, /   D. The, /, the, /

93. Do _____ Chinese _____ Christmas Day?
    A. the, celebrate the   B. /, have
    C. the, usually watch   D. the, observe

94. — Shall I tell Ann how to improve her painting?
    — Yes, but _____ of suggestions may discourage her.
    A. a too long list   B. too long a list
    C. list too long   D. who I think did

95. _____ French believe _____ French is _____ most
    beautiful language in the world.
    A. /, /, a   B. The, /, the
    C. /, the, a   D. /, the, the

96. His health is out of _____, so he has to be examined at once.
    A. the question   B. a question
    C. question   D. questions

97. My health is out of _____, so I don't have to be examined.
    A. the question   B. a question
    C. question   D. questions

98. During _____ Spring Festival most Chinese people like to
    visit their relatives and on _____ New Year's Day they like to
    have a rest at home.
    A. the, the   B. /,/
    C. the,/   D. /,the

99. My parents and I went on a trip last week. On the trip _____
    all fell ill.
    A. two of us   B. the two of us
    C. three of us   D. the three of us

100. He can play _____ violin and I can play _____ erhu.
    A. the, /   B. /, the
    C. /, /   D. the, the

第三十讲 词类(六) 介词

1. More and more young people are fond _____ playing tennis nowadays.
   A. on   B. to
   C. in   D. of
2. — It's a top secret.
   — Yes，I see. I will keep the secret _____ you and me.
   A. with   B. around
   C. among   D. between
3. Dolly wants to cycle round the world and she is really keen _____ the idea.
   A. on   B. for
   C. at   D. with
4. Leaves are found on all kinds of trees，but they differ greatly _____ size and shape.
   A. on   B. from
   C. by   D. in
5. Nowadays a lot of adults go to evening school _____ further education.
   A. after   B. in
   C. for   D. on
6. The two sportsmen congratulated each other _____ winning the match by shaking hands.
   A. with   B. on
   C. in   D. to
7. Four Chinese models were _____ the 14 people awarded prizes on Friday at the World Supermodel Competition.
   A. among   B. between
   C. along   D. beside
8. We are planning to send out several thousand invitations _____

the volunteers.
A. over   B. in
C. on   D. to

9. Seam has formed the habit of jogging _____ the tree-lined
   avenue for two hours every day.
   A. Between   B. along
   C. below   D. with

10. Graduation is a good time to thank those who have helped you
    _____ the tough years.
    A. through   B. up
    C. with   D. from

11. A huge amount of money has been spent _____ the new
    bridge.
    A. in   B. on
    C. with   D. for

12. _____ passion, people won't have the motivation or the joy
    necessary for creative thinking.
    A. For   B. Without
    C. Beneath   D. By

13. Books are the most important records we keep _____ man's
    thought, ideas and feelings.
    A. up   B. to
    C. of   D. on

14. Moving to the warm mountain village cured _____.
    A. her of the disease   B. the disease of her
    C. her the disease   D. the disease from her

15. The modern society requires young people to be able to solve
    problems _____ their own.
    A. of   B. for
    C. on   D. to

16. Let's row over _____ the other side of the lake.
    A. on   B. along
    C. to   D. off

17. Never think _____ sports as the opposite of rest.

A. of   B. over
C. about   D. out

18. His latest book deals with the social problems _____ the day.
    A. on   B. in
    C. for   D. of

19. The flight to Antarctica was delayed by the lack _____ information about the weather conditions there.
    A. in   B. from
    C. for   D. of

20. The work _____ the revised edition of the dictionary was under way.
    A. at   B. of
    C. on   D. about

21. _____ a well-known speaker, he was never at a loss for a word.
    A. As   B. Though
    C. Because   D. For

22. Overworking or playing too hard is a drain _____ one's strength.
    A. to   B. of
    C. off   D. on

23. Shall we cross this field _____ going by the road?
    A. in spite of   B. or rather
    C. because of   D. instead of

24. Make sure that you keep _____ the timetable strictly.
    A. to   B. up
    C. on   D. in

25. The impact _____ modern science _____ society as a whole is greater than ever before.
    A. on, of   B. of, up
    C. of, on   D. about, in

26. You can't miss my house. It's _____ the Sun Hotel.
    A. against   B. opposite
    C. across   D. aside

27. — Bobby wants to go out and play.
    — All right, but not _____ putting on a sweater.
    A. until   B. without
    C. by   D. after

28. Scientists working _____ a problem they do not know sometimes can't even guess what the final result will be.
    A. out   B. on
    C. for   D. to

29. The notice reads _____ follows: "Keep _____ the grass."
    A. like, off   B. as, away
    C. like, away   D. as, off

30. I'm sure you can't possibly carry all that _____. Let me help you.
    A. for yourself   B. of yourself
    C. in yourself   D. by yourself

31. _____ the average, Mr. Blank trades in his old car for a new one every three years.
    A. In   B. For
    C. Of   D. On

32. As far as we know, there are hardly any living creatures on the planets _____.
    A. in addition to the earth   B. besides the earth
    C. other than the earth   D. including the earth

33. _____ the mention of his new discoveries, he can't help _____.
    A. On, laughing   B. On, laugh
    C. With, to laugh   D. At, laughing

34. _____ opening the can, be careful not to spill any of the liquid.
    A. To   B. In
    C. By   D. For

35. The number of the employees has grown from 1,000 to 1,200. This means it has risen _____ 20 percent.
    A. by   B. at

C. to   D. with

36. _____ most students, she was always well prepared and never came to class late.
   A. Like   B. As
   C. For   D. To

37. I wanted two seats _____ Madame Curie for Friday night, so I rang the cinema to see if I could book two tickets.
   A. of   B. about
   C. to   D. for

38. For miles around me there was nothing but a desert, without a single plant or tree _____.
   A. in sight   B. on earth
   C. at a distance   D. in place

39. I know nothing about the young lady _____ she is from Beijing.
   A. except   B. except for
   C. except that   D. besides

40. The sunlight came in _____ the windows in the roof and lit up the whole room.
   A. through   B. across
   C. on   D. over

41. Luckily, the bullet narrowly missed the captain _____ an inch.
   A. by   B. at
   C. to   D. from

42. Your bag is different _____ mine in colour.
   A. for   B. with
   C. from   D. between

43. The new medicine for headache has a very good effect _____ the patient.
   A. on   B. in
   C. of   D. with

44. Rose was wild with joy _____ the result of the examination.
   A. to   B. at

C. by   D. as

45. We offered him our congratulations _____ his passing the college entrance exams.
    A. at   B. on
    C. for   D. of

46. _____ the science exhibition, the art exhibition was also well designed.
    A. Except   B. Besides
    C. Beside   D. Except for

47. Almost everyone fails _____ his driver's test on the first try.
    A. in   B. to passing
    C. to have passed   D. passing

48. _____ his great wisdom, he hesitated in face of the challenge.
    A. All for   B. In spite of
    C. Although   D. No matter how

49. He shook hands with me _____ .
    A. friendly   B. in a friendly way
    C. like old friend   D. as an old friend

50. I'll drop _____ your house and bring you some books.
    A. in   B. on to
    C. in on   D. in at

51. _____ his great wealth, the old king was not at all happy.
    A. Except for   B. In spite of
    C. Other than   D. In addition to

52. They sell cloth _____ here in this country.
    A. by the metre   B. to metres
    C. by metre   D. to the metre

53. Mark wished for _____ rest after having _____ hard time at school.
    A. a, a   B. the, the
    C. a, the   D. a, /

54. The road under repair remained blocked until it was reopened _____ traffic yesterday.
    A. of   B. at

C. with D. for

55. He ran _____ the thief for some time before he lost him in the crowd.
   A. into B. to
   C. after D. up to

56. Everyone should keep a sense of responsibility _____ what he is to do.
   A. of B. for
   C. with D. to

57. Anderson was disappointed when he found that his classmates had gone to the beach _____ him.
   A. except B. but
   C. without D. besides

58. There was no one about and there was no garage open _____ which he could _____ for help.
   A. to, ask B. to, turn
   C. about, ask D. about, turn

59. I rowed to the pilot and went _____ a big ship.
   A. board B. on board
   C. abroad D. on abroad

60. We hadn't got the commercial information _____ great importance that you mentioned in your letter.
   A. on B. of
   C. with D. to

61. Everyone was surprised _____ how quickly he became successful.
   A. to B. at
   C. with D. on

62. I won't invite John, _____ I don't really know him.
   A. after all B. above all
   C. however D. first of all

63. — Would you like to go shopping with me this afternoon?
   — Sorry. I don't like going out _____ a rainy afternoon. You may ask Mary to go with you.
   A. in B. at

C. on   D. during

64. Participants _____ both males and females _____ in age from 12 to 83.
    A. including, ranged   B. included, ranged
    C. including, who ranged   D. included, who range

65. The teachers were treated _____ a movie on the Teacher's Day.
    A. with   B. to
    C. by   D. for

66. I like going to the seaside in summer. It is comfortable to lie _____ the sands _____ the sun.
    A. on, in   B. in, under
    C. on, under   D. in, in

67. — Where did you meet him?
    — I met him _____ 204 _____ Fifth Avenue.
    A. on, the   B. at, the
    C. at, /   D. in, /

68. An international conference _____ community service is going to be held next month.
    A. at   B. in
    C. for   D. on

69. It was not surprising that she wasn't a very good dancer. _____, she had only had one lesson.
    A. At first   B. However
    C. Anyhow   D. After all

70. That is too hot a day _____ February.
    A. in   B. on
    C. at   D. for

71. You can come whenever _____.
    A. it is convenient of you   B. it is convenient to you
    C. you're convenient   D. you will be convenient

72. _____ arriving at the village, the soldiers began to dig defence works.
    A. In   B. On

302

C. For   D. At

73. Don't walk so fast. I can't _____ you.
    A. get along with   B. keep touch with
    C. get away with   D. keep up with

74. David was disappointed to find that his classmates had gone to the seaside _____ him.
    A. except   B. besides
    C. without   D. but

75. I'm sorry that the job is _____ me.
    A. for   B. at
    C. on   D. beyond

76. When you are travelling, you should put labels _____ your luggage.
    A. on   B. to
    C. for   D. with

77. The quickest way to go round the city is _____ underground train.
    A. in   B. on
    C. by   D. with

78. I'm going to see new Beijing _____ . When I _____ came to Beijing ten years ago, it looked old and ancient.
    A. the first time, first   B. the first time, firstly
    C. for the first time, first   D. for the first time, the first

79. The teacher wants us to retell the story _____ our own words.
    A. in   B. with
    C. by   D. at

80. Though she looks young _____ her age, she is _____ mother of three children.
    A. at, a   B. for, the
    C. in, a   D. for, a

81. _____ the two cars that Smith have, the Plymouth is, without any question, the easier to run.
    A. Between   B. Than
    C. In   D. Of

82. We have done many experiments _____ this one.
    A. other than   B. rather than
    C. more than   D. less than
83. He tried to _____ all the trouble he had caused.
    A. make up for   B. make up in
    C. make up at   D. make up on
84. The train leaves at 6:00 p. m. So I have to be at the station
    _____ 5:40 p. m. at the latest.
    A. until   B. after
    C. by   D. around
85. No one could keep calm _____ such an occasion when big
    applause burst again and again.
    A. for   B. in
    C. on   D. to
86. I spent the whole day repairing the car. The work was _____
    easy.
    A. nothing but   B. anything but
    C. something expect   D. all except
87. She insisted on her view point _____ strong opposition.
    A. despite   B. for
    C. because   D. though
88. Contrary _____ we had expected, their first performance was
    a failure.
    A. as   B. from that
    C. what   D. to what
89. He has little patience, and is therefore not likely to succeed
    _____ a teacher.
    A. like   B. for
    C. to be   D. as
90. — Shall we have a farewell party next week?
    — Yes, let's make _____ next Friday.
    A. it   B. ourselves
    C. /   D. on
91. He hesitated, wondering if he had asked too much _____ the

lady.

A. from   B. of

C. for   D. to

92. — Mum, shall we get off _____ Baker Street or at the railway station?

    — I don't know. We'd better ask the driver.

A. on   B. at

C. down   D. in

93. As we lack motors and cars, we must get on the buses _____ them.

A. with   B. out of

C. from   D. without

94. In our country there are still thousands of places inaccessible _____ tourists.

A. for   B. of

C. to   D. with

95. The man searched _____ all his suitcases to find the missing papers.

A. about   B. for

C. through   D. into

96. Buying items _____ sale requires consideration of the reason _____ the sale.

A. on, for   B. at, of

C. for, on   D. in, on

97. The experiment is intended to examine the effect _____ lack of sleep _____ healthy people.

A. for, on   B. of, on

C. on, of   D. from, of

98. The Chinese enjoy their tea _____ it slowly, a little at a time.

A. by drinking   B. only to drink

C. as if drinking   D. so as to drink

99. _____ three years he was so sick that he had to remain in bed.

A. During   B. In

C. For   D. Since

100. Home accidents ususlly result _____ handling electric appliances carelessly.
    A. in   B. to
    C. by   D. from
101. _____ occasional coughs, it was quiet in the examination room.
    A. In addition to   B. Except for
    C. But for   D. In spite of
102. — The day after Philip bought his new sports car, the police took away his driving licence _____ careless driving!
    — Really?
    A. by   B. in
    C. with   D. for
103. Poems let one go _____ the surface and discover poets' feelings.
    A. beyond   B. down
    C. out of   D. from under
104. He chose to live in the suburbs, free _____ crowds and noise.
    A. off   B. away from
    C. of   D. out of
105. The pair of trousers fits me well _____ the waist of it is a little too small.
    A. besides   B. in addition
    C. but for   D. except that
106. These magazines are for adults only. Nothing there is _____ much use to the students.
    A. for   B. in
    C. with   D. of
107. She arrived at the airport only to find that she had missed the flight _____ ten minutes.
    A. by   B. for
    C. in   D. after
108. The plane departs at 8:00. So we have to be at the airport

_____ 7:00 at the latest.

A. until   B. after

C. by   D. around

109. The problem was very difficult. Finally, we decided to solve it as a team _____ our heads together.

A. by putting   B. in putting

C. only to put   D. so as to put

110. _____ the morning of August 1, we had a celebration with the PLA soldiers.

A. In   B. On

C. At   D. From

111. We'll graduate form school _____ coming July.

A. on   B. by

C. in   D. after

112. Your new suit will be ready _____ three days.

A. in   B. on

C. for   D. over

113. The student asked his teacher not to make any mistake _____ him.

A. about   B. on

C. in   D. to

114. My bicycle is _____.

A. in front of his   B. in the front of his

C. in front of he's   D. in the front of he's

115. It happened to be raining _____ the morning of May Day.

A. in   B. at

C. of   D. on

116. Don't stand leaning _____ the door.

A. out   B. against

C. close   D. with

117. The boys are reading the text _____ their voices.

A. on the top of   B. at top of

C. on top of   D. at the top of

118. It's a pleasure to have a talk _____ a cool evening _____

307

autumn.

    A. in, in   B. in, of

    C. on, of   D. on, on

119. I've lost my key _____ the bicycle. Have you seen it?

    A. in   B. for

    C. to   D. about

120. Brown's car is excellent _____ the colour.

    A. except   B. beside

    C. beside   D. except for

121. The story took place _____ Christmas Eve.

    A. on   B. at

    C. in   D. by

122. _____ our great joy, our football team has won the game.

    A. With   B. To

    C. On   D. For

123. The man was arrested, it is said that he _____ an old woman _____ her handbag.

    A. stole, with   B. robbed, of

    C. caught, from   D. struck, at

124. Don't worry. I don't think the medicine will have any ill effect _____ you.

    A. to   B. on

    C. at   D. with

125. Don't _____ the cat _____ the bag.

    A. let, off   B. let, down

    C. let, out   D. let, out of

126. Ellen broke the vase _____ pieces.

    A. at   B. for

    C. in   D. to

127. A tunnel will _____ Britain _____ France.

    A. join, to   B. connect, to

    C. take, to   D. tie, with

128. Being a teacher, I'll be strict _____ my students, but I'll never be too hard _____ them.

A. with, with   B. on, with
C. with, on   D. on, on

129. When you do fine, close work, raise your eyes _____ and look into the distance.
A. once in a while   B. once for a while
C. once at a while   D. once upon a while

130. _____ the help of his teacher, he has made great progress since this term.
A. Under   B. By
C. With   D. For

131. The dictionary my father bought last week is _____.
A. for much use   B. using very well
C. very well used   D. of much use

132. _____ the leadership of the government, Shanghai Book Traders has paid much attention to the exchange between Chinese and foreign cultures.
A. Under   B. With
C. In   D. But for

133. Even at the narrowest of the Pacific, it is about 3,200 km _____.
A. widely   B. with cross
C. crossing   D. in width

134. The man I _____ yesterday is Mr. Li.
A. paid a visit   B. had a talk
C. dropped in   D. came across

135. He _____ the lion _____ head.
A. shot at, by the   B. shot, into its
C. shot at, through its   D. shot, through the

136. It was obvious that the letter was written _____ pencil.
A. by   B. with
C. at   D. in

137. Meal is ready. Let's sit down _____ table.
A. to   B. for
C. to a   D. for the

138. Children like talking with Miss Li as she deals with them
    _____.
    A. very friendly   B. much more friendly
    C. like friend   D. in a friendly way
139. A road accident was reported _____ the first of May.
    A. to   B. on
    C. at   D. for
140. _____ he didn't succeed in passing the examination.
    A. In my surprise   B. I surprised
    C. To my surprise   D. To surprise me
141. He missed too many lessons. _____, he failed in the final
    exam.
    A. On the other hand   B. As a result
    C. Instead   D. Furthermore
142. Albert, dressed in black, walked _____ the door quietly and
    seated himself _____ the table _____ the corner of the
    room.
    A. through, at, in   B. behind, by, about
    C. around, on, at   D. across, beyond, near
143. _____ a fine October morning, Rose went to Paris _____
    the first time in her life.
    A. In, for   B. For, for
    C. On, at   D. On, for
144. They went to the city hall _____ a No. 5 bus. As they were
    caught _____ a traffic jam, they were late _____ the
    meeting.
    A. in, in, for   B. by, by, at
    C. by, in, for   D. on, in, from
145. The great artist devoted all his life _____ in nature.
    A. to search for the beautiful
    B. to searching beautiful
    C. to the search for the beautiful
    D. to search the beauty
146. We must talk _____ the matter now as you are leaving

_____ Paris this evening.

    A. with, to   B. of, in

    C. about, for   D. over, by

147. I read the news _____ the newspaper, but you can also watch it _____ television.

    A. on, on   B. in, in

    C. on, in   D. in, on

148. Please fill this form _____ ink or _____ a ball pen.

    A. with, with   B. in, in

    C. with, in   D. in, with

149. The purpose of learning a foreign language is to communicate and think _____ the language.

    A. in   B. with

    C. of   D. over

150. I wonder why he suddenly changed his point of view _____ this event.

    A. in   B. for

    C. to   D. on

综 合 练 习

2014 年上海高考英语试题
(语法新题型)

Directions: After reading the passages below, fill in the blanks to make the passages coherent and grammatically correct. For the blanks with a given word, fill in each blank with the proper form of the given word; for the other blanks, use one word that best fits each blank.

(A)
My stay in New York

After graduation from university, I had been unable to secure a permanent job in my small town. So I decided to leave home for New York, (25) _____ I might have a better chance to find a good job. (26) _____ (earn) some money to pay the daily expenses, I started work in a local café as a waiter. I believed that (27) _____ _____ _____ I was offered a good position, I would resign at once.

Over time, the high cost of living became a little burden on my already (28) _____ (exhaust) shoulders. On the other hand, my search for a respectable job had not met with much success. As I had studied literature at university, I found it quite difficult to secure a suitable job in big companies. Mother had said that (29) _____ I wanted to have a better career advancement, I had to find work in the city. Perhaps, (30) _____ my mother had told me was deeply rooted in my mind. I just did as she had expected.

Soon I had lived in the city for over six months but I still did not like it. Apparently I had difficulty (31) _____ (adapt) myself to

312

life in the city, let alone finding a job to my delight. After nine months of frustration, I eventually decided to go back to my small town. Not until I returned (32) _____ I realize that a quiet town life was the best for me.

(B)
The giant vending machine (自动售货机) is a village shop

Villagers have long been used to facing a drive when they run out of basic supplies. However, help is now nearer at hand in the form of the country's first automatic push-button shop. Now residents in the Derbyshire village of Clifton can buy groceries around the clock after the huge vending was installed outside a pub in the village this week.

Peter Fox, who is (33) _____ electrical engineer, spent two and a half years working on the project. The machine (34) _____ (equip) with security cameras and alarms, and looks like a mini shop with a brick front, a grey roof and a display window.

Mr. Fox said he hoped his invention, (35) _____ is set to be installed in other villages in the area over the coming months, will mark a return to convenience shopping for rural communities.

He said: "I had this idea a few years ago but I couldn't find a manufacturer who could deliver what I wanted, so I did it by (36) _____. The result is what amounts to a huge outdoor vending machine. Yet I think the term 'automatic shop' is far (37) _____ (appropriate)."

In recent years, the commercial pressure from supermarket chains (38) _____ (force) village shops across the county to close. In 2010, it was estimated that about 400 village shops closed, (39) _____ (urge) the local government to give financial support to struggling shops or set-up new community stores.

Hundreds of communities have since stepped in and opened up their own volunteer-run shops, but Mr. Fox hopes his new invention will offer a solution (40) _____ those villages without a local shop.

第 一 套

(A)

There is a new reason to enjoy hot cocoa (1) _____ a cold winter's night in front of a comfortable fire. Consider it a healthy drink. According to a new study, hot chocolate may actually be good for you.

Scientists at Cornel University in New York State found that hot cocoa may help fight cancer. Chang Lee, a professor of food chemistry, led a team of scientists (2) _____ did the first ever study comparing hot chocolate with other drinks known to help fight cancer. Lee and his team compared hot cocoa with green tea, black tea, and red wine. The results gave hope to chocolate lovers everywhere. "Cocoa came out on top," said Lee.

Lee explained that cocoa is high in antioxidants. Antioxidants are chemical in the body that fight cancer-(3) _____ (cause) substances (4) _____ (call) free radicals. Free radicals naturally occur in the body, (5) _____ if there are too many of them, they can change the body and cause cancer. (6) _____ (Get) a lot of antioxidants from fruits, vegetables and cocoa may help us stay cancer free!

(7) _____ cocoa may help fight cancer, we shouldn't (8) _____ (necessary) drink hot cocoa for breakfast, lunch, and dinner. Experts still recommend eating fruits and vegetables as a way of making sure we get plenty of antioxidants.

(B)

Power has returned to about 80% of Chile more than an hour after a massive power blackout hit most of the country around 8:40 p.m. Sunday, Interior Minister Rodrigo Hinzpeter said. (9) _____ (Follow) the sudden loss of power, people (10) _____ (see) running out of homes, subway stations and theaters in panic, and many people gathered around street parks. Streets (11) _____ (block) by vehicles as drivers pulled over to see what happened. Hinzpeter said the blackout was not directly related (12) _____ the February 27 earthquake, but an investigation would be carried out to see (13) _____ it was indirectly connected.

AC Milan have confirmed that David Beckham has broken his left Achilles tendon, and will be out for a minimum of 3 months, thus ending his Series A season and ruling him out of playing at the World Cup in South Africa, goal. com reported. The injury occurred when Beckham was by himself with the ball at his feet in the closing stages of a game with Chievo Sunday night. He immediately signaled to the bench, hopping towards the touchline (14) _____ his healthy leg before collapsing to the ground in great pain.

A very strange upside-down house created on the grounds of a German zoo will be open (15) _____ the public on March 30, the *Daily Mail* reported. The crazy house stands on a pointed roof and is supported by steel frames. Inside the front door, it has an upside-down kitchen, bathroom, living room and bedroom. It was also built on a slight slope to challenge the viewer's ability (16) _____ (observe) still further.

第 二 套

(A)

Today, air travel is far safer than driving a car on a motorway. But there is a danger that (1) _____ (grow) every year.

From the moment an airplane takes (2) _____ to the moment it lands, every moment (3) _____ (watch) on radar screens. The air traffic controllers around a busy airport may handle 1,000 planes a day. Any plane that flies near the airport comes under the orders of the controllers there. Even a small mistake on their part could cause a disaster.

Recently such a disaster almost happened. Two large jets were flying towards the airport. One was carrying 69 passengers and come from Sydney. (4) _____ was carrying 156 passengers from New

York. An air traffic controller noticed on his radar screen that the two planes were too close (5) _____ each other. He ordered one (6) _____ (turn) to the right and to climb. But he made a mistake. He ordered the wrong plane to do this. So, instead of turning away from the second plane, the first plane turned towards it. Fifteen seconds later, it flew directly in front of the second plane. They avoided each other by the smallest part of a second. The distance between them was less than (7) _____ of a large swimming pool.

(B)

Computer programmer David Jones earns 35,000 pounds a year designing new computer games, yet he cannot find a bank ready to let him (8) _____ (have) a credit card. Instead, he (9) _____ (tell) to wait another two years, until he is 18. The 16-year-old works for a small firm in Liverpool, where the problem of most young people of his age is (10) _____ (find) a job. David's firm releases two new games for the fast growing computer market each month.

But David's biggest headache is (11) _____ to do with his money. Even though he earns a lot, he cannot drive a car, take out a mortgage, or get credit cards. David got his job with the Liverpool-based company four months ago, a year after leaving school with six O-levels and working for a time in a shop. "I got the job because the people (12) _____ run the firm knew I had already written some programs," he said. David spends some of his money on records and clothes, and (13) _____ (give) his mother 50 pounds a week. But most of his spare time is spent working.

"Unfortunately, computing was not part of studies at school," he said. "But I had been studying it in books and magazines for four years (14) _____ my spare time. I knew what I wanted to do and never considered (15) _____ (stay) on at school. Most people in this business are fairly young, anyway," David added: "I would like to earn a million and I suppose early retirement is a possibility. You never know (16) _____ the market might disappear. "

第 三 套

(A)

Apart (1) _____ the Nobel Physics Prize, other 2010 Nobel Prize winners included British scientist Robert Edwards, the "father of the test tube baby", (2) _____ was awarded the Nobel Prize in medicine. An American and two Japanese scientists, who developed an efficient way (3) _____ (create) chains of carbon atoms, shared the prize in chemistry. And this year's Nobel Literature Prize (4) _____ (go) to Peruvian writer Mario Vargas Llosa.

Three former Chinese soccer officials, including Xie Yalong, former vice president of the Chinese Football Association (5) _____ (arrest) for bribery. Meanwhile, investigations against three soccer referees have concluded and the cases (6) _____ (transfer) to the prosecution office. The referees, including Lu Jun, the "gold whistle", are accused (7) _____ taking bribes and fixing matches.

Microsoft has taken Motorola to court over nine smart-phone patents. The software maker said Motorola phones (8) _____ use Google Inc. 's Android software step on Microsoft technology. The functions in question include synchronizing e-mail, calendars and contacts.

(B)

It's parents' nature to love and provide for children. Because our children are part of us, we want to see them happy. Nevertheless, a wish (9) _____ our children have everything that we lacked as youngsters can cause us (10) _____ (spoil) them. One of the most precious gifts you can give your children is true independence. It lets them know (11) _____ to gain what they desire by themselves and become owners of their own happiness. When the time comes

(12) _____ them to go to college or begin to work, you will have the confidence that you have raised a child that can both enter and contribute to society confidently.

When children are not afforded the opportunity to explore self-dependence or to fulfill their own needs, they may have false values. They won't realize the necessity of hard work, and the needs of (13) _____. Yet children who are given love and affection in abundance are often kinder and more responsible than (14) _____ whose parents agree to their every material demand. They develop a strong sense of self that stretches beyond possessions and approval of their peers. As adults, they will understand that each individual is responsible for building the life they desire.

(15) _____ can be difficult to watch children struggle to meet their personal goals, yet it is wonderful to be by their side as they achieve it. Your choice not to spoil your children will bless you with more opportunities to show them understanding and to be (16) _____ (full) present with them as they journey toward adulthood.

第 四 套

(A)

The world today is totally different from (1) _____ it was when I was still a kid. Back then we had no televisions, computers, cell-phones or any of the (2) _____ (hundred) of electronic products available today. Yet we were still happy (3) _____ our lives.

Today, even little kids (4) _____ (expose) to violence. If it doesn't reach them through the news every night, or other shows on television, it reaches them through their video games. Everything seems to be about fighting, or about going to war in order to gain power. It's sad to note that many parents do not care about what the children are watching or playing. Every day they see all kinds of crimes (5) _____ (commit) and think that this is normal and real.

This is surely why young people are much more violent and harder to discipline these days. As an adult, if you witness some young people beating someone up, you'll think twice about intervening, since they (6) _____ easily turn their anger on you. In the old days, you could just stare at the young people and they would crawl into their shells. These days it's the older people (7) _____ are scared.

We have to do something about the entertainment industry if we want to get our normal lives back. All this violence in the media cannot be allowed to continue. Talk to your government representative; get together with your neighbors; set up requests and network through the Internet. The only way the industry will hear us is (8) _____ we speak loudly and with one voice.

(B)

Promises are easily made. Keeping them often proves more difficult because we find (9) _____ simpler to undertake impossible tasks than to say no. When you consistently keep your word, you protect you reputation and promote yourself as someone who can be trusted. Since honesty and sincerity form the basis of all lifelong relationships, your word is one of your most precious and powerful possessions.

(10) _____ when we promise more than we can deliver, (11) _____ (hide) the consequences of our actions through lies, or deny our true selves to others, we hurt those who have been counting on us by proving that their faith has been wrongly given. We are also hurt by the lies we tell and the promises we break. Honesty is the foundation of civilization, (12) _____ (allow) people to live and work side by side without fear or uneasiness. As you develop honesty within yourself, you'll find that your honor and reliability put people (13) _____ ease. Others will feel it comfortable to seek your friendship out and work with you on projects of great importance. They are certain that their positive expectations will be met. If you do catch yourself in a lie, ask

yourself (14) _____ you wanted to hide and why you felt you couldn't be truthful. If life's surprises prevent you from keeping your word, simply admit your error regretfully and quickly apologize.

Since the path of truth frequently represents a more difficult journey, setting out (15) _____ (do) it builds character. You can control and use the power of your word when you do your best to live a life of honesty and understand what motivates dishonesty. In keeping your word and expressing sincerity, you prove that you are worthy of (16) _____ (trust) and see values as something necessary for your daily existence.

第 五 套

(A)

A mother, hoping (1) _____ (encourage) her son's progress at the piano, bought tickets for a performance by the great Polish pianist, Ignace Paderewski. When the evening arrived, they found their seats near the front of the concert hall, and they (2) _____ see the beautiful Steinway piano waiting on the stage. Soon the mother found a friend to talk to, and the boy (3) _____ (slip) away.

At eight o'clock, the main lights in the concert hall began to dim, the spotlights came on, and only then did they notice the boy — up on the piano bench, simply playing *Twinkle*, *Twinkle*, *Little Star*. His mother was shocked and embarrassed, but (4) _____ she could get her son back, the master himself appeared on the stage and quickly moved to the keyboard.

He whispered gently to the boy, "Don't quit. Keep (5) _____ (play). " Leaning over, Packerewki reached down with his left hand and began filling in the bass part (低音部) of the tune. Soon his right arm reached around the other side and played (6) _____ delighted obbligato (伴奏). Together , the old master and the young boy held the crowd fascinated (7) _____ their blended and beautiful music.

(B)

If you are looking to take a break from your everyday life and relax in a fairy-tale world, there's a probably no (8) _____ (good) place than La Balade des Gnomes, near the town of Durbuy, Belgium, (9) _____ (feature) ten amazingly-decorated bedrooms and a special suite (套房) designed in the form of a Trojan horse. This place is truly unique.

Formerly an ordinary Belgian farmhouse, La Balade de Gnomes (10) _____ (change) into a magical tourist spot by architect and owner Dominic Noel. "The hotel was created by people who have a strong interest in nature," he says, but anyone with a rich imagination would certainly appreciate (11) _____ special design and decorations as well. The names of the rooms well represent (12) _____ you can expect to see when you walk through the door: In a Moon Neighborhood, for example, takes you to a distant future (13) _____ human can spend their vacation in a hotel on the Moon.

Every room in La Balade des Gnomes hotel was created and decorated by Dominic Noel with the help of local craftsmen, and offers visitors a unique experience. But the main attraction of this Belgian spot is the two-story Trojan horse suite, (14) _____ actually looks like a giant wooden cow. While it may have been inspired by Greek mythology (神话), this beautiful wooden structure actually is covered in medieval (中世纪的) decorations (15) _____ (base) on fairy tales.

(16) _____ you're looking for a special hotel in Belgium, La Balade des Gnomes is a wonderful choice.

第 六 套

(A)

I had spent my last day in London (1) _____ (visit) friends, taking pictures, and doing some last minute shopping. Among other things, I had bought some presents: a shirt for my brother, a woolen blanket for my sister, and a battery-powered alarm clock for my father.

After travelling in a crowded bus and waiting in the noisy airport building, I was glad to be sitting in the plane at last. (2) _____ a few minutes we would be asked to fasten our seat belts and to turn (3) _____ our cell phones, and then we would soon be up in the sky on our flight to Berlin.

But I had been mistaken. Ten minutes later, instead of enjoying the beauty of the evening sky from high above the clouds, I was sitting in a smoke-filled room with an airline official and a police officer at my side. On the table in front of me was one of my suitcases.

The officials were very polite. They asked me (4) _____ (show) them my passport, my ticket, and my baggage check. Then I (5) _____ (request) to open the suitcase and to spread out its contents on the table. I did (6) _____ I was told. The moment I placed the alarm clock on the table, the two officials looked at each other and (7) _____ (smile).

Hearing the clock ticking away merrily, I suddenly understood. Someone (8) _____ have heard the ticking noise coming from my suitcase and thought there was a time bomb hidden in it.

(B)

Before we start our first lab, I'd like to tell you a little bit about the workbook we'll be using.

The first thing I'd like to point out is (9) _____ the workbook contains a very large amount of material — for more than you could ever handle in a single semester. (10) _____ you're supposed to do is to choose the experiments and activities (11) _____ you want to do, within (12) _____ certain framework, of course. Part of my job is to help you make your choices.

Next, I'd like to mention that in each workbook chapter, there are usually two subsections. The first (13) _____ (call)

Experiments and the second is called Activities. In the Experiments section, the workbook gives you full instructions for all the experiments, including alternate procedures. Choose the procedure you wish — there's plenty of equipment available.

In the Activities section, you will find suggestions for projects that you can do (14) _____ your own time. You'll see that there are usually no detailed instructions for the activities. You (15) _____ (suppose) to do them your own way.

(16) _____ there are no questions, let's turn to Chapter One now.

第 七 套

(A)

Sally Yao talks about her job as a tour guide.

" I usually begin my work at 8 a. m. and go home at 9 p. m.. It is a long but rewarding day. Most days, I pick up tour group at the airport. I usually talk a lot about what we can see on the bus. However, if they're tired, I let them relax and answer any question (1) _____ they have.

Friends always ask me which nationality I like most. I honestly don't have the favorite. I like the variety. It's hard (2) _____ (generalize), but Asian tourists tend to want an organized tour. Maybe they're so busy at work (3) _____ they want someone else to run their holiday for them. Western tourists tend to prefer a bit (4) _____ (much) more freedom. They like (5) _____ (give) time to wander around a city. But as I said, it's not always true.

One example I met today was very demanding! I just kept smiling. They've travelled a long way and spend a lot of money (6) _____ I can't complain too much. I took them to their hotel and they eventually settled in. That couple's daughter wasn't tired, so I took her for a walk round the area. She (7) _____ (do) a degree in Tourism Management. We had a lot in common and I found out some new methods for organizing tours. The great thing about this job is (8) _____ I always meet new people and learn from them.

(B)

The following is part of the speech US president Barack Obama gave (9) _____ the graduation ceremony of a high school in Michigan.

... That's my second piece of advice, very simple: Don't make excuses. Take responsibility not just for your successes; take responsibility where you fall short as well.

Now, the truth is, no matter how hard you work, you're not going to be excellent in every class. You are not going to succeed (10) _____ _____ _____ you try something. There are to be times when you fail. There will be times when you hurt people you love. There will be times when you make a mistake and you stray from the values that you hold most deeply.

And when that happens, it's easiest thing in the world to start looking around for somebody else to blame. Your professor was too hard; the coaches were playing favorites; your friend just didn't understand.

No, but this is an easy habit (11) _____ (get) into. You see it every day in Washington — every day — folks (12) _____ (call) each other names, making all sorts of accusations on television. Everybody is always pointing a finger at somebody else. You notice that?

Now, this community could have easily gone down that road. This community could have made excuses — well, our kids have fewer advantages, our schools have fewer resources — how can we compete? You could have spent years (13) _____ (point) fingers — blaming parents, blaming teachers, blaming the principal.

But that's — Class of 2010, I want you to pay attention to this because that's not what happened. Instead, this community was honest with itself about where you were falling short. You resolved to do better, push your kids harder, (14) _____ (open) their minds wider, expose them to all kinds of ideas and people and experiences.

So, graduates, I hope you (15) _____ (continue) those efforts. Don't make excuses. And I hope that wherever you go, you won't narrow the broad intellectual and social exposure you've had here at high school — instead, seek to expand it. Don't just hang out with people who look like you or share your political views. Broaden your circle to include people with different backgrounds and life experiences, because that's how you'll end up learning (16) _____ it's like to walk in somebody else's shoes. That's how you'll come to understand the challenges other people face.

第 八 套

(A)

Once upon a time and far away, in old Russia (1) _____ was a great and rich trading city (2) _____ (call) Nizhny Novgorod. It sat (3) _____ the banks of the mighty river Volga, and every year the merchants sent their wooden ships to trade at towns and cities near and far. But, far beyond the farthest city they had reached, lay a land (4) _____ no one had ever been, India. The merchants had heard tales of wonder and magic about this faraway land, but they had heard, too, that it was a land of thousand gods and ghosts and they were a little afraid to sail to such (5) _____ far and terrible place.

So one day they called together all the townspeople. (6) _____ (Everyone) of them talked and argued at the meeting until at last old Nikitin, the most daring of the merchants, said, "I have a son, young Aphanasy, who is bold and cheerful and wise beyond his years. And best of all, he is lucky. (7) _____ I am too old to go myself, let us (8) _____ (send) Aphanasy to India."

(B)

Good evening, ladies and gentlemen. I'm very happy to see that so many of you have been able to come this evening (9) _____

_____ _____ weather. I know our speaker will have plenty to say that will be interesting to you all.

Dr. Jane Wilson, whom we are pleased to have with us, (10) _____ (devote) several years to the study of present-day art in Italy, in particular during her four years of lecturing in the University of Milan. She has travelled widely in Britain, France and Italy, (11) _____ (gather) material for the book she's now preparing for publication. She is an expert photographer and has prepared many photos that will be used (12) _____ (help) understand this lecture.

Dr. Wilson will be speaking this evening on the main influences (13) _____ some major 19th century paintings (14) _____ present-day art in Italy, and we all looking forward to (15) _____ (hear) about a subject which I at least know little, but like all of us here, would like to know (16) _____ more. Now without further delay, let's welcome Dr. Wilson.

第 九 套

(A)

In 1977, a dead author of detective stories saved the life of a 19-month-old baby in a most unusual way. The author was Agatha Christie, one of the most successful (1) _____ (writer) of detective stories in the world.

In June that year, a baby girl became (2) _____ (serious) ill in Qatar, near Saudi Arabia. Doctors were unable to find the cause of her illness with confidence, (3) _____ she was sent to a big hospital in London where specialist help was available. A team of doctors hurried to examine the baby only (4) _____ (discover) that they, too, were unable to explain the very unusual disease. Just then, a nurse asked to speak to them.

"Excuse me," said the nurse, "but I think the baby is suffering (5) _____ thallium poisoning."

"What makes you think that?" Dr. Brown asked. "Thallium

poisoning is extremely rare. "

"I read a detective novel by Agatha Christie a few days ago," the nurse explained, "and in the book somebody uses thallium poison, and all the symptoms (6) _____ (describe). They're exactly the same as the (7) _____ (baby)."

The tests showed that the baby had indeed been poisoned by thallium, a rare metallic substance used in making glass. (8) _____ they knew the cause of illness, the doctors were able to give the baby the correct treatment. She soon recovered and was sent back home.

(B)

The most important use of (9) _____ (drift) bottles is to find ocean currents. (10) _____ the position and direction of currents are known, ships can use the forward movement of a current or stay away from currents (11) _____ would carry them off their course. Benjamin Franklin was one of the first to use bottles in the study of currents. He wondered (12) _____ British mail ships needed a week or two longer than US ships needed in order to cross the Atlantic Ocean. Franklin thought the Gulf Stream (13) _____ explain this difference.

Franklin talked with US captains. He found that they knew each turn of the Gulf Stream. They (14) _____ (use) the current in every possible way. (15) _____ his talks with US sea captains, Franklin made his first map of the Gulf Stream. Then he checked his map by using some bottles. The map that he finally made (16) _____ (still use), with only a few changes, today.

第 十 套

(A)

One of the most difficult (1) _____ (problem) that a young person (2) _____ (face) is deciding what to do. There are people, of course, who from the time they are six years old (3) _____ (know)

327

that they want to be doctors or pilots or fire fighters, but the majority of us do not find the time to make a decision about career until somebody or something forces us (4) _____ (face) the problem.

(5) _____ (Choose) an occupation takes time, and there are a lot of things you have to think about (6) _____ you try to decide what you would like to do. You may find that you will have to take special courses to qualify for a particular kind of work, or you may find out that you will need to get some actual work experience to gain enough knowledge.

Fortunately, there are a lot of people you can turn (7) _____ for advice. At most school there are teachers who are professionally qualified to advise you and give you detail information about the job requirements. And you can talk over ideas with family members and friends. But even if you get other people involved in (8) _____ (help) you make a decision, self-evaluation is an important part of the decision-making.

(B)

Colors influence our life more than we can ever imagine. Take language, for example. You may describe a sick person as (9) _____ (be) "a bit green". Sometimes, you may also use symbolic meanings of colors to talk about things. For instance, to describe a depressed person, you may say that the person is "feeling blue". (10) _____ doubt, colors do spice up ordinary conversations.

Additionally, colors can be applied to many parts of your daily life. Have you ever thought about why many school buses and taxis are painted yellow, and stop signs red? Since yellow is the most eye-catching color, it can catch people's attention, especially in heavy traffic. As for red, it is the color which usually indicates warning. That is (11) _____ some traffic signs use this color, and hot-water taps are usually labeled red.

How colors affect appetite may be something (12) _____ most people hardly notice — the colors of a dining environment possibly decide how much you eat. Most fast-food restaurants are often decorated in bright colors such as red, yellow, orange, and white for the purpose of increasing people's appetites. This is (13) _____ bright colors are not only natural colors that (14) _____ (find) in many foods, but also to raise people's spirits. Blue, on the contrary, is said (15) _____ (spoil) people's appetites because few foods are blue in nature. For those who are on a diet, blue dishes and bowls might help! Believe it or not, colors are everywhere in both your daily routine and conversations (16) _____ you may not notice them!

第 十 一 套

(A)

In the United States, (1) _____ is not usual to telephone someone very early in the morning. If you telephone him early in the day, while he is shaving or having breakfast, the time of the call shows the matter is very important and (2) _____ (require) immediate attention. The same meaning is attached to telephone calls (3) _____ (make) after 11:00 p.m. If someone receives a call during (4) _____ (sleep) hours, he assumes it's a matter of life and death. The time chosen for the call communicates its importance.

In social life, time plays a very important part. In the US guests tend to feel they are not highly regarded if the invitation to a dinner party is extended only three or four days before the party date. (5) _____ it is not true in all countries. In other areas of the world, it may (6) _____ (consider) foolish to make an appointment to far in advance because plans which are made for a date more than a week away tend (7) _____ (forget). The meaning of time differs in different parts of the world. Thus, misunderstandings arise between people from cultures that treat time differently. In the US no one would think of keeping a business associate waiting for an hour. It would be too impolite. A person (8) _____ is 5 minutes late is expected to make a short apology. If he is less than 5 minutes late, he will say a few words of explanation, though perhaps he will not complete the sentence.

(B)

Welcome to Everglades National Park. The Everglades is a watery plain (9) _____ (cover) with saw grass that's home to numerous species of plants and wildlife. At one and a half million acres, it's too big to see it all today, but this tour will offer you a good sampling. Our tour bus will stop first at Taylor Slough. This is a good place to start (10) _____ it's home to many of the plants and animals typically associated (11) _____ the Everglades. You'll see many rare birds and, of course, our world-famous alligators, an extinct species of crocodile. Don't worry. There's boardwalk (12) _____ goes across the wetland so you can look down (13) _____ the animals in the water from a safe distance. The boardwalk is high enough to give a great view of the saw grass land. From there we'll head to some other muddy and even jungle-like areas that feature wonderful tropical plant life.

For those of you who'd like a closer view of the saw grass land, you might consider renting a boat sometime during your visit here. However, don't do this unless you have a very good sense of direction and can negotiate your way through all grass. We'd hate to have to come (14) _____ (look) for you.

You have the good fortune of being here in the winter — the best time of year to visit. (15) _____ the spring and summer the mosquitoes will just about eat you alive! Right now they're not so bothersome, (16) _____ you'll still want to use an insect repellent.

第 十 二 套

(A)

Not all inventions have been the result of careful planning. Some were just discovered by chance, as the following two stories show.

In 1853, when a cook (1) _____ (name) George Crum was making French fries, a man sent some fries back, (2) _____ (say) that the fries were not thin enough. Crum cut and fried some thinner ones, (3) _____ these were also not thin enough. Crum was angry. To make the man (4) _____ (leave), Crum cut some potatoes really thin and fired them. (5) _____ the man liked them, and soon other guests were ordering this same delicious snack. The potato chip was born.

In the later 1940s, an American scientist, Percy Spencer, was trying to make a machine. (6) _____ would use radio waves to detect German warplanes. One day, after the experiment, Spencer found that a chocolate bar in his pocket had melted. Spencer then stood farther away from the machine and placed some corn in front of it. Soon, the corn was popping everywhere. Spencer had just "invented" the microwave oven.

These two stories show that chance can play an important role (7) _____ invention. Some inventions take lots of hard work, while others require that their inventions (8) _____ (be) in the right place at the right time.

(B)

I am glad to see (9) _____ many of you here. We've become really alarmed over the health center by the number of students who are seeing, who (10) _____ (experience) hearing loss. First, I want to go over some basics about hearing. Then we can take a look at our school environment and see if we can figure out some ways (11) _____ (protect) hearing. Too much moderate noise for a long time or some types of intense noise for even a short time can damage hearing.

Loudness is measured in units (12) _____ (call) decibels. Sounds up (13) _____ 80 decibels generally aren't harmful. That's noise like traffic on a busy street. anything louder than 80 decibels, especially with continuous exposure, may eventually hurt your hearing. Once you are up to around 140 decibels, that's like a jet plane taking (14) _____, then you might even feel pain in your ears. And pains are sure signs that your hearing is at risk. Even one exposure to a really loud noise at close range can cause hearing loss.

So what you need to do is to limit your exposure to harmful levels. If you pass along this handout, we can take a look at the decibel level of some common campus sounds. Notice (15) _____ loud those horns are that people take to football games. They are really dangerous if (16) _____ (blow) right behind you. Now, let's try to produce a list of damaging noises.

第 十 三 套

(A)

I often think of the event (1) _____ occurred when I was about ten years old. One day, while I (2) _____ (shop) with my mother at a store, I stole a chocolate bar and put it in my pocket. When we arrived home, I secretly took it out and was (3) _____ to eat it, but I had a feeling of guilt about taking something that did not belong (4) _____ me.

I soon realized that (5) _____ I should do was (6) _____ (tell) my mother about this. I went to my mother and told her what I had done (7) _____ a quiet voice. She did not yell at me as I (8) _____ (expect). Instead, she gently told me what I needed to do.

We went back to the store. I was very (9) _____ (scare), and I hesitantly told the manager what I had done. He told me that (10) _____ (steal) was bad but being honest was great. Afterward, he allowed me to pay (11) _____ the chocolate bar. My mother hold my hand the whole time. And (12) _____ (have) her by my side helped me to be strong.

(13) _____ the way home, we talked about the lesson that I (14) _____ (learn). Then, she told me to put it all behind me and (15) _____ (enjoy) my chocolate bar. That guilt-free chocolate tasted great. The way (16) _____ my mother treated me turned this event into a lesson of forgiveness and honesty, and I will always be thankful to her.

(B)

County fairs are a tradition in New England towns. They offer great entertainment. One popular event is the pie- (1) _____ (eat) contest. If you want to take part (2) _____ the contest, (3) _____ is a good idea to remember guidelines: first, make sure your stomach is nearly empty of food. (4) _____ (eat) a whole pie can be hard (5) _____ you have just finished a meal. Next, it is helpful to (6) _____ (like) the pie you are going to eat. The cream types are a good choice. They slide down the throat more easily. Placing your hands in the right position adds (7) _____ the chances of (8) _____ (win). There is a temptation to reach out and help the eating process. This will result in becoming (9) _____ (disqualify). Don't just sit on your hands. If your hands (10) _____ (tie) behind your back, you will not be tempted to make use (11) _____ them.

Now you are ready (12) _____ (show) your talent at eating pies. The object, of course, is to get to the bottom of pie plate before the other people. It is usually (13) _____ (good) to start at the outside and work toward the middle. The method gives you a goal to focus (14) _____. Try not to notice (15) _____ the other people near you are doing. Let the cheers from the crowd (16) _____ (stimulate) you. But don't look up. All you should think about is eating that pie.

第十四套

(A)

I am a British woman social anthropologist (人类学家). I once spent a year in Moldova , in Eastern Europe, (1) _____ (study) everyday life in the country. I stayed with a Moldovan family to see from the inside how people managed their lives. I had a wonderful time and made many new friends. What I observed is of course based on my own experience at a particular place and time.

I often found (2) _____ surprisingly difficult to see life there through the eyes of a Moldovan This was (3) _____ the people I met were extremely hospitable and I was treated as an honored guest at all times. As my hosts, they wanted me to enjoy myself and not to get (4) _____ (involve) in shopping, cooking or other domestic jobs. Most mornings I was encouraged to go out to explore the city, or carry out my research, and I returned later to find that my elderly landlady and her sister had travelled across the city on buses to the central market (5) _____ (bring) back heavy loads of potatoes, a whole lamb, or other large quantities of products.

I was often invited to people's homes, and was always offered food on entering. Most of the adults I met enjoyed inviting friends, family, neighbors, colleagues and even strangers into their homes, (6) _____ they treated them to food, drink, and a lively hospitable atmosphere. Hosts hurried to serve guests as well and as quickly as possible. (7) _____ a household was expecting guests, large amounts of food were prepared in advance, usually by the women. Wine had already been made, generally by the men, (8) _____ were also responsible for pouring it. Unexpected visitors were still offered as much food and drink as the household (9) _____ provide in the circumstances.

(B)
How English family life has evolved
since the eighteenth century?

The majority of English families of the pre-industrial age, roughly until the mid-eighteenth century, lived in a rural location. Many of them owned or had the use of a small place of land, and actually all family members were busy with agricultural work in one form or another, usually (10) _____ (grow) food for their own consumption and sometimes also producing food or other goods for sale.

The labor was controlled by the husband, (11) _____ _____ his wife and children, too, had an economic value as their contributions to the family income were likely to make the difference between starvation and survival.

Children worked from an early age, girls helping their mothers, and boys their fathers. School was an occasional factor in their lives. Instead, children learned by doing (12) _____ their parents showed them. Knowledge of caring (13) _____ animals, sewing was handed down from parent to child.

Also, most people engaged in handicraft production in the home, and the family (14) _____ (pay) to work with cloth, wood or leather. In general, this work could be put aside and taken up again when there was a break such as agricultural work.

The process of industrialization in the second half of the eighteenth century and during the nineteenth transformed life for the majority of population. It was the use of steam to power machinery (15) _____ required large buildings, and it resulted in the construction of numerous factories in many towns and cities. These in turn (16) _____ (encourage) migration from the countryside in search of work. If electricity had preceded steam, domestic industry might have survived more fully.

第十五套

(A)

Michelle walked out the theater humming (哼唱) a tune. She'd just seen a wonderful musical at the beautiful Paramount Theater. (1) _____ she closed her eyes, she could still see the beautiful costumes and stage sets. It was now after 11 p. m. , and she really didn't like being out late by (2) _____ . Since no one else had wanted to go to the show, she (3) _____ go alone. She headed down the dark Seattle Street toward her car. The parking space was empty. "That's odd," she thought. "Am I on the wrong street ?" She checked the street signs. No, she was on Pine Street. And she was sure that this was (4) _____ she'd left her car. But her car was nowhere to be seen. She began to feel nervous. Someone had stolen her car! What was she going to do?

Should she call the police or call someone to give her a ride? She decided to call someone. She took out her cell-phone only (5) _____ (find) that her battery was dead! Now what? Maybe she could take a cab. She only had $1 in cash (6) _____ she checked every corner of her wallet. And to her horror, her credit card was missing! Then she remembered she'd ordered something on the Internet and left the card by her computer. She headed back toward the theater and the lights on Pike Street. Then she saw something familiar. Her car! She realized she (7) _____ (park) on *Pike* Street not *Pine* street! Once again (8) _____ (sing) a song from the show, she got into her car and headed home.

(B)

Most religions have some kind of holy text on which the religious beliefs are based. For Christians this text is the *Holy Bible*, for Jews it is the *Torah* and for Muslims it is the *Koran*.

Muslims believe that the *Koran* (9) _____ (consist) of revelations from God to Muhammad during the years 610 to 632 when Muhammad died. These revelations were written down by those (10) _____ were close to him during this time and for several years after his death. They were gathered into the text (11) _____ (know) as the *Koran* during the years 630 to 650.

The interpretation of the *Koran* has always been a difficult task, even for Islamic scholars. For example, the meaning of some words are determined by dots above the vowels (元音). In ancient Arabic, however, very often these dots (12) _____ (omit). As a result some letters looked identical. Thus, the meanings of these words depended in many cases (13) _____ the memories of the men who had written them. Early Muslims had to try to get the exact meanings of the words (14) _____ these people died and it was too late.

Unlike the *Bible*, in which the events are provided in time order, There is no reference to (15) _____ things occurred in the *Koran*. In any case, unlike the *Bible*, most the suras section are composed of orders and warnings. Unlike in the *Bible*, there are very few stories in the *Koran*.

Muslins believe that by (16) _____ (recite) the book, they create a holy atmosphere, and there are many Muslims who have learned the *Koran* by heart.

第 十 六 套

(A)

Many people underestimate the importance of writing skills. They think that as long as they (1) _____ speak and understand the language, they know it. Truth is, we live in the age of internet and smart phones where most of the communication happens in writing. An ability to express ideas (2) _____ a clear and literate way has become extremely necessary for work, study and everyday life.

Do you have trouble (3) _____ (express) yourself in written English? Don't worry, even native speakers find it difficulty.

Here are some tips that will help you improve your English writing skills:

1. Read as much as you can. It is the best way (4) _____ (learn) sentence structures and build a wide vocabulary. We will share a writing for you to read on Facebook every week.

2. Translate from your native language into English (5) _____ vice versa. However, if you write more, you would start thinking in English. You will know you have become fluent (6) _____ you no longer need to translate your thoughts.

3. Use social media. By posting on Twitter or Facebook, you can get comments and feedback from your peers. It also helps overcome a fear of writing in public. You can always get your writings (7) _____ (check) by reviewers at Daily Themes before you share it on other channels.

4. Take an online course. There are a few very good free online courses on writing. English composition, and grammar on Cousera, Alison, edX, and Future Learn. You can take courses

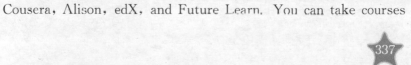

on these websites, and share your learning by writing on Daily Themes.

5. Get a writing coach at Daily Themes. The fastest way to learn is to have someone, (8) _____ has already mastered the language, check your writings.

Happy writing!

(B)

Children have their own rules in playing games. They seldom need a referee (裁判) and rarely trouble to keep scores. They don't care much about who wins or loses, and it doesn't seem to worry them (9) _____ the game is not finished. Yet, they like games that depend a lot on luck, (10) _____ _____ their personal abilities cannot be directly compared. They also enjoyed games that move in stages, in which each stage — the choosing of leaders, the picking-up of sides, or the determining of which side shall start — is almost a game in itself.

Grown-ups can hardly find children's game exciting. And they often feel puzzled at (11) _____ their kids play such simple game again and again. (12) _____, it is found that a child plays games for vey important reasons. He can be a good player without having to think whether he is a popular person , and he can find himself being a useful partner to someone of whom he is ordinarily afraid. He becomes a leader when it comes to (13) _____ turn. He can be confident, too, in particular games, that it is his place to give orders, to pretend to be dead, to throw a ball actually at someone, or to kiss someone he (14) _____ (catch).

It appears to us that when children play a game they imagine a situation (15) _____ their control. Everyone knows the rules, and (16) _____ (importantly), everyone plays according to the rules. Those rules may be childish, though. They make sure that every child has a chance to win.

第 十 七 套

(A)

The rise of the so-called "boomerang generation" is revealed in official figures showing that almost one in five graduates in their late 20s now live with their parents.

By contrast, only one in eight university graduates had failed (1) _____ (fly) the nest by the same age 20 years ago. It also found that grown-up sons are twice as likely as their sisters to still be living with their parents in their late 20s. With a nearly quarter of men (2) _____ (approach) 30 still living at home, the findings are bound to lead to claims of a "generation of mummy's boys".

Young professionals in their late 20s or early 30s have been nicknamed the "boomerang generation" because of the trend (3) _____ returning to the family home having initially left to study. Recent research has suggested (4) _____ young people in Britain are twice as likely to choose (5) _____ (live) with their parents in their late 20s (6) _____ their counterparts elsewhere in Europe.

Growing housing prices, rising student debts and the effects of recession (衰退) on the job market have forced (7) _____ wave of young people to move back into the family home at an age when they would normally be moving out. But commentators warned the phenomenon may have more to do with young people facing "dire" prospects than simply a desire to save money.

While the proportion of those of university or college age moving out from the family home (8) _____ (continue) to rise in the last 20 years, among those in their mid and the late 20s the trend has been reversed. Overall 1.7 million people aged from 22 to 29 now share a roof with their parents including more than 760,000 in their late 20s. In 1988, 22.7 per cent of men aged 25 to 29 were still living with their parents but last year the proportion was 24.5 percent.

(B)

(9) _____ important we may regard school life to be, there is no (10) _____ (deny) the fact that children spend more time at home than in the classroom. Therefore, the great influence of parents cannot be ignored or discounted by the teacher. They can become strong allies of the school personnel or they (11) _____ consciously or unconsciously hinder and frustrate curricular objectives.

Administrators have been aware of the need to keep parents informed of the newer methods used in schools. Many principles have conducted workshops explaining such matters as the reading readiness program, manuscript writing and developmental mathematics. Moreover, the classroom teacher with the permission of the supervisors, can also play an important role in enlightening parents. The informal tea and the many interviews carried on during the year, as well as new ways of reporting pupils' progress, can significantly aid in achieving a harmonious interplay between school and home.

(12) _____ (illustrate), suppose that a father has been drilling Junior in arithmetic processes night after night. In a friendly interview, the teacher can help the parent sublimate (升华) his natural paternal interest into productive channels. He might be persuaded to let Junior participate in discussing the family budget, buying the food, using a standard or measuring cup at home, setting the clock, calculating mileage on a trip and engaging in scores of other activities (13) _____ have a mathematical basis.

If the father follows the advice, it is reasonable to assume that he will soon realize his son is making satisfactory progress in mathematics, and at the same time, enjoying the work. Too often, however, teachers' conferences with parents (14) _____ (devote) to petty (不重要的) accounts of children's misdeeds, complaints about laziness and poor work habits, and suggestion for penalties and rewards at home.

(15) _____ is needed is a more creative approach in which the teacher, as a professional adviser, plants ideas in parents' minds for

the best utilization of the many hours that the child spends out of the classroom.

In this way, the school and the home join forces in fostering (16) _____ (full) development of youngsters capabilities.

第 十 八 套

(A)

The world's great cities are engines of wealth creation. Places like London and San Francisco account (1) _____ a disproportionate share of economic output. They are the combustion chambers in which ideas and capital are combined (2) _____ (generate) new riches.

To an alarming extent, such cities are also playground for the rich — and only the rich. The soaring cost of housing in these places pushes those of more modest means away, toward spots (3) _____ homes are cheaper but opportunity is more limited. The pressure has serious consequences. A recent paper reckons that over the past 50 years this dispersing effect left American output 13.5% below the level it would otherwise have reached. Poor Americans (4) _____ (live) in rich cities survive longer than their counterparts in poor (5) _____. Finding (6) _____ (effective) ways to reduce housing costs would thus not only save money but prolong lives. Economics is all about supply and demand, and high housing costs are the product of too little of the former in the face of lots of the latter. Strict planning roles in pricey cities make building new homes a nightmare for developers. In London, for example, they face myriad rules about (7) _____ they can build, including one that demands that nothing (8) _____ impede the view of the dome of St Paul's Cathedral from a gap in a hedge ten miles away.

(B)

Cigarette smoking kills. That we know. So, manufactures made electronic cigarettes as a safer smoking choice — safer than tobacco.

341

E-cigarettes contain the drug nicotine like cigarettes. But they do not use tobacco. And you do not light (9) _____. They are powered by battery.

So, if e-cigarettes are so safe, why have poison control centers around the United States seen an increase (10) _____ telephone calls about e-cigarette poisonings? The answer is children.

Most of the calls are from people worried about children who have played with the devices. In the period of one month this year, the United States Centers for Disease Control say 215 people called the Center with e-cigarette concerns. More than half of these calls were for children (11) _____ (age) five and younger. The devices apparently had made them sick.

Tim McAfee is director of the CDC's Office on Smoking and Health. He says the problem is regulation, meaning the US Federal government does not control e-cigarettes (12) _____ they contain liquid nicotine.

Mr. McAfee adds that liquid nicotine is a well-known danger.

"Nicotine historically has been used as a pesticide in the United States. And that's where we have really had for many, many decades significant poisonings when people got exposed to nicotine that was in liquid solutions."

Mr. McAfee explains that nicotine poisoning happens (13) _____ the substance gets into the skin, gets into the eyes or is swallowed. Even a small amount, he says, (14) _____ make a person sick. Nicotine poisoning can cause stomach pain or a sense of imbalance. Headaches and seizures (突发疾病) are also common sighs of nicotine poisoning. And too much nicotine can kill.

Tim McAfee says e-cigarettes do not create the level of risk to people as tobacco products do. He notes that almost 500,000 Americans die each year from cigarettes.

"So, cigarettes are the winner in that contest. And we don't really know what's going to happen with e-cigarettes."

E-cigarettes do not contain hundreds of harmful chemicals (15) _____ are found in real cigarettes. So, the US Surgeon

General has suggested that e-cigarettes may be a useful tool for adults (16) _____ (try) to end their tobacco use, or quit.

But McAfee worries that teenagers may think electronic cigarettes are harmless. They could become addicted, or hooked, on the nicotine and then start smoking real cigarettes. In other words, he fears that for young people fake (假装) e-cigarettes could be a "gateway" to the real thing.

2015 年上海高考英语试题
（语法新题型）

Directions: After reading the passages below, fill in the blanks to make the passages coherent and grammatically correct. For the blanks with a given word, fill in each blank with the proper form of the given word; for the other blanks, use one word that best fits each blank.

(A)
Gift from a stranger

My local supermarket is always busy. The first parking space I found was convenient, but I'd noticed a woman in a blue car circling for a while. (25) _____ I was in a good mood, I let her have it. On the edge of the car park I backed into the next available spot — it was a tight fit.

Pretty soon I'd made my way through the supermarket and was back in the fresh air. Feeling good, I (26) _____ (empty) my purse change into the hands of a homeless man and helped a struggling woman reverse park (倒车).

Just as I approached my car, 1 saw the woman I'd let have my car space earlier. She was giving me (27) _____ odd look — half puzzled, half intent (热切的). I smiled and wished her a pleasant day. As I squeezed back into my car, I spotted the same lady (28) _____ (look) in at me. "Hello," she said, hesitantly. "This (29) _____ sound crazy but I was on my way to drop some of my mother's things off at the charity bins. You are just so much (30) _____ her. You helped those people, I noticed, and you seemed so happy." She looked at me meaningfully and passed a box in through the window. "I think she would like you to have it." (31) _____ (shock), I took it from her automatically. She smiled and walked away.

After a pause, I opened the box. Inside was a beautiful gold necklace with a large grey pearl. It was (32) _____ (nice) gift I'd ever received, and it was from a complete stranger. The necklace was around my neck, a warm reminder of human kindness.

(B)
Ask helpful Hannah

Dear helpful Hannah,

I've got a problem with my husband, Sam. He bought a smart phone a couple of months ago and he took it on our recent ski vacation to Colorado, it was a great trip except for one problem. He has a constant urge (33) _____ for next messages; he checks his phone every five minutes! He's so addicted to it that he just can't stand the idea (34) _____ there may be an important text. He can't help checking even at inappropriate times like when we are eating in a restaurant and I am talking to him! He behaves (35) _____ any small amount of boredom can make him feel the need to check his phone even when he know he shouldn't. The temptation to see (36) _____ is connecting him is just too great. When I ask him to put down the phone and stop (37) _____ (ignore) me, he say, "In a minute." but still checks to see if (38) _____ has posted something new on the Internet. Our life (39) _____ (interrupted). If we go somewhere and I ask him to have the phone at home, he suffers from withdrawal symptom. May this dependency on his smart phone has become more than an everyday problem.

I recently read an article about "nomophobia", (40) _____ is a real illness people can't suffer from the fear of being without your phone! I am worried that Sam maybe suffering from this illness because he feels anxious if he doesn't have his phone with him, even for a short time.

Who would have thought that little devices like these could have brought so much trouble!

中学英语常用词组和短语

A

abandon

    abandon himself to despair　陷入绝望

    abandon medicine for literature　放弃医学,从事文学

    with abandon　尽情地;任意地

aboard

    aboard the ship, the Beagle　在 Beagle 号船上

    It is time to go aboard.　现在是上船或登机的时间了。

about

    ask about him　了解他的情况

    be about to give up　即将(正要)放弃

    The boy was about to cross the road.　这孩子正要过马路。

    get about; be about　(病后)起来走动;起床活动

    come about　发生;成为现实

    How has it come about?　它是怎样发生的?

above

    above all　最最重要的是

    above everything else　最最重要的是

    the techniques outlined above　上面概括的技巧

    over and above...　除……之外

    He got a number of perquisites, over and above his salary.　除工资外,他还得
        到一些津贴。

abroad

    go abroad for one's holidays　出国度假

    both at home and abroad　在国内外

absent

    be absent from class　上课缺席

    be absent from school　上课缺席

    look at me in an absent way　心不在焉地看着我

absorb

    be absorbed in...　专注于;聚精会神(干……)

abstract

    in the abstract   抽象地说;一般地说

access

    have access to the President   有见到总统的机会

    provide access to...   提供对……的享用权

    have no access to the health service   没有享受医保的权利

accessible

    be accessible to sb.   容易接近、得到、到达或使用

    The headmaster is always accessible to the students.   学生总是能找到那位校长。

    The house at the top of the hill was not accessible to a car.   山顶上的那栋房屋
      过去轿车不能到达。

accident

    by accident   意外地;偶然地

accomplish

    accomplish the task   完成任务

    accomplish the goal (purpose)   达到目的(目标)

according

    according to...   根据,按照

account

    open an account at the bank   在银行里开了个账户

    take... into account (consideration)   把……考虑进去

    account for the fact...   说明了……事实的原因

    give an account of...   解释……的理由

    on no account   决不

    on account of his health   由于他的健康缘故

    take account of the interests of our country   考虑国家的利益

accountable

    He was accountable for his action.   他对他的行动负责。

accuse

    accuse sb. of...   指控某人……

    I accused him of stealing my bike.   我指控他偷我的自行车。

accustomed

    be (get, become, grow) accustomed to cold climates   习惯于寒冷天气

ache

    He ached all over.   他全身都疼。

acid

    the level of acid   酸的浓度

across

across the Arctic　横穿北极

throw it across the room　把它扔到房间的另一头

get across quickly　迅速过马路

swim across this big lake　游过这个大湖

Don't get across your mother.　别惹你母亲不高兴。

put my idea across　讲清楚我的想法

He put one across his teacher.　他欺骗过他的老师。

shout across the room　在房间里大声叫喊

come (run) across an unknown word　偶尔碰到不认识的词

across the board　普遍地

The workers at the store got a pay rise across the board.　这家商店的工人普遍
　　涨了工资。

act

　　act as　充当;担任

　　act on.../act upon...　对……作用;按照……行动

　　He acts on his mother's advice.　他按照他母亲的忠告去做。

　　act out that story　比划着讲那个故事

　　act for me　代理我的职务

action

　　take action on...　对……采取行动

　　They came into action again.　他们又开始战斗(行动)。

active

　　take an active part in...　积极参加……

　　be active in politics　积极参加政治活动

adapt

　　Every species is adapted to life in...　使每种物种适应在……地区的生活。

　　We should adapt ourselves to climate here.　我们应该使我们自己适应这里的
　　气候。

add

　　add sth. to...　把某物加到……里

　　Please add some salt to the soup.　请在汤里加些盐。

　　be added to...　被加到……里

　　add to my interest　增加了我的兴趣

　　His whole school education added up to no more than one year.　他所受的全部
　　学校教育加起来的总和仅仅一年那么少。

addition

　　in addition　再说,除此之外

　　in addition to object test　除了客观测试外(还有……)

admiration

    with admiration　钦佩地

    have（display）an admiration for him　对他非常佩服

admire

    admire sb. for sth.　对某人的……钦佩

admit

    admit（to）stealing the TV set　承认偷了那台电视机

    admit one's mistake　承认自己的错误

    He was admitted to Fudan University.　他被复旦大学录取。

    He was admitted to hospital suffering from burns.　他因烧伤住院。

    The regulations do not admit of your doing that.　规则不允许你那样做。

advance

    advanced English　高级英语

    in advance　事先,预先

    in advance of the others　在别人的前面

advantage

    take advantage of　利用……（机会;条件）

    have the advantage over sb. of　……与某人相比,有利条件是……

    He had the advantage over the boy of being born into a rich family.　他与那个
        男孩相比,有利条件是出生在一个有钱人的家庭。

advertisement

    an advertisement for a cook　一个招聘厨师的广告

advice

    follow my advice　听我的忠告

    give you a piece of advice on sth.　给你提一条关于某事的意见

affection

    I have strong affection for their children.　我对他们的孩子有着强烈的感情。

after

    ask after him　探问他

    after all　毕竟,终究

    He is after you.　他在找你。

    day after day　日复一日

    year after year　年复一年

    look after　关心;照顾

    one after another　一个接一个

    run after...　追赶……

    take after　长得像……

    He takes after his father.　他长得像他的父亲。

afraid

    be afraid of...　害怕……

    be afraid to repeat what they hear　不敢重复他们听到的话

against

    He was strongly against slavery.　他强烈反对奴隶制度。

    take a picture against the sun　拍张逆光照

    against the law　违法

    against the will　违背意愿

    against the sky　衬着天空

    lean against the door　斜靠在门上

    against the wind　顶着风,逆风

    fight against the enemy　与敌人斗争

age

    at this age　在这个年龄

    I am of age today.　今天我已是成年人了。

    of one's own age　和某人同龄

    at the age of eighty-four　在八十四岁时

    orphanages or homes for the aged　孤儿院或养老院

    under the age of fourteen　十四岁以下

    aged from four or up　年龄从四岁到略大一点

    He is a boy aged fifteen.　他是个 15 岁的男孩。

ago

    more than 2,500 years ago　两千五百多年前

agree

    Most people agree with the doctor.　大多数人同意那位医生的看法。

    agree with sb.（what sb. said；what sb. did）　同意某人(某人说的话；某人干的事)

    agree to your plan（suggestion）　同意你的计划(建议)

    agree on your idea（way, opinion, agreement...）　同意想法(方法；观点；协定……)

agreement

    in agreement　持相同意见

    in agreement with your decision　同意你的决定

ahead

    Go ahead!　说吧! /去吧!……

    ahead of you　在你的前面,超过你；比你强

    an hour ahead of your cousin　比你的堂兄早一小时

    be one point ahead　领先了一分

ahead of schedule (time)　提前

aid

aid the elderly and the disabled　帮助年老和丧失劳动力的人

with the aid of him　在他的帮助下

come to my aid　来帮助我

air

in the open air　在露天

be on the air　作广播

by air　乘飞机

Don't put on airs with me.　别给我摆架子。

aim

aim at　瞄准;以……为目的;计划;打算

They were aimed at stopping the war.　他们的目的是停止这场战争。

aim at the lion　瞄准那只狮子

He aimed at finishing her letter by two o'clock.　他计划两点钟写完那封信。

achieve one's aim　达到目的

airport

at the airport　在机场

alarm

in alarm　惊恐地

a false alarm　一场虚惊

alert

on the alert　处于紧急状态

alike

The two twins are very much alike.　这两个双胞胎非常像。

alive

He was alive to the dangers of the work.　他意识到这工作的危险。

The street was alive with people.　这条街到处都是人。

all

above all　最重要的是,首先

in all　总共

all at once　突然

all of a sudden　突然

all but (＝almost)　几乎

all the same　仍旧(照样)

not...at all　根本,完全(常用于否定句)

all in all　总之

first of all

for all I know　据我所知

for all　尽管

For all his wealth, he felt unhappy.　尽管他有钱,但是他感到不快乐。

for good (and all)　永远;长期地

once (and) for all　一劳永逸地

all over the world　全世界

all right　行;好吧;没问题

and all that　等等

He followed me all the way down the street.　他一路上一直跟着我。

alone

let (leave) him alone　别理他

let alone　更不用说

The child had not enough money for food, let alone go to school.　那孩子那时连饭都吃不饱,更不用说去上学了。

along

all along　一直

walk along the bank of a river　沿着河岸行走

come along　一起走

along the centre of the Great Plains　沿着大平原的中部

get along better with sb.　与某人相处得更好

drive along a main road　沿着大路行驶

walk along the street　沿着街走

Sth. is used along with sth.　某物和某物被一起使用。

alongside

stand alongside him　站在他的旁边

allow

allow me to do it　允许我做此事

be allowed to do...　被允许做……

He allowed helping me.　他同意帮助我。

aloud

read aloud　大声地朗读;出声地朗读

alter

alter the mistakes　改正错误

alternative

alternative source of energy　可替代的能源;另一种能源

amazement

in amazement　惊奇地

To my amazement, he was ill.　使我惊讶的是,他病了。

among

    among（one of）the first on the scene　是第一批到达现场的人员之一

amount

    the amount of＋不可数名词　……的总量

    the amount of money　钱的总数

    a large amount of money　大量的钱

    His income for that year amounted to \$1,000,000.　他那年的收入多达 1 000 000 美元。

and

    and so on　等等

    and so forth　等等

    and the like　等等

analysis

    in the final analysis 归根结底；说到底

angry

    be angry with him for...　为……对他很生气

    be rather angry at what he said　对他说的话很生气

    He was angry at finding that I had done nothing.　他发现我什么事也没做很生气。

anger

    He spoke in anger.＝He spoke angrily.　他愤怒地说。

another

    one after another　一个接一个地；一个又一个地

    rescue one child after another　营救一个个孩子

    one another　互相

    one way（thing, time...）or another　以某种方式（在某个时候，做某件事）

    Tom is always busy with one thing or another.　汤姆总是忙着某件事。

answer

    the answers to the questions　这些问题的答案

    answer for...　对……负责

    in answer to...　作为对……的回答/响应/反击

    In answer to the question, he shook his head.　他只是摇了摇头，就算回答了问题。

anti-

    some anti-pollution laws　一些反污染的法律

anxiety

    with great anxiety　焦急地

anxious

    be anxious about her　为她担忧

    be anxious for a map　急于得到一幅地图

They were too anxious to leave. 他们急着要走。

any

if any 如果有的话

There are few trees there if any. 如果有树，也没几棵。

anyone

Anyone who wants...（＝People who want...＝Those who want...＝Whoever wants...） 凡是要……的人

anything

anything but 决不；一点也不

The little bridge is anything but safe. 那座小桥一点也不安全。

like anything 拼命地

He would work like anything. 他总是拼命地工作。

apart

apart from 除……之外

take the watch apart 把这块手表拆开

apologize

apologize to sb. for sth. 为某事向某人道歉

apologize to you for my forgetfulness 为我的健忘向你道歉

apology

My apologies! 对不起！

appeal

appeal to sb. 投合某人所好；向某人呼吁；请求某人

Jogging appeals to old people. 慢跑受到老年人的欢迎。

appear

appear to be true 显得正确的

application

The application of what we've learned to practice is very important. 把我们学到的东西付诸实践是很重要的。

apply

apply oneself to... 致力于……

They apply themselves to learning French. 他们致力于学习法语。

The invention will be applied to our production. 这项发明将被运用到生产上去。

She has applied for a passport. 她已申请了护照。

appoint

appoint Johann the conductor 任命 Johann 为指挥

make an appointment 预约

appreciate

appreciate music 欣赏音乐

appreciate getting some advice from you　感激从你那儿得到忠告

appreciate your kindness in doing sth.　感谢你好心做某事(不能用人作宾语)

appreciation

　　have an appreciation of books　喜爱书籍

approve

　　approve of your plan　赞同你的计划;赞许你的计划

argue

　　argue about sth. with sb.　为……和某人争论

　　argue against...　据理反对……

arise

　　arise from...　从……产生/出现/发生

arm

　　arm in arm　手挽手

　　be armed with...　用……武装起来

around

　　He worked around the clock.　他日夜不停地工作。

　　around the corner　在拐角处;即将到来

　　put her arms around his neck　她搂着他的脖子

　　around the world　全世界

　　around my home　在我家附近

　　bring your son around　带你儿子来玩

arrange

　　arrange for me to do...　安排我做……

　　arrange a taxi for him　为他安排了一辆出租车

arrangement

　　make arrangements　作安排

arrest

　　be arrested　被逮捕

　　He was put under house arrest.　他被软禁了。

arrive

　　The day finally arrived.　那天终于来到了。

　　arrive in/at (＝get to＝reach)　到达

　　arrived at a simple system　做出一种简单的(文字)系统

　　arrive at some conclusion　得出某个结论

　　What decision did you finally arrive at?　你最后做出什么决定?

as

　　live about the same time as sb.　和某人生活在同一个时代

　　even as...　正当……

move as they do　像他们原来一样活动

as their first or second languages　作为他们的第一或第二语言

as a foreign language　作为一门外语

as a search and rescue craft　作为一架探索和救生艇

as for alcoholic drinks　至于含酒精的饮料

as for me　至于我

as follows　如下

as（so）far as I know　就我所知道的而论；据我所知

as good as　实际上

Everything was as good as settled.　一切实际已经被解决了。

as it is　根据现在情况看；就以现在的样子

as（so）long as　只要

so as（not）to do...　为了（不）做……

so...as to do...　如此……以至于做……

such...as to do...　如此……以至于做……

as soon as　一……就……

would as soon not do...　宁愿不做……

as well　也

may（might）as well do...　不妨做……

as time went on　随着时间的推移

as dark as a moonless night　像无月光之夜一样漆黑

as if（＝as though）　好似，好像

As bees love sweetness, so flies love rottenness.　就像蜜蜂喜欢甜食一样苍蝇喜欢腐烂的东西。

ashamed

　　look ashamed　显得难为情

　　be ashamed of...　为……感到羞愧

ask

　　ask sb. for sth.（＝ask sth. of sb.）　向某人要某物

　　ask favours of other people（＝ask other people for favours）　请别人帮忙

　　ask about his private affairs　问关于他的私事

　　ask after...　问候……

asleep

　　fall（drop）asleep　入睡了

assist

　　assist sb. with sth.　帮助某人做……

　　assist sb. to do sth.　帮助某人做……

　　assist sb. in doing sth.　帮助某人做……

associate

associate... with... 把……和……联系起来

It is associated with warmth. 它和温暖联系在一起。

be in association with him 和他有交往

assure

I assure you that you are wrong. 我保证你错了。

assure sb. of sth. 向某人保证……

assure him of his safety 向他保证一定安全

be assured to spread quickly 被认为传播得很快

at

stand at the blackboard 站在黑板旁

at the news 一听到这消息

at the word "go" 一听到"开始"令下

at the sight 一看到这情景

at about 80 to 96 km an hour 以每小时 80 到 90 公里的速度

at all costs 不惜一切代价

at a loss 不知所措

at large 逍遥法外;尚未捕获

at least 至少

at most 至多

at last 最后

attach

attach the label to your luggage 把标签拴在你的行李上

I was much attached to her. 我对她很有感情。

attack

make an attack on... 对……攻击

make a sudden attack on the enemies 向敌人突然攻击

attend

attend concerts and plays 参加音乐会和看戏

attend on (upon) her 侍候她

attend to the matters 处理(办理)这些事情

attentive

be attentive in class (=pay attention in class) 上课专心

attention

stand at attention 立正

call attention to sth. 把注意力引到某事上

attitude

develop a good attitude about (to/towards) tests 培养好的测验态度

attract

    Flowers attract bees.　花吸引着蜜蜂。

    Like attracts like.　物以类聚。

attractions

    enjoy various attractions　游览各种名胜；欣赏各种吸引人的东西

audience

    before a large audience　在很多观众面前

    have an audience of 500　有 500 名听众

    give an audience to him　接见他

audio

    the audio-visual aids　视听辅助器

    video and audio tapes　音像带

aunt

    at my aunt's　在我阿姨家；在我舅妈家

average

    an average man　一个普通男子

    on (the) average　平均起来；一般来说

avoid

    can't avoid going...　不可避免去……

    avoid making any spelling mistakes　避免犯任何拼写错误

    avoid taking that nap　避免打瞌睡

    avoid taking sleeping pills　避免吃安眠药

await

    await the ship (＝wait for the ship)　等候那艘船

awake

    keep people awake　使人们醒着

    stay awake night after night　夜夜不能寐

    The noise awoke me.　那噪音吵醒了我。

    I awoke at 7.　我在 7 点醒来。

    be awoke to the difficulties　认识(明白)这些困难

award

    award Noble Prizes to sb. for outstanding services　把诺贝尔奖授予有突出贡献的人

    The judge awarded her 2,000 dollars.　那位法官判决给她 2 000 美元。

aware

    be keenly aware of　敏感地意识到

    be aware of　意识到，知道

    They are still not aware of the harm of smoking.　他们仍不知道抽烟的危害。

away

do away with... 废除；取消

get away with... 携带……跑掉

The thief got away with several thousand pounds' worth of jewellery. 那贼携带价值两千英镑的首饰跑掉了。

get (break) away from... 从……强行脱离

pass away 去世

give sth. away 把某物赠送掉

The hotel is only five minutes/one mile away. You can walk there. 这家旅馆不远，你可以步行去那里。

awful

That's awful! 太糟糕了！/太可怕了！

He was awfully glad. 他非常高兴。

awkward

He felt awkward and uncomfortable. 他感到别扭和不舒服。

She is an awkward girl. 她是个笨手笨脚的女孩。

B

back

fall back 后退，撤退

get back her breath 喘口气

go back to his childhood 回顾他的童年

at the back of the classroom 在教室的后面（室内）

on the back of the envelope 在信封的背面

have the whole country at his back 有全国人民作后盾（支持）

He turned his back on me. 他不理（背弃）我。

The enemy fell back. 敌人后退了。

keep back his tears 忍住他的眼泪

bad

go bad 变坏了

be bad for one's health 对健康有害

The situation went from bad to worse. 情况（变得）每况愈下（越来越糟）。

badly

We badly need rain now. 我们现在非常（迫切）需要雨水。

baggage

a piece of baggage 一件行李

balance

upset the balance of nature 扰乱了生态平衡

the balance of the work 剩下的工作

bamboo

Some bamboo never blooms. 有些竹子从不开花。

a long piece of bamboo 一根长竹子

ban

ban all smoking here 这里禁止抽烟

bank

blood bank 血库

on the banks of the river 在河岸上

in the bank 在银行里

He banks half his salary every month. 他每月把一半工资存在银行里。

bank on your help 依靠(指望)你的帮助

banner

under the banner of... 以……名义

barely

It was barely ten o'clock at night. 时间才刚刚晚上十点钟。

Barely had he arrived when he had to leave again. 他一到那里就又要走了。

bargain

drive a hard bargain 使劲讨价还价

That is a bargain. 我同意了。

bark

bark at... 对着……叫

base

be based on other people's idea 基于别人的思想

be based on... 建立在……基础上

on the basis of... 在……前提下

a base action 一个恶劣的行动

bath

have a bath 洗澡

Your bath is ready. 你的洗澡水准备好了。

bean

bean curd 豆腐

bear

bear a share of the responsibility 承担一份责任

bear... in mind 记住……

a born teacher 一名天生的教师

He was born deaf. 他生下来就是聋的。

He was born poor. 他天生很穷。

Everybody is born with one of these four types of blood. 每个人生来就具有这四种血型其中的一种。

beat

beat his opponent 打败他的对手

beat you at chess 在围棋上赢了你

The rain beat against the window. 雨水有(节奏地)拍打着窗。

My heart beats very fast. 我的心跳得很快。

The sun beat down on my head. 太阳照在我的头上。

bed

go to bed 去睡觉

in David's bed 在戴维的床上

be sick in bed 卧病在床

lie in bed 躺在床上

Sit on my bed 请坐在我床上

make one's bed 铺床

before

before long 不久

It will not be long before he comes back from work. 过不了多久,他就会下班回来。

It was long before they got the flood waters under control. 过了很久,他们才控制住了这场洪水。

It was 3 months before I was seven. 再过3个月,我七岁。

beg

beg us to stay longer 恳求我们多待一些时间

beg sb. for a favour 乞求帮助

beg a favour of sb. 乞求帮助

beg your pardon (没听清楚)请再说一遍

go begging 去乞讨

beginning

at the beginning of this month 在本月初

at the beginning of the journey 在这次旅程开始时

in the beginning of my learning English 在我初学英语时

to begin with 首先;在开始时

begin with... 以……开始

begin with an opening ceremony 以开幕式开始

behave

behave strangely 表现反常

behind

behind bars　在监狱里

fall (lag) behind　落后

stay behind　留下(不走)

belief

　　The rumour is beyond belief.　谣言不可信。

　　To (the best of) my belief，he...　据我看来,他……

believe

　　believe in sb.　信赖某人

　　believe it or not　信不信由你

bell

　　The bell has gone.　铃声响过了。

　　ring one's bell　按铃

belong

　　belong to　属于

　　belong to him　属于他的

below

　　Her hair reached to below her knees.　她的头发到她的膝盖以下了。

　　3 degrees below zero　零下 3 度

　　Read the paragraph below.　请读下一段。

beneath

　　The air is trapped beneath ground.　空气被圈在(气垫船)下面。

　　the earth beneath my feet　我脚下的泥

bench

　　sit on a bench　坐在长凳上

bend

　　bend before(to) his father　先向他父亲屈服

　　He bends his mind to his studies.　他把心思集中在学习上。

benefit

　　benefit sb.　使某人得益

　　The sharing of knowledge should benefit people.　知识的共享使人们得益。

　　Sb. benefits from sth.　某人从某事得到好处。

best

　　make the best of...　尽量利用;(不爱做的事)好好去做

　　at best　至多;再好;说得再好一点

　　All the best!　祝一切好!(临别语)

　　do one's best to do...　尽力做……

better

　　had better do...　最好做……

be better off　较富裕

know better than（to）do sth.　懂得不宜做某事

The more，the better.　越多越好。/多多益善。

beyond

hide the sun and the view of beautiful mountains beyond　遮住了阳光和远方美
丽山脉的景色

wouldn't last beyond a month　用不到一个月（last 持续）

be beyond all praise　夸不胜夸

beyond repair　无法修理

beyond description　无法形容

birth

give birth to a healthy baby　生出一个健康的婴儿

at birth　在出生时

by birth　论出身

bit

not a bit　一点儿也不

bit by bit　一点点地

black

He was black and blue all over.　他全身青一块紫一块。

blame

He is to blame for some of the pollution that exists.　他应为存在的某些污染受
责备。

Hc will be blamed for some of the pollution that exists.　他将为存在的某些污
染受责备。

He blamed me for being late. 他责备我迟到了。

bleed

bleed for...　为……感到难受

blind

He blinded himself in both eyes.　他弄瞎了自己的双眼。

be blind to the fact　对事实视而不见

block

be blocked　被阻塞

High-rise buildings block the sunlight from other buildings.　高层建筑挡住了
其他大楼的阳光。

blood

stop the flow of blood　制止流血

Blood is thicker than water.　血浓于水。

in cold blood　残酷地

He murdered her in cold blood.　他残酷地谋杀了她。

　　make my blood boil　使我很生气

bloom

　　be in bloom　开花

blow

　　blow the candle out　吹灭了蜡烛

　　He always blows his own horn.　他总是自吹自擂。

　　give the enemy a heavy blow　给敌人一次沉重的打击

　　He killed 6 flies at（with）one blow.　他一下子杀死了 6 只苍蝇。

　　blow up　爆炸

　　wind-blown trees　防风林

board

　　notice board　布告牌

　　with all on board　船上所有的人

　　the board meeting　董事会会议

　　It is perfectly above board.　这件事是光明正大的。

boast

　　He always boasts of his achievements.　他总是夸耀自己的成就。

body

　　keep body and soul together　维持生命（生活）

boil

　　boiling hot　滚烫的

　　boiling water　正在沸腾的水

　　cold boiled water　冷开水

　　boil over　煮得溢出来

bone

　　He is all skin and bone.　他瘦得皮包骨头。

book

　　speak like a book　说话文绉绉，咬文嚼字地说

　　All the students must book in.　所有学生都得签到。

　　booking office　售票处

bore

　　be bored with...　对……厌烦

　　get bored sitting here　厌烦地坐在那儿

borrow

　　borrow it from my teacher　从老师那儿借来的

　　by borrowing words from other languages　通过外来语或向别的语言借来的词

bottom

at the bottom of the stairs　在楼梯底部

at the bottom of P. 48　在 48 页下边

at bottom　实际上；内心里

He is a kind man at bottom.　实际上他是个善良的人。

I'll thank you from the bottom of my heart.　我将由衷感谢你。

from top to bottom　从上到下；全部

bound

be bound to succeed　一定会成功

bow

bow to each other　互相鞠躬

break

break away from him　从他那里强行脱离

break away from a bad habit　改掉坏习惯

break down　抛锚(坏了)

make... break down　使……抛锚

break into one's house　闯入某人的家

break soil up　穿破土壤

break out　爆发；突然发生

Fighting broke out.　战争爆发了。

when a fire broke out　当火灾发生时

broke his leg　摔断他的腿

break your words　不遵守你的诺言

breakfast

skip a breakfast　不吃早饭

breath

catch one's breath　因惊恐或激动一时屏住气；歇口气

hold our breath　屏住气

out of breath　上气不接下气

stop to take breath　停下来喘口气

brief

in brief（＝briefly）　简短地；扼要地；总而言之

brilliant

be brilliant at playing the piano　演奏钢琴很出色

bring

bring... together　把……汇集在一起

bring about a crisis　引起(造成)危机

bring it back　把它带回来

bring it out　把它讲清楚；把它拿出来

bring out a book 出版一本书

bring them up 把它们带上来；养育他们

bring a child into the world 生孩子

bring. . . back 使……回想起来

bring. . . into an end 使……结束

broadcast

be broadcast 被广播

browse

browse through books 翻阅书籍

bump

bump into him 撞在他身上

bump into the fence 撞在篱笆上

bunch

give her a bunch of flowers 给他一束花

burden

He was burdened with a big family. 他要负担一大家子。

burn

Don't eat the burnt meat. 别吃烧焦的肉。

be burnt by the sun 被太阳光灼伤

burn one's bridge 下决心；不留后路

burn down the house 烧毁房屋

Exam time is near and he is burning the midnight oil. 考试即将来临，他正在开夜车。

burst

burst into laughter (tears) 放声大笑（哭）

burst out laughing (crying) 突然大笑（哭）

burst with a loud noise 突然发出很响的声音

bury

become buried in the ground 被埋葬在地下

business

in international business 在国际贸易中

It's none of your business. 不关你的事。

busy

be busy at their work 忙于他们的工作

but

But for his help, I wouldn't have finished the task. 要不是他的帮助，我就完不成这任务。

But for her, the book is better. 但是对她来说，这本书更好。

not...but...　不是……而是……

They found not one but ten dead lions.　他们发现的不是一只死狮子，而是十只死狮子。

There was clearly nothing she could do but sit down.　她只能坐下来。

can't help but wait here　我只能在这里等候

can't but wait here　只能在这里等候

can't choose but wait here　只能在这里等候

can't do anything but wait here　只能在这里等候

There is nothing left to do but wait here.　只能在这里等候。

I have no choice but to wait here.　我只能在这里等候。

There is no choice but to wait here.　只能在这里等候。

by

by the time the doctor came　到医生来的时候为止

I'm taller than her by a head.　我比她高一头。

shorten the trousers by 2 inches　把这裤子改短两英寸

by adding two words　通过把两个词合起来的方法

by the week　按周

by the hour　按小时

by the day　按天

by 50%　按 50％的比例

by mistake　错误地

He took my umbrella by mistake.　他错拿了我的伞。

It is seven by my watch.　我的表现在七点了。

by the clothes he wears　按他穿的衣服

The cloth in that shop is sold by the metre.　这家商店的布按米出售。

Tom pulled me by the hand.　汤姆拉住我的手。

You are paid by the hour.　我按小时付给你工资。

Some sorts of fruit are sold by weight; others are not sold by weight.　有几种水果是按重量出售；其他的不按分量出售。

mean by　是(什么)意思；指(谁)

What do you mean by that?　那是什么意思？

What do you mean by coming so late?　那么晚来什么意思？

Whom did he mean by they?　他说的他们是指谁？

C

cake

can't eat one's cake and have it　二者不可兼得

You spend your money on beer and then complain about being poor, but you can't expect to eat your cake and have it. 你既要喝酒又想要不花钱,这是不可能的。

calculate

　　calculate on　预计;指望

　　You can't calculate on earning much money. 你不能指望赚很多钱。

　　greater than she had calculated　超出她的预算

call

　　call an ambulance　打电话叫救护车

　　call for you at nine　九点来接你

　　call for help　要求帮助

　　call him up　打电话给他

　　call him back　给他回电

　　call in a doctor　请个医生来

　　call out　请(叫)出来

　　call (one's) names　骂人

　　call on him　拜访他

　　call at his home　拜访他的家

　　the so-called expert　那个所谓的专家

　　on call　随时可用;随叫随到

　　The nurse is on call tonight. 那个护士今晚随叫随到。

calm

　　calm her　使她镇静下来

　　make her calm　使她镇静下来

campus

　　on the campus　在校园里

can

　　a can of...　一罐……

　　canned food　罐头食品

　　can't help but do...　不能不做;只能做

capable

　　be capable of handling the job　有能力处理这项工作

capital

　　the capital of China　中国的首都

　　working capital　周转资金

　　make capital of...　利用……

car

　　in my car　乘我的轿车

　　get in the car　上了轿车

get out of the car　下了轿车

care

　　care for the future of Europe　关心欧洲的前途

　　care so much for gold　那么喜欢黄金

　　take care of others　关心别人

　　Take care that you don't break it.　当心别打碎了它。

　　take care of herself　她自己照顾自己

　　with great care　仔细地

　　medical care　医疗

careful

　　Be careful　当心!

　　be careful in doing sth.　仔细做某事

　　be careful with that glass　当心那面镜子(玻璃杯)

carelessness

　　carelessness in using it　使用时粗心大意

carry

　　carry on　进行;继续下去

　　How about carrying on our decision tomorrow?　明天继续讨论我们的决定怎
　　　么样?

　　carry out　贯彻;执行;完成

　　carry out your plan　完成你的计划

　　be carried in a separate part of the paper　被刊载在报纸的专栏里

　　carry a section of "features"　刊载了特写栏目

case

　　in that case　若是那样的话

　　in one's case　在某人的情况下

　　in some cases　在某些情况下,有时

　　in most cases　在大多数情况下

　　in no case　决不

　　in case anything happens　万一有事发生

　　In case of fire, pull the alarm.　万一着火,请拉警报器。

cash

　　pay in cash　用现金支付

　　cash the cheque　把这张支票兑换成现金

catch

　　catch John by the arm　抓住约翰的手臂

　　catch John around the neck　勾住约翰的脖子

　　be caught up　被钩住

My coat caught in the door. 我的衣服挂在门上。

My sleeve caught on the corner of... 我的袖子钩在……的角上

catch hold of... 抓住……

catch a bad cold 患重感冒

catch up with others 赶上别人

be caught in the rain 被雨淋

catch fire 着火

Do you catch me? 你听懂我意思了吗?

castle

castles in the air (in Spain) 想入非非;空中楼阁

cause

the cause of the accident 事故的起因

cause your fewest health problems 引起你最少的健康问题

cause Mr. White a lot of trouble 给怀特先生造成很多麻烦

be caused by carelessness 由粗心而引起

centre

in the centre of the city 在市中心

financial centre 金融中心

century

in the early part of this century 在本世纪初

in the nineteenth century 在十九世纪

ceremony

at a special ceremony 在特殊的仪式(典礼)上

Don't stand on ceremony. 别客气了。

certain

a certain scientist 某位科学家

a certain kind of breakfast 某种早饭

for certain (=surely=for sure) 肯定

I am certain (sure) that... 我肯定……

We are very pretty certain to be drowned. 我们肯定会被淹死。

chair

sit down in her tall chair 在她的高椅上坐下

be in the chair 任主席

take the chair 主持会议;担任主席

chance

meet him by chance 意外(偶然)地碰到他

You might take a chance. 你可以碰碰运气。

Chances are that we can save ourselves. 有可能我们能拯救自己。

change

    change to Bus No. 42　换乘 42 路公共汽车

    Languages change with the times.　语言随着时代而变化。

    change 200 American dollars into Japanese money　把 200 美元换成日元

    change it for a new one　把它换成新的

channel

    the English Channel　英吉利海峡

    on Channel 8　在八频道

charge

    free of charge　免费

    in the charge of sb.　由某人负责

    in charge of sth.　负责某事

    He is in charge of the reading-room.　他负责这个阅览室。

    charge sb. with sth.　指控某人……

    The police charged him with breaking the law.　警察指控他犯了法。

    How much do you charge for your medicine?　这药要价多少?

chat

    have a nice chat　进行闲谈

    chat with him　和他聊天

cheap

    on the cheap　便宜地

check

    check up (on) the washing machine for me　为我检查洗衣机

    check-in　检票处

    check in　报到;签到;到达

    check out　结账后离开;把……检查一遍

cheer

    cheer for...　为……欢呼(喝彩)

    cheer to our hearts' desire　尽情欢呼

    cheer him up　使他高兴

chemical

    the chemical industry　化学工业

    chemical fertilizer　化肥

chemistry

    a chemistry teacher　一位化学教师

    a chemistry book　一本化学书

    a chemistry lab　一间化学实验室

chief

chief electrician　总电气师
Chinese
    What is the Chinese for...?　……的汉语是什么？
    Chinese cabbage　白菜
choice
    He has no choice but to lie in bed.　他只能躺在床上。
choose
    his chosen subject　他所选择的学科
    to be chosen as the international language　被选为国际语言
    choose to accept my present　愿意（决定）接受我的礼物
    I cannot choose but wait for him here.　我只能在这里等他。
Christmas
    at Christmas　在圣诞节
    on Christmas day　在圣诞节
circumstance
    under (in) no circumstance　决不
    under (in) the circumstances　在目前情况下
claim
    claim the suitcase　说这只箱子是自己的；认领了这只箱子
    make claims about...　认领了……
class
    in a first class compartment　在头等车厢里
    The class are very clever.　全班同学都很聪明。
clean
    A new broom always sweeps clean.　新官上任三把火。
    do a clean job　干得很出色
    clean up your room　收拾你的房间
    a good cleaning　大扫除
clear
    if it clears up　如果天晴
    clear up　清楚了；晴朗起来；开朗起来；整理，收拾
    Her meaning is clear to everybody.　大家都清楚地知道她的意思。
    make clear　讲清楚；表明
    I have made it clear that I support you.　我已讲清楚我支持你。
clever
    be clever at　擅长于
    be clever with...　擅长使用……
climb

climb down the mountain　爬下山

climb up the mountain　爬上山

close

pay close attention to...　密切注意……

a close game　势均力敌的比赛

be close to the ground　接近地面

close to my place　靠近我的地方

be as close to perfect as possible　尽可能地趋于完美

make it possible for the entire world to be closer than ever before　使整个世界
比以前更密切成为可能

clutter

clutter up the house　把家里弄得乱七八糟

coal

carry (take) coals to Newcastle　班门弄斧

coat

cut one's coat according to one's cloth　量入为出

cold

cold wave　寒潮

cold storage　冷藏

have (get) cold feet　畏缩不前

make his blood run cold　使他吓得要命

pour (throw) cold water on...　给……泼冷水

in cold blood　冷酷无情地

coffee

black coffee　清咖啡

a coffee (＝a cup of coffee)　一杯咖啡

collect

collect butterflies　收集蝴蝶

volunteer to collect food　志愿募集食物

collect taxes　征税

colour

My tie is red in colour.　我的领带颜色是红的。

be in full colour　深浓的颜色

be televised in colour　用彩色电视播放

Her face had lost its color.　她的脸色惨白。

under the colour of...　在……的借口下

with flying colours　出色地；成绩优异地

colour TV　彩色电视机

coloured coats　有颜色的衣服

colourful coats　颜色鲜艳的衣服

combine

　combine. . . with. . .　把……和……结合（合并）起来

　It combines with carbon dioxide in the air.　它在空气中与二氧化碳结合。

come

　come across an unknown word　偶尔碰到不认识的词

　come about　发生；造成

　How did this thing come about?　这件事是怎么发生的？

　He came at the enemy.　他向敌人扑去。

　come clean　坦白交代

　come down from. . .　从……传下来

　A thick fog has come down.　一阵浓雾降下来了。

　The price of meat has come down this week.　本周肉价已降下来了。

　come from. . .　来自……

　come from all over the city　来自全城

　Most of our energy comes from the sun's rays.　我们大多数能量来自太阳光。

　come into existence　形成

　come into being　形成

　come into use　付用，开始采用

　come into effect　开始生效

　come into power　开始执政

　Come on!　赶快！过来！

　come out　出来；出版；开花

　come out first　得第一

　come out of a side road　从小马路上出来

　He comes of a peasant's family.　他出生于一个农民家庭。

　come to anything difficult　遇上困难

　Don't stop every time you come to a new word.　每次遇到生词时不要停下来。

　come to life　恢复了生机；活跃起来

　He began to come to his life.　他苏醒了。

　come to one's sense　神志恢复正常

　come to the point　谈正题

　come to love him　渐渐爱上他

　That comes to 2 yuan.（＝That'll be 2 yuan.）　共两元。

　come to a. . . end　有……结局（结果，下场）

　come running to help　跑过来帮忙

　His dream has come true.　他的梦想已实现了（变成现实）。

374

come up 走过来

come up 上来;发芽;被拒绝

come up with... 赶上……

come up from behind the bush 从那棵灌木后面伸出头来

on the coming Saturday 本周六

command

at my command 我已掌握了

have a good command of... 掌握;控制

comment

comment on (upon) sth. 评论某事

commit

commit himself to doing... 致力于;献身于

common

common knowledge 人所共知的事;共识

They have a lot in common. 他们有很多共同之处。

out of the common 异乎寻常,不平常

communicate

communicate with sb. 与某人交际

communicate...sth. to sb. 把……传递给某人

company

keep sb. company 给某人做伴

keep company with him 陪伴着他

compare

compare A with B 把"A"和"B"相比较

Let's compare Shanghai with New York. 我们把上海和纽约相比较。

compare A to B 把 A 比作 B;把"A"和"B"相比较

People often compare Shanghai to a paradise. 人们常把上海比作天堂。

Compared with John's, your composition is not good. 与约翰的作文相比较,
  你的不好。

after comparing notes 交换意见以后

comparison

beyond comparison 无可比拟地

by comparison 比较起来

This computer is cheaper by comparison. 比较起来这台电脑更便宜。

in comparison with... 和……比较起来

There is no comparison between the two coats. 这两件衣服没有可比性。

compete

compete with (against)... 和……竞争(竞赛)

375

compete for... 为……而竞争

competition

    gymnasium competitions 场馆比赛

    riding competitions 骑马比赛

    He is in competition with 10 others. 他和其他十个人比赛。

complain

    make complaints 进行投诉

    complain about sth. to sb. 向某人投诉某事

    complain about (of) the amount of homework and everybody did. 埋怨回家作业的总量,并且人人埋怨。

    He is complaining to me about it. 他正在向我投诉这件事。

compose

    be composed of... (＝be made up of...＝consist of...＝contain...) 由……组成

    On the other hand，white is composed of the entire spectrum of colour. 另一方面,白色是由所有色彩的光谱组成的。

composition

    a composition for the guitar 吉他的曲子

    fill my teeth with some composition 用某种化合物补牙

conceal

    conceal sth. from sb. 对某人守……秘密

concentrate

    concentrate on (upon)... 集中思想在……上

    concentrate on (upon) their lessons for a longer period of time 专心于他们的功课较长的时间

    concentrate on some masterpieces 把精力集中在一些杰作上

concern

    be concerned about... 为……而担忧

    be concerned for (over)... 对……关心

    be concerned with 与……有关

    so (as) far as... be concerned 就……来说;就……而论

    It is impossible so (as) far as we are concerned. 就我们来说,这件事是不可能的。

conclusion

    form their own conclusion 得出他们自己的结论

    draw their own conclusion 得出他们自己的结论

    come to their own conclusion 得出他们自己的结论

    arrive at their own conclusion 得出他们自己的结论

    reach their own conclusion 得出他们自己的结论

in conclusion 最后

condition

in condition 身体很好

out of condition 身体不适

in good condition 安好无损地

Everything arrived in good condition. 每样东西都安好无损地到达。

under all kinds of conditions 在各种条件下

on no condition 决不;绝对不要

on condition that he came 如果他来

confidence

in confidence 推心置腹地

with confidence 满怀信心地

take me into your confidence 对我说出你的心里话

confident

We are confident of success. 我们对成功充满信心。

congratulate

Let me congratulate you on your success. 让我祝你成功。

rush forward to congratulate the pilot on a perfect landing 冲向前去祝贺那位
飞行员作了一次完美的着陆

congratulation

Congratulations on your success. 祝你成功。

connect

connect... with... 把……和……联系起来

be connected with... 与……有关系

conscience

have a guilty conscience 感到内疚

have a clear conscience 无愧于心

conscious

be conscious of... 觉察到……

consequence

as a consequence 结果

as a consequence of... 由于……的结果

in consequence 结果

consideration

take... into consideration 把……考虑进去

consider

consider going... 考虑去……

consider changing his mind 考虑改变他的主意

consider breakfast（as/to be）the most important meal　把早餐看作是最重要的一餐饭

considering the weather　考虑到天气（considering 是介词）

consideration

　　be under consideration　在考虑中

　　in consideration of...　考虑到……；由于……

　　on no consideration　决不

　　take...into consideration　把……考虑进去；考虑到……

considerate

　　be thoughtful and considerate　考虑周到、体贴他人的

　　It was considerate of you to do sth.　你做某事是体贴人的；谢谢你做某事

consist

　　consist of saying poetry aloud or giving speeches　由朗诵诗篇和演讲组成

　　consist of different families　由不同的鸟科（家庭）组成

　　consist mainly of a high plateau　主要由高原组成（无被动）

construction

　　under construction　在修建中

consult

　　consult with...　和……协商

contact

　　contact him　与他接触

　　make contact with him　与他接触

　　contact lenses　隐形眼镜

　　contact officer　联络军官

contain

　　How much water does this bottle contain?　这瓶子装有多少水？

　　contain his tears　忍住眼泪

　　contain the enemy attack　遏制敌人攻击

container

　　container ship　集装箱运货船

content

　　to one's heart's content　尽情地

　　He contents himself to dry bread.　他对干面包感到满足。

contest

　　attend the speech contest　参加演讲比赛

　　a composition contest　作文比赛

　　contest against him　和他对抗（比赛）

continue

continue into the future　持续到将来

continue with their work　继续干他们的工作……

continue to use a loose plug on a cleaner　继续使用插头松的吸尘器

contrary

on the contrary　相反地

His opinion is contrary to mine.　他的观点与我的观点相反。

to the contrary　相反的

Is there any evidence to the contrary?　有相反的证据吗?

contrast

by contrast　对比之下

in contrast with（to）our old house　与我们的旧房相比

contribute

contribute to a new law　对新的法律起了一份作用；有助于新法律

control

have some control over...　控制……

have the fire under control　使这场火灾得到控制

have（hold，gain，take）control of...　控制住……

beyond control　控制不了

out of control　失控

convenience

at one's convenience　在某人最方便的时候

convenient

be convenient to sb.　对某人方便

if（it is）convenient to you　如果你方便的话

conversation

in conversation with...　在和……谈话

get into conversation with...　和……攀谈

cooperate

cooperate with...　和……合作

corner

in one corner　在一个角落里

in the northwest corner　在西北角

in the corner of the room　在房间的角落里

at/on the corner of the street　在马路的拐角处

at the corner of the street　在马路的拐角处

on the corner of the table　在桌子角上

drive（put/force）me into the corner　使我陷入困境

She has turned the corner.　她病情已好转了。

cooker

a new kind of cooker 一种新的炊具

cost

at a low cost 以最低的成本

The gold watch chain cost her 21 dollars. 这根金表链花了她 21 美元。

cost him his life 使他失去生命

at a (the) cost of... 以……为代价

at all costs (at any cost) 不惜一切代价

count

Every minute counts. 每一分钟都是重要的(有价值的;起作用的)。

count... as... 把……算作是……

Count off, please. 请报数。

counter

check-out counter 付款台

country

in the country outside Rome 在罗马郊外

couple

miss a couple of hours of sleep 少睡两三个小时

a couple of... (少数)几个;一两个,一对(夫妇)

a couple of rabbits 一对兔子

The couple are young. 这对夫妇很年轻。

course

during the course of... 在……期间

in the course of... 在……期间

in the course of their reading 在他们阅读过程中

of course 当然,自然

as a matter of course 自然地;理所当然的事

court

on a small court 在一块小的球场上

hold court 开庭

take sb. to court 对某人起诉(控告)

cover

The band was under cover. 乐队在遮篷下。

cover... with... 用……盖住……

be covered with... 被盖上了……

cover the cost of living 够付生活费

cover losses from such accidents as car and plane crashes 涉及诸如汽车、飞机坠毁等事故的损失

It covers 71 percent of the earth. 它占有地球的百分之七十一。

The Central Zone covers the plains area. 中时区包括平原地区。

cram

 cram for an examination 临时应付考试;临时抱佛脚

crash

 A plane crashed last night. 昨晚一架飞机坠毁了。

 The car crashed into a lamp post. 那辆轿车撞在路灯柱子上了。

crazy

 be crazy about... 热衷于;对……喜欢得要命

 work like crazy 拼命地工作

credit

 to buy a car on credit 赊购一辆轿车

 buy by credit card 用信用卡购买

crime

 in crime of violence 在暴力罪行中

cross

 make a cross 画个大叉

 cross the street 横穿马路

 cross at the zebra crossing 过斑马线

crowd

 very crowded 很拥挤

 be crowded with... 挤满了……

 The hall is crowded with people. 礼堂里挤满了人。

 in a crowded bus 在拥挤的公共汽车里

 a small crowd of people 一小群人

cruel

 be cruel to people 对人们很残忍

cry

 cry down 贬低

 cry for 哭嚷着要求

 cry for the moon 要求不能得到的东西;想入非非

 cry out against... 大声疾呼地反对……

 a cry of surprise 一阵惊叫声

 cry over 为……哭泣;哀叹

 Don't cry over spilt milk. 不要为打翻的牛奶哭泣。

 cry up 夸耀,吹捧

 a far cry from... 和……大不相同;相距很远

 This car is a far cry from that one. 这辆车和那辆大不相同。

cue

　　cues for. . .　对……的提示

cucumber

　　He is always cool as a cucumber.　他总是非常冷静。

cup

　　a cup of coffee（＝a coffee）　一杯咖啡

cure

　　cure him of his illness　治好他的病

curious

　　be curious about. . .　对……好奇

cut

　　cut at his enemy　向敌人砍去

　　cut across the yard　穿过院子

　　cut away a tumor　切除肿瘤

　　cut back expenses　减少开支

　　cut down its trees　砍倒树木

　　Tom cut in,"…"　汤姆插进来说"……"

　　cut off　切断,割掉,截断(退路等)

　　cut the hair off　把头发剪掉了

　　have a bad cut on his head　头上有个严重的裂口

　　cut through rock　炸穿(切割)岩石

　　take a short cut　走捷径

　　cut through the playground　穿过操场

D

daily

　　most daily English language newspapers　大多数英语日报

　　China Daily　中国日报

　　He came here daily.　他每天都来这里。

dam

　　dam that river　在那条河上筑坝

　　dam up your anger　克制(抑制)你的怒火

damage

　　do sb. damage（＝do damage to sb.）　对某人身体有损害

danger

　　be out of danger　脱险

　　in danger (of). . .　处于(……的)危险

　　in danger from water　遇上灭顶之灾

dare

   I dare say   可能，或许，我猜测

   I dare say he will come.   可能他会来。

dark

   in the dark   在黑暗里

   keep (leave) him in the dark   使他蒙在鼓里

   You must keep this dark.   你必须保密。

dash

   dash into the room   冲入房间

   dash out of the room   冲出房间

   dash after the dog   猛追那条狗

   dash the chair against the door   用椅子猛砸门

   dash water over him   用水浇他

date

   out of date   过时

   up-to-date   跟上时代的

   have a date for...   有个……约会

   up to date   到目前为止

   date back to the 12th century   追溯到十二世纪

   The castle dates from the 12th century.   这座城堡在十二世纪就已存在了。

dawn

   at dawn   黎明时分

   The day is dawning.   天渐渐亮了。

day

   day and night   日日夜夜

   all day long   整天

   day after day   日复一日

   day by day   日复一日

   have one's day   有得意的时候

   Every dog has its day.   凡人皆有得意时。

   one day   从前或将来某一天

   some day   将来某一天

   the other day   前几天

   the day after tomorrow   后天

   the day before yesterday   前天

   to this day   直到今天

   a person in the news of the day   当代的新闻人物

   on International Labor Day   在五一国际劳动节

daytime

    in the daytime　在白天

dead

    half dead　精疲力竭

    I laid him down dead.　我把他放下，他死了。

    dead center　正中心

    The arrow hit at the dead center.　那支箭射中正中心。

deal

    a great deal of...　大量的……（＋不可数名词）

    deal with the job interview　对付这次求职面试

    What subject does it deal with?　它涉及什么题材？

    how to deal with it　怎样处理它

dear

    The oranges are very dear.　这些橘子很贵的。

    Dear me!　我的天哪！

death

    be squashed to death　被挤死了

    He was sentenced to death.　他被判处死刑。

    to the death　一直到死

debt

    be in debt　负债；受某人的好处或恩惠

    get out of debt　不再负债

    pay off his debt　还清债务

    get（run）into debt　开始负债

decide

    decide on（upon）every step　决定每一步

    decide against the plan　决定不执行这个计划

decision

    make a decision about.../as to...　做出关于……的决定

    make a decision of this problem　对这个问题做出决定

    come to such a decision　做出这么一个决定

deck

    on deck　在眼前；即将来到

declare

    Have you anything to declare?　你有什么要申报？

decline

    decline an offer of help　谢绝提供帮助

    His health is declining.　他的健康日渐衰退。

on the decline　在衰退中

dedicate

dedicate his life to the cause of science　把他的一生献身于科学事业

be dedicated to doing sth.　献身于做……;作……之用

deed

in deed　在行动上

defeat

defeat his purpose　达不到他的目的

defeat them　打败他们,赢他们

take defeat well　败不馁,坦然接受失败

defend

defend the goal　守门

defend women and children from...　保护妇女和儿童免受……

definite

with a definite purpose in mind　思想上有明确的目标

degree

The temperature rose by 5 degrees.　温度上升了五度。

by degrees　渐渐地,一点一点地

in a certain degree　在某种程度上

to a certain degree　到某种程度,在某种程度上

delay

without delay　毫不拖延地;立即

delight

be delighted to do sth.　因做某事很高兴

take delight in doing...　喜欢干……;从……中取乐

To my delight, he will...　使我高兴的是,他将……

depend

depend on (upon)　依靠;依赖;取决于

depend on us for a home and for food　依靠我们得到安身之处和食物

depend on it　请相信;没问题

Depend on it, I will win the game.　请相信,我会赢取这场比赛的。

It all depends.　得看情况而定。这很难说。

deposit

pay a deposit on the house　付房屋定金

deposit his money in the bank　把钱存在银行里

be deposited in a unfavorable environment　(被)落在不利的环境里

depth

the depth of colour　颜色的浓度

The well is not deep in depth.　这口井不深。

describe

He described himself as a doctor.　他自称是医生。

be described as the worst　被讲成最坏的

description

beyond description　无法形容

deserve

deserving of...　应受到；值得

This is a problem deserving of study.　这是个值得研究的问题。

They were never deserving of trust.　他们从未受到信任。

design

be designed for...　为……而设计

by design　有意地

Did you do it by design or by accident?　做这件事你是有意的还是无意的？

have designs on you　对你别有用心

desire

desire to do sth.　渴望做某事

have desire to do...　希望做……

desk

sit at a desk　坐在写字台旁（办公）

despair

cry in despair　绝望地哭了

determine

be determined to do...　决定做……

detail

in detail　详细地

develop

develop one's physical skills　培养一个人的身体技巧

develop films　冲洗胶卷

development

be under development　在发展中

devote

devote one's life to...　献身于；把……用在……

devote time and care to the service of others　奉献时间和爱心，为别人服务

devote all his time to his new system　把他的时间都用在新系统上

a devoted friend　一个忠实的朋友

He is devoted to his teaching.　他献身于教书事业。

diamond

diamond wedding　钻石婚(结婚六十周年)

die

　　die from the effects of acid rain　死于酸雨的影响

　　die of…　因患……而死

　　die out　绝种,熄灭;消灭

　　die down　平息;静下来

　　die for a cup of coffee　迫切想要杯咖啡

　　be slowly dying　将慢慢地死去

　　The old year is slowly dying.　旧的一年正在慢慢地逝去。

　　Her only pay was in smile from the lips of dying soldiers.　她的唯一报酬是来
　　　　自将死的士兵嘴唇上的微笑。

diet

　　if you are on a diet　假如你在节食的话

　　go on a diet　节食

differ

　　He differed from (with) me.　他跟我不同。

difference

　　tell the difference between A and B　区别 A 与 B 之间的不同

　　make no difference　没关系

different

　　be different from…　不同于……

　　be different from any other language　不同于其他语言

　　Tom is different from what he was 10 years ago.　汤姆不同于十年前。

difficulty

　　get (run) into difficulty　陷入困境;遇到困难

　　in a difficulty (in difficulties)　处境困难;经济困难

　　out of a difficulty　摆脱困难;脱离困难

　　with difficulty　困难地;费事地;吃力地

　　have difficulty in sleeping　睡眠有困难

　　without any difficulty　毫不费力地

dip

　　have (take) a dip　洗一会儿澡;游一会儿泳

　　dip into them　浏览它们

　　dip into these books　浏览这些书

direction

　　in the direction to (of/for) London　向伦敦方向(去)

　　three lanes in each direction　每个方向三车道

　　He went back in the direction from which he had come.　他朝来的方向走回去。

follow the directions on the bottle 按瓶上的说明办

disagree

　　disagree with sb. about... 与某人关于……意见不一致

disappointment

　　to his disappointment 使他失望的是

disapprove

　　disapprove of his plan 不赞成他的计划

discuss

　　Let's discuss the matter with... 让我们和……一起讨论这件事

discussion

　　under discussion 正在讨论

dislike

　　have a dislike of (for)... 不喜欢……

dismiss

　　The students were dismissed at 11:30. 学生 11 点半下课。

　　He was dismissed yesterday. 他昨天被解雇了。

　　He dismissed my suggestion. 他不考虑我的建议。

display

　　be on display 陈列;展出

distance

　　at a distance 隔开一段距离

　　at some distance 隔开一些距离

　　in the distance 在远方

　　It's no distance at all. 一点也不远。

distinguish

　　a most distinguished scientist 一位非常卓越的科学家

　　distinguish the difference between A and B 区别 A 与 B 之间的不同

　　be distinguished for 以……闻名

　　The Curies are distinguished for... 居里夫妇以……闻名

disturb

　　Don't disturb the other readers. 别打扰其他的读者。

divide

　　be divided into... 被分成……

　　be divided into two equal parts 被分成两个相等的部分

　　divide the information into parts 把信息分成几个部分

　　The country is divided into 4 time zones. 这个国家被分成 4 个时区。

　　be divided in half 被分成两半

　　be divided into halves 被分成两半

do

    do well in sth.　把某事做好

    I don't think that'll do.　我认为那是不够的(不行的)。

    do away with pollution　消除污染

    do nothing but work hard　只能努力工作

    what to do with him　怎样对付他/怎样与他相处

    what to do with the old newspapers　怎样处理这些旧报纸

    What have you done with the bottle?　你动过那瓶子吗?

    do for...　使……完蛋;使失败;使不行

    do more good to...　对……更有好处

    do more harm to...　对……更有害处

    The heavy rain did for our crops.　那场大雨把我们的庄稼毁掉了。

    do up　整理;修理;打扮

    She is doing up her hair.　她在整理头发。

dog

    dog days　一年中最热的日子,三伏天

    a dog-eared book　卷了角的书

door

    answer the door　给敲门的人去开门

    from door to door　挨家挨户

    next door　隔壁

    open the door to finding a good job　为找到份好工作创造条件

doorstep

    on the doorstep　在门口的台阶上

double

    double your reading speed　成倍提高你的阅读速度

    double up　使身子弯曲

    cause a diver to double up in pain　使潜水员疼得身子弯曲

    at the double　快步走

doubt

    doubt of his success　对他的成功表示怀疑

    beyond all doubt　毫无疑问

    be in doubt about...　怀疑……

    There is no doubt that we all need to sleep.　无疑我们都需要睡觉。

    There is no doubt that...　毫无疑问……

    No doubt it also is gold.　无疑它也是黄金。

    throw doubt on sb.　对某人怀疑

    I doubt that...　对……我表示怀疑。

down

    walk down the road to the well　沿着通向那口井的路散步

    down the river　沿着那条河

    come down that bridge　沿着那座桥来

    be down with a cold　因感冒病倒了

    Down fell that pile of lovely brown hair.　一长股褐色的美发垂了下来。（倒装句）

    down with…　打倒……

    let you down　让你失望；辜负你的期望

    get down to work　认真开始工作（学习）

    up and down　来回地

    upside down　颠倒过来

    write (take) down　写下来；记下来

dozen

    dozens of eggs　几十个鸡蛋

drag

    drag myself out of bed　起床

    drag myself around　慢吞吞地

drain

    be a great drain on electrical power　大量消耗电力

draw

    draw him down under the water　把他拉到水下去

    draw away in terror　惊骇地缩了回去

    draw level with her opponent　与对方打成平局

    draw near　临近

    draw his sword　拔出剑

    Draw me a line.　请给我写封短信。

    draw up a map　制定，草拟一幅地图

dream

    dream of　梦想；渴望

    dream of letting you do that　渴望着让你做那件事

dress

    dress you up　把你打扮得漂漂亮亮

    dress him down　责备他

    He was dressed in a tight racing parka.　他穿着紧身的派克式赛衣。

    He was very well-dressed.　他穿着很讲究。

drink

    Let me drink to your success.　让我举杯祝贺你的成功。

    drink tea with milk and sugar　喝甜奶茶

drink up all the water　喝完所有的水

drinking water　食用水

drive

　drive through... and you will see...　如果你驾车通过……你将会看见……

　be driven out of business　被驱赶出商界

　drive me crazy/mad　使我受不了;使我发疯

drop

　drop his tin of food for fish into the river　把一听鱼食扔到河里

　drop a bag on the ground　把一只包掉在地上

　Jim dropped down on the old couch.　吉姆倒在旧的长沙发上。

　drop in on him　顺便拜访他

　drop in at his house　顺便拜访他的家

　drop out of high school　高中退学

drown

　a drowning boy　一个将淹死的男孩

　The waves drowned out his words.　波浪声淹没了他的话。

dry

　The well has dried up.　这口井已干涸。

　dry one's eyes　拭干眼泪

　dry clothes in front of unguarded fires　在没有防护措施的火炉前烘烤衣服

due

　due to　由于(作表语);归功于

duel

　in a duel　在决斗中

during

　during the night of November 29　在 11 月 29 日夜里

　during the spring of 1973　在 1973 年的春天

Dutch

　go Dutch　各付各的钱;AA 制

E

each

　each other　互相

　each and every man　每个人(强调)

eager

　be eager for a car　渴望一辆轿车

　be eager to buy a car　渴望买一辆轿车

eagerness

in their eagerness to do sth.　为了急于做某事
ear
　　turn a deaf ear to...　不理睬……
　　We are all ears.　我们都在仔细听。
　　box your ear　打耳光
　　by ear　凭记忆
　　go in one ear and out the other　左耳进右耳出;只当耳边风
early
　　as mentioned early　正如前面提到的
　　as early as the 16th century　早在十六世纪
　　keep early hours　早睡早起
　　The early bird catches the worm.　捷足先登。
ease
　　with ease　容易地
　　put (set) me at ease　使我不拘束
　　stand at ease　稍息
easy
　　take it easy　不要紧张,放松一些,慢一点
eat
　　Acid can eat metals.　酸能腐蚀金属。
　　eat one's words　食言
　　eat out　在外面吃饭
　　eat up　吃光;吃完
　　man-eating fish　吃人的鱼
economy
　　in economies　在经济上
　　Economy is a good thing.　节省是件好事。
edge
　　at the edge of...　在……边缘
　　on the edge of the table　在桌子的边上
　　have an edge on...　比……略胜一筹,比……强
　　on edge　兴奋,紧张,不耐烦
　　We are all on edge.　我们都很兴奋。
education
　　senior high school education　高中教育
　　an education　一种教育;一段时间的教育
effect
　　have a great effect on...　对……有很大的影响

has the effect of lifting up the vehicles　产生了把气垫船升起的作用

have a great effect on science　对科学有很大影响

The rule is in effect tonight.　这条规则今晚生效。

put（bring，carry）... into effect　使……生效

The law will take effect tomorrow.　这条法律明天生效。

produce an effect upon...　对……产生作用

effort

　make（an）effort　做出努力

　with（an）effort　费力地

　without effort　毫不费力地

　spare no effort to do...　不遗余力做……

egg

　He will put all his eggs in one basket.　他将孤注一掷。

　teach one's grandmother to suck eggs　班门弄斧

elderly

　aid the elderly and the disabled　帮助年老的和丧失劳动力的人

elimination

　have an elimination match　进行淘汰赛

else

　No one else in my family has...　我家里没有别的人……

emphasis

　place great emphasis on...　着重……

empty

　empty into the Atlantic Ocean through the St. Lawrence River　通过圣劳伦斯
　　河流入大西洋

enable

　enable... to survive under difficult condition　使……在困难的条件下生存下来

end

　at the end of...　在……结尾

　in the end　最后

　come to an end　结束

　right at the other end of the aeroplane　就在飞机的另一端

　at the end of the court　在球场的一端（尽头）

　end in failure　以失败告终

　end up inside the lion　结果被狮子吃了

　end up gaining weight instead of losing　结果体重没减轻，反而增加了

energy

　play with all his energy　用全幅精力进行比赛

engage

    be engaged to sb. 和某人订婚

    be engaged in doing sth. 忙于做某事

English

    a knowledge of English 一门英语

    spoken English 英语口语

    written English 书面英语

    The English have a wonderful sense of humor. 英国人富有幽默感。

    in English 用英语

enjoy

    enjoy such songs as this one 喜欢像这首歌一样的歌

    enjoy oneself 过(玩)得很好

    enjoy letters with news from home 欣赏着带有家乡消息的来信

    enjoy oneself at the picnic 野餐时玩得很开心

enlarge

    enlarge on (upon)... 详细论述……

enough

    They are more than enough for this kind woman. 他们对于这位善良的女人来说,已是足够了。

    Ten dollars is enough and to spare. 十美元绰绰有余。

    more than enough 很多

enquire

    enquire after you 向你问好

    enquire for him 问他在哪里;找他

enroll

    be enrolled at the college 被录取到这所学院

ensure

    I ensure that you are wrong. 我保证你错了。

    ensure you good results 使你一定得到好成绩

enter

    enter for... 报名参加……

    I entered him for the exam. 我叫他报名参加考试。

    He was entered for the exam. 他报名参加考试。

    enter into... 开始(谈话,讨论等);缔结(契约,婚约等)

entertain

    entertain us with singing, dancing and acting 向我们提供唱歌、跳舞和表演

entertainment

    have English performance for entertainment 为英语节目助兴

enthusiasm

   with enthusiasm　热情地

entitle

   entitle you to travel　使你有权得到旅游

   be entitled to try again　有权再试一次

entrance

   the entrance to the hall　礼堂的入口处

   at the entrance to an office　在办公室的入口处

   the college entrance examination　大学入学考试/高考

environment

   in the environment　在周围的环境里

equal

   be equal to...　等于,和……相等;能胜任;能应付

   I'm not equal to the position.　我不能胜任这个职务。

equip

   be equipped with...　用……装备

   be equipped to do sth.　配备就绪做某事

equipment

   faulty electrical equipment　（不可数)有毛病的电器设备

error

   by trial and error　通过不断的摸索(反复试验)

   be in error　错了

   fall into error　犯错误

   lead sb. into error　使某人犯错误

escape

   escape from the enemy's prison　从敌人的监狱里逃跑

   escape from his mind　记不起来了

   escape being punished　逃避惩罚

essential

   be essential to...　对……是必不可少的

   Food is essential to life.　食物对生命来说是必不可少的。

estimate

   estimate...at...　估计……为……

   I estimate her age at thirty.　我估计她的年龄为三十岁。

   estimate for...　为……进行估价(估计费用)

   estimate for the repair of the building　为大楼的修理费用进行估价

   at a rough estimate　据大致估计

eve

on New Year's Eve　在元旦前夜

on the eve of the wedding　在婚礼前夕

even

even worse than they had expected　比他们预料的糟糕得多

even though　即使

even if　即使

even then（now）　尽管这样,即使在这样的情况下

even so　尽管如此,尽管这样

even as　正当……的时候

even number　偶数

evening

Let's have an English evening.　让我们举行一次英语晚会。

at an English Evening　在英语晚会上

in the evening　在傍晚

event

team events　团体项目

in any（all）event(s)　尽管如此,不管怎样

in that event　如果那样

in the event（that）+（从句）　如果……

in the event of fire　万一着火

ever

Why ever not?　究竟为什么不……?

Who ever?　究竟谁?

Which ever?　究竟哪一个?

for ever　永远地

every

every other day　每隔一天

every second day　每隔一天,每个第二天

every two days　每隔一天,每两天

every other week　每隔一周

once every four years　每四年(每隔三年)一次

every time he goes...　每当他去……

in every way　在多方面

evidence

in evidence　明显,显而易见

The effects of the war are in evidence.　战争的影响是很明显的。

examination

take the final examinations　参加期终考试

do the examination to the best of our ability　进行最佳能力的考试

have a medical examination　进行体格检查

be under examination　在审问中

example

　e. g.　例如

　set a good example to us　给我们树立一个好榜样

　for example　例如

　take my sister for example　以我姐姐为例

　make an example of the boy　处罚这孩子以警诫别人

　education by example　以身作则

　Education by example is more important than speeches.　以身作则比语言更重要。

except

　except the south　除了南部地区外

　powerless to do anything except wait　除了耐心等待外,无能为力做任何事情,
　　只能等待

exception

　with the exception of me　除去我

　without exception　毫无例外

　take exception to...　对……生气

　take exception to what you said　对你的话很生气

exchange

　exchange... for...　把……换成……

　I'll exchange my dollars for pounds.　我将把美元兑换成英镑。

　exchange a few words　交谈几句

　in exchange　作为交换

　He gave me a book and I gave him a pen in exchange.　他给我本书,而我给他支
　　钢笔作为交换。

excuse

　excuse... for...　原谅

　excuse me for my being late.　请原谅我的迟到。

　Excuse from...　使免于……,允许不……

　I've excused him from housework for this evening.　我已允许他今晚不做家务。

　He excused himself by doing...　他通过……为自己开脱。

　be excused to do sth.　准许离开做……

experiment

　make (do) their experiment　做他们的实验

exhaust

　I am exhausted.　我累极了。

exhibition

　　on exhibition　展览

　　make an exhibition of oneself　出洋相

　　Yesterday I made an exhibition of myself.　昨天我出了个洋相。

existence

　　be in existence　存在

　　come into existence　开始存在;形成了

expect

　　expect me for supper at six o'clock sharp　期待我六点整吃晚饭

　　expect...of sb.　期待某人……

　　Don't expect too much of me.　请别对我抱太大期望。

expectation

　　beyond expectation　出乎意料

　　contrary to expectation　和预料相反

　　come up to one's expectation　达到期望(的水平)

expense

　　spare no expense to do...　不惜一切代价做某事;不遗余力做某事

expose

　　expose me to a new kind of vocabulary　使我接触新的词汇

　　be exposed to the sun　接触太阳光

express

　　He can express himself.　他能表达清楚自己的意思。

expression

　　beyond expression　无法形容

　　without expression　毫无表情

eye

　　catch my eye　引起我的注意

　　close one's eyes to...　不理会某人或某物,视而不见某人或某物

　　give an eye to...　照看,照顾

　　have an eye on...　密切注意……

　　in my eyes　在我眼里,在我看来

　　keep an eye on...　照看,对……注意

　　turn a blind eye to...　对……视而不见

F

face

　　face the fact　面对事实

　　face even more dangers and problems　面临着更多的危险和问题

face with floods and starvation　面临着洪水和饥荒

slap sb's face　打某人的耳光

make (a) face(s)　做鬼脸

stand face to face　面对面站着

have the face to do so　竟敢这么做

in (the) face of danger　面对着危险

look him in the face　正面看着他

lose (one's) face　丢面子

on the face of it　表面看来

pull (wear) a long face　板着脸

in (to) his face　当着他的面

Face about!　向后转!

face out his objection　顶住他的反对

face to the south　面向南面

fact

in fact　实际上;事实上

as a matter of fact　实际上;不瞒你说

fail

He will come without fail.　他肯定(一定)来。

fail to do so　没这么做

fail to get the job　没得到这份工作

began to fail　开始变弱了

Words failed me.　我无法用语言表达。

fair

fair play　公平的比赛;光明磊落

The visiting team did not get fair play in the match.　客队在比赛中不公道。

fair to cloudy　晴转多云

fairly

a fairly clear picture of...　一幅关于……的十分清楚的图片

faith

in good faith　真诚地,信赖地

keep faith with them　对他们守信

break faith with them　对他们不守信

fall

fall behind　落在后面

fall down　跌倒,垮下来

fall one's feet　很幸运,顺利(克服困难)

They always fall on their feet.　他们总是很幸运。

fall on one's knees　跪下

fall to pieces　垮台；解体，倒塌

when the empire fell to pieces　当这个帝国瓦解时

fall in love with her　爱上了她

fall into the water　掉到水里

fall on me　落在我身上

fall to the floor　倒向地上

fall onto the road　落在路上

fall into deep sadness　陷入悲伤

It fell around her like a cloak.　它像外衣一样披在她身体四周。

fall out of his pocket　从他的口袋里掉出来

fall over her　倒在她身上

familiar

His name is familiar to us.　我们很熟悉他的名字。

We are familiar with his name.　我们很熟悉他的名字。

get familiar with the following names　对下列名字很熟悉

famous

be famous for...　以……闻名

far

be far more advanced than...　比……先进得多

be far away from...　离……很远

as (so) far as I can remember　就我所能记得的

so far as I know　据我所知

so far　至今（用现在完成时）

so far from...　不仅没有……相反……

so far from taking my advice　不仅没有接受我的意见，相反……

by far the best　（三者或三者以上）更好的

by far the better　（两者中）最好的

far and near　到处

go far　有出息；起很大作用

farewell

have a farewell party　开个告别会

farm

live on a little farm　生活在小农场里

live on a farm far from any city　住在离城市很远的农场里

fashion

be in (follow) the fashion　赶时髦，随大流

be (go) out of fashion　过时

faulty

　　a faulty wire　一根有毛病的电线

favour

　　Do me a favour, please.　请帮个忙。

　　do a favour for sb.　帮助某人

　　do me the favour to fetch some water　帮忙取些水来

　　be in favour of...　同意……，赞成……

　　do me the favour to carry the box　请帮我拿这只箱子

　　in his favour　对他有利

　　ask sb. for a favour　求人帮个忙

　　ask a favour of sb.　求人帮个忙

favourite

　　What's your favourite sport?　你最喜欢的运动是什么?

fear

　　I fear that...（＝I'm afraid that...）　恐怕……

　　fear for me　为我担忧

　　in fear　害怕地，惊恐地

　　throw out his arms in fear　害怕得伸出他的手臂

feed

　　feed the chickens　喂小鸡

　　feed on...　靠吃……维持生命，用……喂养

　　feed on the crops　以庄稼为主食

feel

　　feel lonely　感到孤独

　　feel nervous　感到紧张

　　feel comfortable　感到舒服

　　feel for the switch on the wall　摸索着找墙上的开关

　　by feeling them with his fingers　用手指摸字母

　　feel one's way　摸索着走(十)

　　feel oneself　感到身体正常

　　feel like to do sth.　想做……，愿意做……

　　feel free to do sth.　随意做……

　　get the feel of...　习惯于……

ferry

　　by ferry　乘渡船

　　cross the river by ferryboat　乘渡船过河

festival

　　during the kite festival　在风筝节

at the kite festival　在风筝节

the Festival of Ascending on High　登高节,重阳节

fever

have a high fever　发高烧

run a fever　发烧

He has two degrees of fever.　他有两度寒热。

feverish

be feverish　发烧

field

on the field　在运动场上;在战场上

in the field of medicine　在医药领域里

in the field of health　在保健领域里

in the field of book publishing　在出版界

field event　田赛

field hospital　野战医院

take the field　参加战斗

win the field　打胜仗

fight

fight my way back　打回,打出

fight the diseases　与疾病斗争

fight the flames with extinguishers　用灭火器与火焰搏斗

fight against the enemy with him　和他一起与敌人作斗争

fight against each other　互相冲突(打架)

fight for the freedom of slaves　为奴隶的自由而斗争

figure

figure out　合计,计算出;断定;弄明白;理解

figure on　估计到,指望

I figure on him to leave at 6:00.　我估计他六点走。

He is a fine figure of a man.　他身材魁梧。

She is a fine figure of a woman.　她身材苗条。

fill

fill in the blank with...　用……填空

fill requirements　满足要求

be filled with...　充满了……;(某地方)放满(装满,挤满)了

... has to be filled in　……必须填写

find

find out　了解,调查,打听,弄清楚

find a system of reading for the blind　找到一种供盲人阅读的系统

fine

    pay a fine　付罚款

    He was fined $200.　他被罚款两百美元。

    Thread is finer than rope.　线比绳子细。

finger

    have a finger in the pie　插手,参与其事

    lay one's finger on the vase　碰一下那只花瓶

finish

    from start to finish　从头到尾

    fight to the finish　斗争到底

fire

    catch fire　着火了

    be on fire　着火了

    The house was on fire.　那房子着火了。

    open (cease) fire　开(停)火

    He would go through fire and water for you.　我愿为你赴汤蹈火。

    light a fire　点火

    make a fire in the old stove　生火炉

    There was some wood to make a fire with.　有一些用来生火的木头。

    die in the fire　在火灾中死了

    There is no smoke without fire.　无风不起浪。

    dance around a fire　围着火堆跳舞

    fire at the enemies　向敌人开火

    set fire to the house　纵火烧那栋房子

    He was fired.　他被解雇了。

    fire up　勃然大怒,激动

    play with fire　干危险的事

first

    at first　开始,起初

    first aid　急救

    first name　名(last name 姓)

    for the first time　第一次

    from first to last　从头到尾

    First things first.　要紧的事要先干。

    stand first on the list　名列前茅

    first of all　首先

fish

    a fish-shaped kite　鱼形风筝

two fish　两条鱼

two fishes　两种鱼

fit

The coat is fit for me.　这件衣服(款式)适合我。

The pair of shoes fits me very well.　这双鞋(尺寸上)很适合我。

fit in with their surroundings　适应它们周围的环境

fit in with...　适应,适合

keep fit　保持健康

fit...in (into)...　把……放入……

fit the new coat on you　给你试穿这件新衣服

have a fit　大为吃惊;大为生气

fix

fix one's eyes on (upon) sb. (sth.)　盯着某人(某物)看

His eyes are fixed on me.　他盯着我看。

fix on a date for the meeting　选定(确定)开会的日子

fix up a visit　安排一次访问

flame

be in flames　燃烧着

flare

flare up　突然发火

flat

a flat tyre　一只瘪的轮胎

flesh

They are my flesh and blood.　他们是我的亲骨肉。

floor

On the floor there lay a bottle.　那只药瓶就在地板上。

on the third floor　在三层楼(美语),在四层楼(英语)

The library has four floors.　这个图书馆有四层。

on the ocean floor　在海底

The whole fourth floor is very angry.　四楼的全体住户很生气。

the floor of the bridge　桥面

I managed to get the floor in the afternoon.　下午我设法得到发言的机会。

floor the room with...　用……给房间铺地板

The boxer floored the opponent.　那位拳击手击败了对手。

fluent

He is fluent in Spanish.　他西班牙语掌握得很熟练。

flutter

flutter in the wind　在风中随风飘动

fly

    fly kites　放风筝

    fly to San Francisco　飞往旧金山

    fly out of the window　飞到窗外去了；不知去向了

    fly from...　从……(地方)逃跑

    fly at...　向……进攻(袭击)

    This was a flying visit.　这是一次闪电式的访问。

focus

    focus on...　集中思想在……上

    focus on the physical disease　针对身体的疾病

fold

    a folding chair　一张折叠椅

    fold her hands　合拢她的双手

    fold her arms　把手臂交叉在胸前

    fold up　使折起；(因笑或疼)使弯起身子；破产,停止营业

follow

    follow the instructions of sb.　遵照某人的指示

    follow the directions　遵照指示；按所指引的路线(方向)走

    follow a music career　从事音乐生涯

    follow a satisfying hobby　培养一种令人满意的爱好

    He was followed by questions.　接着问他问题。

    Do you follow me?　你听懂(理解)我的话吗？

    as follows　如下

    His arguments are as follows.　他的理由(论点)如下。

    the following morning　第二天早晨

fond

    be fond of...　喜欢……

fool

    make a fool of...　欺骗,捉弄

    play the fool　出洋相

    fool about (around)　无所事事,胡混

foot

    at the foot of the tower　在塔的脚下

    at the foot of the stairs　在楼梯脚下

    keep a foot in both camps　脚踏两只船；两边都支持

    on foot　步行；在筹划中

    A plan is on foot.　一个计划正在筹划中。

    rise to one's feet　站起身来

drag one's feet 拖延不走,迟不行动
for
    for all 尽管
    for certain (sure) 肯定
    for example (instance) 例如
    for ever (forever) 永远,老是
    for good 长期地,永远地
    for short 简称
    The United States of America is called the U. S. A. for short. 美国被简称为
      USA。
    for sale 供出售
    for the time being 暂时
    So much for the topic. 这个题目就讲到这里。
    word for word 逐字逐句地
    The car is for hire, not for sale. 这轿车是供出租用的,而不是出售的。
    be for him 支持他
    Don't take me for a fool. 别把我当傻瓜。
forbid
    forbid sb. to do sth. 禁止某人做某事
force
    by force 靠武力,强行
    put... into force 使……生效
    come (go) into force ……开始生效
forget
    forget our arguments 不要计较我们的争吵,别把我们的争吵放在心上,别介意
form
    in the form of... 以……的形式
    in the form of a gold medal 以金质奖牌(勋章)的形式
    if he is in form 如果处于他处于良好的竞技状态
    be formed from... 由……组成,由……构成
former
    our former English teacher 我们从前的英语老师
    a former classmate of mine 我的一位老(从前的)同学
forth
    back and forth 前前后后,来来回回
    and so forth 等等
    bring forth his suggestion 提出他的建议
fortune

try one's fortune　碰碰运气

make a large fortune from...　靠……发财

a fortune-teller　一位算命先生

forward

look forward to meeting them　期待着见到他

bring (put) forward　提出

backwards and forwards　透彻地,充分地

understand the theory backwards and forwards　充分理解这个理论

four

on all fours　趴在地上

He is on all fours for...　他趴在地上找……

free

be free and easy with...　对……很随便(无拘束)

be free of...　没有,摆脱

They must free themselves from...　他们必须从……中解放出来。

set him free　释放他

free of charge　免费

supply him with lunch free of charge　免费供应他午餐

freedom

a way of freedom from worry　一种解脱忧愁的方法

with freedom　无拘无束地,随便地

freeze

He was half frozen.　他有点冻僵了。

freezing cold　冰冷的

freezing point　冰点,零度(摄氏)

freeze Tom out of the club　不让汤姆参加这个俱乐部

make one's blood freeze　使某人吓得要死

freeze one's blood　使某人吓得要死

fresh

remain fresh in my mind　使我头脑保持清醒

fresh water　淡水

friend

be friends with...　和……交朋友,和……友好

make friends with...　和……交朋友

make friends with others by playing　通过玩耍和别人交朋友

friendly

in a friendly way　友好地

fright

in fright　惊恐地，害怕地
　　take fright　受惊
frighten
　　frighten me with...　用……来吓我
　　be frightened by...　被……吓住了
　　be frightened of...　害怕……
　　frighten the birds away (off)　吓跑了那些鸟
　　be frightened to death　被吓死了
from
　　from now on　从现在起
　　from then on　从那时起
　　apart from　除……外
　　far from satisfactory　很不满意
　　from bad to worse　每况愈下
　　from hand to mouth　勉强糊口
　　from time to time　不时地
　　from a literary point of view　从文学的观点来看
　　from the heart　从心里，诚恳地
front
　　in front of her　在她的前面
　　stand in front of the plane　站在飞机(外)的前面
　　at the front of the plane　在飞机(内)的前部
　　die at the front　在前线死去，阵亡
full
　　be full of...　装满；充满了
　　The room is full of dust.　这个房间都是灰尘。
　　He is always full of himself.　他总是想到自己。
　　I'm full (up).　我吃饱了。
　　to the full　尽情地，非常
fun
　　have a lot of fun　玩得很高兴
　　What fun!　一件多么有趣的事！
　　make fun of sb.　和某人开玩笑；取笑某人
　　for fun　为了高兴
　　He learns French for fun.　他学法语只是为了高兴。
　　half in fun　半开玩笑地
function
　　function as a teacher　起到老师的作用

furnish

    be furnished with...　用……布置

    The book furnished us with facts.　这本书提供给我们许多事实。

further

    for further studies　为了进一步学习,为了深造

    go further　往下说,继续谈

    furthermore　还有,此外

G

gain

    gain our destination　到达目的地

    The clock gains five minutes.　这个钟表快了五分钟。

    gain control of oneself　控制住自己

    with the warships to gain itself an empire　用这些战舰把自己扩张成一个帝国

    gain on (upon)...　赶上……,跑到……前头,与……缩短距离

    gain the other runners　赶上了其他跑步运动员

game

    play games　做游戏

    video game　电子游戏

    make game of him　嘲笑他

    play the game　按规矩办事,讲信义

    I think he will play the game and return your book.　我想他会按规矩办事,归
       还你的书。

    He has the game in his hands.　他有必胜的把握。

    a game soldier　一个勇敢的战士

    be game for walk　愿意步行

gap

    There is a great gap between his ideas and mine.　他的想法和我的想法差距很大。

    go through the gap in the fence　从篱笆的缺口穿过去

gate

    at the school gate　在校门口

gather

    gather around him　围在他的周围

    gather in the crops　收割庄稼

    gather... together　把……收拾好

    gather up the child in his arms　把那个孩子抱起来

gaze

    gaze at him　凝视着他

gaze into the distance　凝眸远眺

gaze round the shop　出神地环顾商店的四周

general

general knowledge　常识，人所共知的事

in general　总的来说

as a general rule　一般来说

generation

from generation to generation　一代代地

generous

be generous to everybody　对大家很宽厚

a generous lunch　一顿丰盛的午餐

genius

have a genius for painting　对画画有天赋

geography

physical geography　自然地理

get

get about　传开；到处跑

The news soon got about.　这消息很快传开了。

get my ideas across　把我的想法讲清楚

get along (on) with...　……进展；与……相处

How are you getting along with your studies?　你学习进展得怎样？

get along (on) well with them　与他们相处得很好

get away from poverty　摆脱贫穷

get away from the smell　避开这股气味

get far　有出息

get hold of...　抓住……

get in the crops　收割庄稼

get in touch with...　与……有联系

get into trouble　闯祸

get into the habit of sleeping　养成睡觉的习惯

get a kite into the sky　把风筝放入空中

get home from class　放学回家

get my opinion home　使我的观点被听懂

get action on...　对……有所行动

to get by on the examination　为了敷衍(过去)考试

get down to business　开始谈正经事；言归正传

They sat down and got down to business.　他们坐下来开始谈正经事。

get money to pay for her lessons　挣钱付学费

get to know about him　渐渐了解他

get sth. all out　把它们取出来

get off at the next stop　在下一站下车

get off the horse　下马

get off the boat　下船

get off the elevator　下电梯

get out of the habit of sleeping　去掉打瞌睡的习惯

get over it　克服它；从(病)恢复过来

get the tin out of the river　把这罐头从河里拿上来

struggle to get my breath back　挣扎着使呼吸回过来

get rid of...　摆脱掉；除掉；处理掉

get round　传开

get to...　到达……

get through...　通过；完成

get me through to my mother　帮我接通我母亲的电话

a get-together　一次聚会

get up　起床；站起身

get well（＝recover）　恢复健康

gift

a gift for your birthday　一件生日礼物

a gifted man　一个有天赋的人

He has a gift for music.　他有音乐天赋。

in the gift of...　由……决定给予

The scholarship is in the gift of the college.　这份奖学金由学院决定给予。

give

at a given time　在规定的时间

his given name　他的名字(不包括姓)

give away　赠送人，分发

give all his books away　把他所有的书赠送(分发)掉

give back　归还；恢复(健康)

The medicine has given me back my health.　这药已使我恢复了健康。

give in（to...）　（向……）屈服；让步；投降

give him a hand with...　帮忙(做……)

give his life to his cause　用一生献给他的事业

give his life to helping the poor　用一生帮助穷人

give oneself airs　显得很神气

He always gave himself airs when he won the first prize.　当他得了第一名时，他总是显得很神气。

411

give my regards (greeting) to him 代我向他问好

give off a strange power 发出一种奇怪的力量

give out poisonous gases 发出有毒气体

give out radiation 发出射线

give out the prize 颁发奖品

He gave out. 他累极了。

glance

glance at sb. 看了一眼某人

glance at the list of contents 扫视书的目录

glance around (about, round) him 向他的四周望了望

at a glance 一眼(就……)

The doctor saw at a glance that the child was ill. 医生一眼就看出这孩子病了。

glare

glaring light 耀眼(刺目)的光

glare at him 怒视着他

glory

He was in his glory. 他很得意。

He gloried in his cause. 他为他的事业而自豪(得意)。

go

have nothing to go 没有东西剩下

go about 四处走动;做(干)……事

go about their business 忙着他们的事

go after... 追捕;设法得到;追求

go ahead 往前走;继续下去

go all out (to do...) 全力以赴(做……)

go along 一同去

Go along with you. 去你的吧！

go around 足够分配

Don't worry! There is enough coffee to go around. 别担心！咖啡足够大家用。

go at each other 互相攻击

go back to the past 回到过去

go back to Rome times 追溯到罗马时代

go back to one's seat 回到座位上去

go back and forth to work 来回运送(工作)

a helpful go-between 有益的中介

go by 过去,经过

Two years went by. 两年过去了。

go do sth. (=go to do sth.) 去做某事

go down （船）下沉;（价格）下跌;（温度）下降

The sun has gone down. 太阳已落山了。

go far 有出息,有成就

go far wrong 出严重的差错

go for an outing 去郊游

go in for... 参加……;喜欢……

go into some place for sth. 为某事进入某个地方

go into 调查,了解,研究;讨论

Go it! 加油!

go on 发生;继续干

I am going on for seventy (years old). 我快到七十岁了。

go on for rather a long time 持续相当长的时间

go on with her work 继续她的工作

go out of the front door 从前门走出去

go out of our minds quickly 很快忘了

go over 复习;核对

go over your notes 复习你的笔记

That means going over the lecture. 那意味着要复习这个讲座。

feel himself go red 感到自己脸都变红了

go round 传开

go swimming 去游泳

go through 查看;经历;看一遍;用完;通过

go through other objects 穿透别的物体

go through with... 把……进行到底

Many crimes go unrecorded by the police. 许多犯罪行为没被警察记录下来。

keep going up 继续上升

go well with sth. 与某物很相配

go with (match) the correct answer 与正确答案一致（相配）

go with their neighboring color 与其邻色相配

The bell goes. 铃响了。

My hair is gone. 我的头发剪下卖掉了。

He was gone. 他死了。

My bike was gone. 我的自行车丢了。

have a go 试一试

gold

gold bar 金条

gold fish 金鱼

a gold mine 大赚其钱的买卖

The restaurant is a gold mine. 饭店是大赚其钱的生意。

as good as gold 表现好极了

golden

    golden wedding 金婚

    a golden opportunity 一次宝贵的机会

    golden rule 金科玉律

good

    be good at... 擅长于,善于

    as good as 和……一样好;几乎

    He as good as promises to marry her. 他几乎(差不多已经)答应娶她。

    have a good time 玩得很好

    for good 长期地,永远

    What is the good of...? ……的益处是什么?

    be good to me 待我好一点

    be better for your health 对你健康更有益

    do more good to us 对我们更有益

    The harder the problems are, the more good they will do us. 题目越难,对我们越有好处。

    a good many questions 好多问题

gracious

    Good gracious! 天哪!

grade

    in Grade One (＝in the first grade) 在一年级

    grade the papers 给试卷评分

    The eggs are sold in grades. 鸡蛋分等级出售。

graduate

    graduate from... 从……毕业

    a graduate student 研究生

    graduate with a B. S. degree 毕业,并取得学士学位

grant

    take... for granted 视……为理所当然;认为……没问题

    She took it for granted that he could enter a good university. 她认为他考进所好大学是没问题的。

grass

    sit on the grass 坐在草地上

grateful

    be grateful to sb. for sth. 为某事对某人表示感激

    be grateful to you for your advice 感激你的忠告

414

be grateful to you for writing me　感谢你写信给我

greedy

be greedy for knowledge　渴望得到知识

be greedy of...　贪恋……

green

be dressed in green　穿绿色衣服

greenhouse effect　温室效应

greenback　美钞

He is a green boy in business.　他生意上是个没经验的人。

give sb. the green light　对某人开绿灯

ground

ground crew　地勤人员

ground force　地面部队

We have no ground for doing it.　我们没有做这件事的根据(原因,理由)。

the ground floor　底层,铺面,一楼(英国人用)

group

a large group of students　一大群学生

Huge stores are grouped together.　大型商店连成一片。

grow

grow red in the face　脸变红了

grow from ten to twenty-one sports　从一项体育运动发展到二十一项

grow out of　产生于……;因年岁增大而嫌……小,因年岁增大改掉(……习惯)

He used to tell lies in his childhood, but he grew out of that later.　他小时候常
说谎,但后来改掉了。

grow vegetables　种蔬菜

grow quiet　变得安静

grow up　长大成人;长大成熟

a grown-up　成年人

growth

with his growth　随着他的成长

guard

They are on guard at the gate.　他们正在大门口站岗。

keep guard　站岗

stand guard　站岗

be on guard　站岗,(保持)警惕

The soldiers are on guard at the gate to prevent anyone in and out.　士兵们把守
着大门,不让任何人进出。

guard your face against/from the sun　保护你的脸免受太阳的灼伤

guess

    at a guess　粗略估计

    by guess　靠猜测

guilty

    feel guilty for. . .　对……感到内疚

    have a guilty conscience about. . .　对……感到内疚

    be guilty of. . .　犯(某种罪或错误)

H

habit

    form the habit of. . .　养成……的习惯

    lose the habit of. . .　失去了……的习惯

    be in the habit of. . .　有……的习惯,经常爱……

    He was in the habit of eating porridge in the morning.　他早晨有吃稀饭的习惯。

    get (fall) into the habit of. . .　染上了……的习惯

    break away from the habit of. . .　改掉……的习惯

    get rid of the habit of. . .　改掉……的习惯

hack

    hack sb. to death　把某人劈死

    hack sb. into pieces　把某人砍成碎块

    hack open a path with. . .　用……开辟条小路

    hack a farm out of the wilderness　把荒地开辟成农场

hair

    His black hair was going grey.　他的黑发正在变白。

    a few white hairs　几根白头发(本句中的 hair 是可数名词)

    A white-haired man sits on the porch.　一个白头发的男子坐在门廊里。

    make my hair stand on end　使我毛骨悚然

    without turning a hair　不动声色

half

    only half as big as the Pacific　只有太平洋的一半大

    one half of the world's population　世界人口的一半

    halfway down the street　沿街走到半路

    divide the apple in half　把这个苹果分成两半

    divide the apple into halves　把这个苹果分成两半

    Which book is better? Just half-and-half.　哪本书更好? 差不多(不相上下)。

    half an hour　半小时

    one hour and a half　一个半小时

    one and a half hours　一个半小时

half the oranges　一半橘子

half my wages　我的一半工资

don't half like...　非常喜欢(有时也表示:一点也不喜欢……)

hall

in the hall　在礼堂里

a concert hall　音乐厅

a dance-hall　舞厅

an exhibition hall　展览厅

hand

He writes a good hand.　他写了一手好字。

the hour (minute) hand　时(分)针

on (the) one hand　一方面

on the other hand　另一方面

by hand　用手工

with their hands　用他们的手

at hand　在手边;在眼前

hand in hand　手拉手

from hand to hand　从一个人(传到)另一个人

give him a big hand　给他鼓掌

Spring is at hand.　春天就要到来。

(at) first hand　直接地,亲自

learn about the accident at first hand　亲自了解这个事件

lend (give) us a hand (helping) with...　帮助我们做……

hand in your work　请你交作业

hand his orchestra over to his brothers　把他的交响乐队交给他的几个兄弟

shake hands with sb.　和某人握手

handle

handle these books　处理这些书

hang

hang from steel cable　从钢索上悬挂下来

hand on　紧紧抓住不放;别放下电话

hang out　晾晒,挂出去;坚持;闲逛(俚语)

hang round　闲逛

hang up　挂上电话,搁置

happen

happen to make the sun stop burning and shining　正巧使太阳停止燃烧和照耀

What happened to you?　你发生了什么事?

as it happens　恰好,碰巧

As it happens, they are here.　他们恰好在这里。

whatever happens　不管发生什么情况

happy

be very happy with the system　对这制度很满意

The people were so happy with his funny stories.　人们对他的故事如此满意。

hard

It's hard for me to do sth.　做某事对我来说是困难的。

Don't be hard on me.　别对我太苛刻(严厉)。

I am not afraid of hard work.　我不怕艰苦的工作。

He is a hard-working man.　他是个勤劳的人。

We must work hard.　我们必须努力工作。

by working hard　通过努力工作

harm

do no harm to your health　对你的健康无害

do more harm to you (＝more harm done to you)　对你更有害

harmful

be harmful to animals　对动物是有害的

harmony

in harmony　和睦地,和谐地

in harmony with...　和……一致

have

have to do...　不得不做……

had better (best) do...　最好做……

have a wonderful time　玩得很好

have a word with...　和……讲一句话

have an edge on (over)　比……略胜一筹

have an impact (effect) on (upon)...　对……有影响

have confidence (faith) in...　对……有信心,相信……

have control of (over)...　能控制住……

have doubts about...　对……有怀疑

have it that...　传说

An old saying has it that...　一个古老的谚语说……

have none of doing...　不允许做……

have no business doing sth.　无权做某事;没有理由做某事

have your TV on so loud　把电视开得那么响

have a shirt on　穿一件衬衫

have nothing on　没穿衣服

have one eye on sth.　分一部分精力看着某物,留神一下某物

418

have nothing to do with... 与……没有关系

have much to do with. 与……很有关系

head

be (go) out of his head 神志不清，昏了头

stand on his head 倒立

use your head 动动脑筋

lose one's head 失去理智，惊慌失措

put our heads together 集思广益，共同商量

droop his head 低下头

head for 向……走去(前进)

health

be in good (bad) health 身体好(不好)

drink to your health 为你的健康干杯

hear

hear from... 收到……的来信或来电

hearing-aid 助听器

hear these words from her father 从她父亲那儿听到过这些话

heart

heart attack 心脏病

heart trouble 心脏病

go home with a light heart 怀着轻松的心情回家去

learn... by heart 记住……

heart and soul (＝whole-heartedly) 全心全意地

heat

have much heated discussion 进行非常热烈的讨论

help

help you with your studying/studies 帮助你学习

help sb. with all the work 帮助某人做所有的工作

help to show... 有助于显示出……

can help not thinking 能忍住不考虑……(can't help 不能忍住)

come to one's help 帮助某人

be of help (＝be helpful) 有用的

be of great help to... (＝be greatly helpful to...) 对……有很大帮助

with the help of open-door policy 在改革开放政策帮助下

come to one's help 来帮某人忙

help out 帮助克服困难

help in the growth 有助于生长

here

Here comes a bus now.　一辆公共汽车来了。
hesitate
　hesitate for long　犹豫好长时间
　never to hesitate to ask sb.　毫不犹豫地问某人
hesitation
　without hesitation　毫不犹豫
hike
　hiking trip　步行旅游
himself
　He'll be himself.　他会恢复正常的。
　come to himself　恢复正常
history
　throughout history　整个历史
hold
　Room 101 can hold more than 50 students.　101 号房间能容纳 50 多个学生。
　She held back, not knowing what to do.　她踌躇不定,不知干什么。
　hold on to the letters　保存这些信件
　hold out　坚持(抵抗),顶住(压力)
　hold up　(交通)堵塞,举起
　hold up his hand　举起他的手
　hold it out to him in her open hand　她摊开手,把它拿出来给他
hole
　with a hole in the roof　在屋顶上有个洞
holiday
　be on holiday　在度假
home
　at home　在家里
　Being a guest in an American home will be...　在美国人家里作客将会……
　take it home　把它带回家去
　a nursing home for women　一所女子护理院
honest
　to be honest　说老实话
honour
　in honour of his 30 years teaching in our school　为了对他在我们学校的 30 年
　　教育表示敬意
　in honour of a Japanese brave boy　为了对勇敢的日本男童表示敬意
　graduate from college with honours　作为优等生从大学毕业
　She was honoured for her service.　因为她的贡献而给与她荣誉。

Nurses are honoured today.　护士们今天才受到尊敬。

hope

   hope for sth.　渴望某物

   hope for the best　最好的希望

   Hope for the best，prepare for the worst.　作最好的打算（希望），最坏的准备。

horizon

   on the horizon　在地平线上

   Computers have already widened people's horizons.　电脑已经开阔了人们的眼界。

horror

   have a horror of...　害怕；讨厌

   in horror　恐惧地

   to his horror　使他感到惊慌的是

   with horror　因为害怕

horn

   blare one's horn　鸣喇叭

hour

   hour after hour　一个小时又一个小时

house

   go about from house to house　挨家挨户地到处走动

how

   How careless of me!　我是多么粗心！

   How brave of him!　他多勇敢！

   How come?　怎么会……的？

   How about swimming?　游泳怎么样？

   How long will it take the letter to reach London?　这封信到达伦敦需要多久？

   how soon　多久以后

humour

   with good humour　心情愉快地

   keep in a good humour　保持好的心情

hundred

   hundreds of...　成百上千的……

   tens of hundreds of...　成百上千的……

   hundreds and hundreds of...　成百上千的……

hurry

   in a hurry　匆匆忙忙地

   He was in a hurry.　他匆匆忙忙。

   hurry to the post office　匆匆忙忙地向邮局走去

   in a great hurry　非常匆忙

leave in a hurry　匆匆忙忙离开

in such a hurry　这么匆匆忙忙地

husband

　　Husband and wife sat together.　夫妇俩坐在一起(省略冠词"the")

hurt

　　My stomach hurt.　刚才我胃疼。

I

ice

ice water　冰(镇)水

break the ice　打破沉默

I broke the ice at the meeting by telling a story.　在会上我讲了个故事打破了沉默。

cut ice with him　对他起作用

What I said cut no ice with him.　我说的话对他不起作用。

skate on thin ice　冒风险

idea

have any idea　知道,了解

Have you any idea(of)what he said?　你知道他刚才说什么吗?

I have no idea.　我不知道。

I have no idea(as to)what it means at all.　我根本不知道那是什么意思。

get a general idea of the content　大致了解了内容

get a rough idea of what the book is like　大致了解是什么样的书

identify

identify... with...　把……和……联系起来;与……共鸣

i. e.

i. e. ＝That is　即

I like three sports, i. e. basketball, football and volleyball.　我喜欢三项运动,即篮球、足球和排球。

if

if necessary　如有必要

If only she still had her hair!　要是她的头发还在就好了!

If only I had been more careful(＝I wish I had been...)　但愿我那时更仔细

if so　假如如此

if any　如果说有的话

if possible　如果可能的话

if you like(please)　如果你愿意;劳驾

If you please, sir, can you do me a favor?　劳驾,先生,你能帮个忙吗?

even if it rains　即使下雨

ignorance

be in ignorance of...　不知道(了解)……

be in total ignorance of sth.　对某事完全不了解

ignorant

be ignorant of (about)...　对……不了解,不知道……

ill

fall ill　病倒了

It is three months since he fell ill.　他病了三个月。

It is three months since he was ill.　他病好三个月了。

speak ill of him　说他的坏话

ill-treatment　虐待

illness

pain in illness　疾病的疼痛

importance

The meeting is of great importance.　这次会议很重要。

impress

impress everything on my mind　把一切深深印在我的脑海中

be quite impressed　印象很深

impression

under the impression　认为,有……这样的印象

We are under the impression that they are brothers.　我们认为他们是兄弟。

in

in a day or two　一两天以后

in a low　一连

He wrote three letters to me in a low.　他一连给我写了三封信。

be in for the examination　参加考试

in a sense　从某种意义上

in conclusion　最后

in detail　详细地

in a friendly fashion　以友好的方式

in other words　换言之

in my opinion (view)　在我看来

in person　当面,本人

in public　在公众面前;公开地

in return　作为报答;回过来

in short (a word)　总之

in that　因为;在……方面

in the long run　从长远来说

in the meantime　（与此）同时

in turn　轮流；回过来又……

in vain　白白地，徒劳

day in，day out　一年到头

I worked day in，day out without a holiday.　我一年到头工作，没有一天假期。

inaccessible

The island is inaccessible to me.　这个岛屿我不可到达。

The cake is inaccessible to me.　这块蛋糕我无法得到。

include

I include eggs on the list of things to buy.　我把鸡蛋列在购物单里。

income

the total of their income　他们的总收入

independent

You are independent of trains and buses if you have a car.　如果你有轿车，就不依赖火车和公共汽车了。

The factors are independent of each other.　这些因素互相约束。

infect

He is infected with the flu virus.　他感染上了流感。

inferior

be inferior to...　比……差，地位比……低

influence

have (an) influence on (over) him　影响他

inform

inform sb. of (about，as to) sth.　通知（告诉）某人关于某事

keep us informed of...　使我们知道……

inhabit

inhabit that island　居住在那个岛上

inherit

Blood type is inherited from parents.　血型是从父母亲那儿继承来的。

injure

injure her feelings　伤害了她的感情

be killed or injured in road accidents　在交通事故中丧命或受伤

inquire

inquire about...　打听（询问）……的情况

inquire after his health　问候他的健康

inquire for...　要求见到……；设法买到……

inquire into...　调查，了解，追究

inquiry

   make an inquiry about friends or family　问询关于朋友和家人的情况

insist

   insist on (upon) doing sth.　坚持做某事;坚决主张做某事

instance

   for instance　例如

instant

   instant noodle　方便面

instead

   instead of　代替,而不

   I'll go instead of you.　我将代替你去。

   instead of obeying　而不服从

   They are made of leather instead of plastic.　它们是皮革制成而不是塑料制成的。

intend

   be intended to deal with...　打算处理……

interest

   have (show) an interest in...　在……方面有兴趣

   take little interest in...　对……几乎没兴趣

   be interested in...　对……感兴趣

   places of interest　使人感兴趣的地方,游览胜地

   It is likely to interest him.　多半有可能使他感兴趣。

   with interest　感兴趣地

interval

   at intervals　每隔一会儿;每隔一段距离

   in the interval　在(课间,工间)休息时

interview

   a week before the interview　在面试前一周

introduce

   introduce oneself　自我介绍

   introduce the lecture to the audience　向观众介绍这个讲座

   be introduced into the Olympics　被介绍进入奥林匹克运动会

invest

   invest in a new car　购买辆新车

investigation

   under investigation　在调查中

invite

   invite sb. to do sth.　邀请某人做某事

   That is an inviting house.　那是幢吸引人的房子。

involve

    be involved in the trouble　　陷入困境

    involve with those people　　和那些人有密切联系

    an involved story　　一个复杂的故事

iron

    iron the shirt　　熨烫衬衫

    The prisoner was out in irons.　　那个囚犯被戴上了镣铐。

isolate

    be isolated from the rest of Europe　　被与欧洲的其余部分隔开

issue

    be issued to him　　……被签发给他

    issue from. . .　　来自……

    issue sb. with. . .　　发给某人……

    the next issue　　下一个问题

J

jail

    be put in jail　　被打入监狱

    be sent to jail　　被打入监狱

jam

    in the traffic jam　　（交通)阻塞,拥挤

    I am in a jam.　　我处境困难。

jealous

    be jealous of him　　妒忌他

    be jealous of one's freedom　　珍惜自由

job

    in a job interview　　在求职面试时

    Do a good job next time.　　下次要好好干。

    odd jobs　　杂活

    on the job　　在上班时

join

    join hands to sing　　手拉手地唱歌

    join her in her work　　和她一起干

    join. . . to. . .　　把……和……连在一起

    join an island to the mainland by a bridge　　桥把岛屿和大陆连在一起

    join the wires up　　把这些电线连接起来

joke

    have a joke with me　　和我开玩笑

play a joke on sb.　和某人开玩笑

joke about sth.　拿某事开玩笑,取笑

make a joke　讲笑话

He hid my keys for (as) a joke.　他把我的钥匙藏起来只是(为了)开玩笑。

journey

go on a journey　去旅游

take a journey　去旅游

make a journey　去旅游

an hour's journey　一个小时的路程

have a good journey　一路顺风,一路平安

joy

to my joy　使我高兴的是

to the joy of my brother　使我哥哥高兴的是

with joy　高兴地

go wild with joy　欣喜若狂

judge

judge from...　根据……可以看出

judging from what he said, he ought to succeed.　根据(从)他说的话来判断,他
应该成功的。

judge by...　通过……来判断

Judging by the response of the audience, I had made an effective speech.　通过
(从)观众的反应来判断,我的演讲很有成效。

judgment

pass judgment on sb.　对某人判决;说短道长

Don't pass judgment on your neighbours.　别对你的邻居说短道长。

in my judgment　在我看来

jump

jump about　四处蹦跳

jump into the river　跳入河里

jump up　(大幅度)上涨,迅速上升

jump on him　严厉批评他

junior

be junior to him　年龄比他小;职务比他低

just

just now　刚才;就在现在

just then　就在那时,那时候

justice

bring sb. to justice　使某人受到法律制裁

bring those who break the law to justice　使那些犯法的人受到法律制裁

K

keen

He didn't seem very keen on（about）English.　他好像对英语不感兴趣。

be keen on（playing）table tennis　热衷于（渴望着）打乒乓

be keen to do sth.　渴望着做某事

The wind outside is keen.　外面的风很冷。

keep

keep your promise（word）　遵守诺言

keep your head　保持冷静

keep disciplines　遵守纪律

keep Christmas　庆祝圣诞节

keep a shop　经营一家商店

keep two children　养活（照顾）两个孩子

keep hens　饲养鸡

Keep my coats for me.　请照看一下我的衣服。

keep a diary　记日记

keep goal　守门

How are you keeping?　你情况怎么样?

keep...in mind　记住……

keep away a tiger　远离（不要接近）老虎

keep off...　避开……，不要踩（吃，谈）……

keep off the grass　勿踏草地

An apple a day can keep the doctor away.　每天一只苹果可远离（不看）医生。

keep it for two days　借两天

keep them from getting into fights　防止他们打架

keep a patient from feeling pain　使病人免于（感到）疼痛

keep in touch with civilization　与文明保持联系

keep the readers in touch with the world　使读者与世界保持联系

keep...out　不让……进来

keep out the bad weather　把坏天气隔在外面

keep to　遵守,按……行事

traffic keeps to the left　交通靠左边

keep to himself　不与人交往

Don't keep it to yourself.　不要保守秘密了。

keep up quality　保持质量

keep prices down　降价

keep oneself warm　使自己保持温暖

keep on trying　坚持试下去

keep sb. on　继续雇佣某人

keep body and soul together　维持生命,活命

be kept under lock and key　严密保管好

keep money in the bank　把钱存在银行里

keep up　保持,维持,继续,使……不下降

keep up my languages　使我的语言保持下去

keep up with sb.　赶上某人

goal keeper　守门员

keep most people at home　使大多数人待在家里

for keeps　永远(不变);长期的;严肃认真

keep an eye on...　照看……,对……留个神

keep the truth back　隐瞒了事实真相

The two teams played for keeps.　这两个队比得很严肃认真。

key

keys to these questions　这些问题的答案

a key man　一位关键人物

kill

kill time　消磨时间

kill me　杀死我,使我难受至极,使我极感尴尬

kill the audience　使观众笑得要死

by killing food supply for birds　通过除掉鸟的食物供应

kind

many kinds of apples　多种苹果

medicine of any kind　任何一种药

We buy hair goods of all kinds.　我们收购各种各样的头发。

kind of　有点儿

I'm feeling kind of tired.　我感到有点儿累。

be so kind as to do...　劳驾做……

It's kind of you to do sth.　难为你做某事,谢谢你做某事

kindness

do me a kindness (to do...)　做件好事,帮个忙(做……)

kite

fly a kite　放风筝

knack

have a knack for...　有……的技巧

knee

go/get down on your knees　跪下

kneel

　　kneel on one knee　单膝跪下

knife

　　under the knife　在做手术时

knock

　　knock him down　把他撞倒

　　be knocked down　被撞倒

　　knock about all over the world　在全世界旅游(到处跑)

　　knock the bottle over　打翻了那杯水

　　be knocked off　……被拍掉(被敲掉)

　　knock hard on the door　拼命敲门

　　knock at the door　(有礼貌地)敲门

　　knock into him　撞在他身上

　　the knocked-out teeth　被脱下的牙齿

know

　　know better than to...　应懂得不该……

　　know better than to spend all her money on clothes　应懂得不该花所有的钱买
　　　衣服

　　know about...　知道……的情况,了解……的情况

　　know nothing about it　不了解这件事

　　be known as...　作为……而出名,被认作……

　　know her as a woman of ability　把她看作为一个有能力的女人

　　be known as proverbs　被认为是谚语

　　He became known as "The Waltz King" through Europe.　他以华尔兹舞曲之
　　　王风靡全欧。

　　be known as air cushion vehicles　被称为气垫交通工具

　　be known for...　以……闻名

　　be known to everybody　大家都知道

　　know right from wrong　辨别是非

　　know the difference between right and wrong　分辨是非

　　know the songs by heart　能背出(记住)这些歌

knowledge

　　a knowledge of first aid　一门急救知识

　　have a knowledge of...　对……有所了解

　　common knowledge　人所共知的事

L

lack

lack the major source of heat power　缺乏热能的主要来源

The tree died from lack of water.　由于缺水,那棵树枯死了。

lady

Be a lady.　做个有身份有教养的女士。

land

It landed on the red-hot stove.　它正好落在火红的炉子上。

We landed at Liverpool from the ship.　我们在利物浦上岸。

We landed at the airport in Chicago.　我们在芝加哥机场降落。

land on one's head　头着地

lane

six lanes of cars　(有)六个车道

Lane 545 No. 36 Chang-de Road　常德路 545 弄 36 号

large

at large　(囚犯)在逃;逍遥法外;一般来说;随便地

It is reported that the prisoner is still at large.　据报道那个囚犯仍逍遥法外。

last

at last　最后

last but not least　最后一点,也是最重要的一点

the last thing　最后,最不喜欢或最不合适的事

these last few days　最近几天

last four years　持续四年

last for ninety minutes　持续 90 分钟

It lasts less than 30 seconds.　它持续不到 30 秒钟。

late

be a bit late　晚了一点儿

be late for school　上学迟到

I was late (in) arriving.　我到晚了。

be late with dinner　迟开饭

later in the day　当日晚些时候

not later than 10:00　不迟于 10 点

later on　后来

in later life　在往后的岁月里

seconds later　几秒钟后

sooner or later　迟早

laugh

laugh at people in trouble　嘲笑在困难中的人

One who laughs last laughs best.　谁笑在最后谁笑得最好。(别高兴得太早。)

have the last laugh　最后胜利了

laughter

    burst into laughter（tears）　放声大笑(哭)

law

    go to law about...　打⋯⋯官司

    take the law into one's own hands　（不找法院)自己执法

lay

    lay a new oil pipe　铺设一条新油管

    lay eggs　下蛋

    lay aside　放在一边;存蓄

    lay down one's arms　放下武器

    lay emphasis on...　强调⋯⋯

    lay him off　解雇他

    lay the table　摆桌子(准备吃饭)

    lay a finger on him　轻轻碰(打)一下他

lazy

    a lazy morning　一个悠闲的早晨

lead

    lead me（going）to London　带领我去伦敦

    What led him to run away?　什么导致他逃跑?

    lead me by the nose　牵着我的鼻子走

    lead a full life　过着充实的生活

    lead a normal life　过着正常的生活

    lead to...　引起,导致;导向(to＋动名词)

    lead to their quarrelling　引起他们吵架

    lead to better understanding　导致更好的理解(to 是介词)

    give a good lead（in...）　（在⋯⋯方面)起带头作用

    in the lead　领先

leader

    leader of the 1950's and 1960's　20 世纪 50 和 60 年代的领袖

leadership

    under the leadership of...　在⋯⋯领导下

leaf

    leaf by leaf　一片片地

    burst into leaf　长出叶子

lean

    lean forward　前俯

    lean on(upon)　依靠

    lean over the side of the bridge　前俯在桥沿上

lean against a door　斜靠在门上

lean meat　瘦肉

learn

learn...by heart　记熟(背下)……

learn about...　听说(了解)……事

learn from...　向……人学习

learn from their mistakes　向错误学习

learn from each other　互相学习

learn a lesson　得到教训

least

at least　至少

not in the least　一点也不

not least　也是相当重要的(原因)

leave

CA Flight 983 leaves at 12:30.　中航 983 航班将在十二点半起飞。

leave for big cities　前往大城市

leave a little to show he has had enough　留一点点以示他已够了

leave the door open　让门开着

on the left/right　在左边/右边

have nothing left　没有东西剩下

had only one shot left　只剩下一颗子弹

There must have been 25 or 30 tablets left in the bottle.　在药瓶里一定剩下 25 到 30 片药片。

leave...to chance (fate)　……听天由命(碰运气)

on leave　休假

ask for half a day's leave　请半天假

take (one's) leave　告别

lecture

give...a lecture　给……作讲座;训斥……

Don't lecture me.　别教训我了。

at my left　在我的左面

leg

pull my leg　跟我开玩笑,哄骗我

stand on one's own legs　自立,自己管自己

stretch one's legs　溜达

stretch one's arms and legs　伸懒腰

leisure

at leisure　从容地,慢慢地

at your leisure　在你有空的时候

lend

lend it to Peter　把它借给彼特

lend a hand＝give a little help　助一臂之力,帮个忙

lend an ear to…　倾听……

length

at length　详细地;周密地;最终;终于

in length　长度是……

This river is short in length.　这条河很短。

less

no less than 100 yuan　多达 100 元,有 100 元之多

more or less　基本上,大体上;左右,大约

It is an hour's journey, more or less.　大约一个小时的路程。

lesson

take lessons in music　上音乐课

teach (give) me a good lesson　给了我一个教训

learn a lesson from the mistake　从错误中得到一个教训

let

let it fall its full length　让头发全部落下来

Let's go to… for…　为某事,让我们一起去……地方

let alone go to school　更不用说去上学

let out　发出;泄露

Let him be　随他去,别理他

Let him alone.　随他去,别管他。

let go　放开,放手

Hold it tight, and don't let go.　请握紧,别放手。

Let me see.　让我想一想。

letter

get a letter from him　收到他的一封信

a capital letter　大写字母

a red-letter day　喜庆的日子

level

5,000 feet above sea level　海拔 5 000 英尺

contain high levels of acid　含酸量很高

at a professional level　以职业(球队)的水平

lie

China lies (in the) east of Asia.　中国位于亚洲的东面。

Japan lies (to the) east of China.　日本位于中国的东面。

434

The Pacific Ocean lies on the east of China.　太平洋位于中国的东面。

There lies a river in the distance.　在远方有一条河。

lie in one another's arms　紧紧依偎地躺着

lie back　仰躺

He lay bach in her chair.　他仰躺在她的椅子上。

lie down　在床上躺下(休息或养病)

take ... lying down　甘心接受……(不愉快的情况或事情)

He didn't take his defeat lying down.　他不甘心他的失败。

tell a lic　说谎

life

all through life　一生中

in my life　一生中(从出生到现在)

I have never seen such a foolish man in my life.　我一生中从未见过这么傻的人。

all my life　一生中(从现在到死)

I'll wait for you all my life.　我会等你一辈子。

the lives of great and famous people in history　历史上伟大而有名的人物的生平

between life and death　生命垂危

bring him (back) to life　使他苏醒过来

He came (back) to life.　他苏醒过来了。

for one's life　为了活命

The music is full of life.　这首乐曲充满了活力(生气)。

I am reading *The Life of Newton*.　我正在读《牛顿传记》。

lift

Lift your feet (up).　请抬(挪动)一下你的脚。

take the lift to the 10th floor　乘电梯到十楼

Give (get) me a lift.　请让我搭个便车。

lift sth. onto the horse　把某物抬上马背

light

He came over and begged for a light.　他走过来要求点个火。

light his cigar　点燃他的雪茄

His eyes lit up.　他的眼睛发亮了(露出了喜色)。

light railway　轻轨

light blue　淡蓝色

a light heart　轻松的心情

some lights　几盏灯

some light　一些光

like

do as you like　爱怎样就怎样

You can do exactly as you like.　你爱怎样就怎样。

How do you like...?　觉得……怎么样?

How do you like the film?　觉得这部电影怎么样?

What is the book like?　这本书怎样?

if you like　如果你愿意

something like　有点(像)

She looks something like your sister.　她看上去有点像你的妹妹。

as like as...　和……相像

and the like　等等之类的东西,等等

I like... best　我最喜欢……

I'd like to do... (=I'd love to do... =I want to do...)　我想要做……

Would you like to do...?　你要做……吗?

what I would like best is...　我最想要做的事是……

There's no place like home.　出门一里,不如家里。

likely

He is likely to fail.　他很有可能会失败。

It is likely that he will fail.　他很有可能会失败。

limit

limit on the gasses given out from cars　对汽车排出的气体有严格限制

There's a limit to the amount of money we can spend.　我们花钱的总数是有限制的。

within (one's) limits　在一定限度内,在某种程度上

I'm willing to help you, within limits.　在某种程度上,我是愿意帮助你的。

line

in line　排成行

He set the chairs in line along the wall.　他把椅子沿着墙排成一行。

drop (send) a line　写封短信

in a straight line　以一条直线

The street was lined with a lot of people. (=A lot of people lined the street.)　马路两边有许多人排队。

Line up, please.　请排队.

link

be linked to (with)...　和……联系起来

Fingerprints linked the suspect to the crime.　指纹把那个嫌疑犯和那个罪行联系起来了。

The campaign was closely linked with their future.　那次战役和他们的前途紧密地联系起来了。

list

a list of new words　一批新单词

make a list of things　列一张该做的事情的表

listen

listen to me report… in detail　听我详细汇报……

little

not a little　非常；十分

wait a little longer　等候时间长一点

such a little child　这么小的一个孩子

so little a child　这么小的一个孩子

so little milk　那么少的牛奶

live

live a poor life　过着穷困的生活

live a full and active life　过着充实和积极的生活

live up to…　不辜负某人；按……行事

live up to people's expectation　不辜负人民的期望

live broadcast　现场直播

living

make his living　谋生

earn his living　谋生

make a living by teaching　以教书谋生

locate

Shanghai is located in the east of China　位于中国的东面(国内)

Japan is located to the east of China　位于中国的东面(国外)

The Pacific Ocean is located on the east of China　位于中国的东面(相切)

be located in the suburbs　位于郊区

be located on the rivers　位于河流的两岸

be located on the North American continent　位于北美洲

long

as (so) long as I am free　只要我有空

as long as an hour　长达一小时

long for a holiday　渴望着一个假日

long for even greater wealth　渴望着更大的财富

long to do sth.　渴望做某事

long-lived people　长寿的人

look

look a passage over quickly　快速地全部看一篇文章

take a close look at…　仔细观察……

look around him　环顾他的四周

look around the house for sth. 环顾房子的四周找某物

look around me for sth. 环顾我的四周找某物

look around him for sth. 环顾他的四周找某物

look dead 看上去死了

look down over everything within sight 俯视万物（视野中的一切）

look pretty sick 看上去病得很重

the look on the young man's face 这位年轻人脸上的表情

Look out! 当心！

look out sadly 难过地朝外面看

look sad 显得难过

look for mystery 寻找神秘的东西

look forward to... 盼望着……

look both ways 看马路两边

look the word up in the dictionary 请在词典里查一查这个单词

look a little stupid 显得有些愚蠢

look about the room 环顾房间的四周

look around 环顾四周

as I look back 当我回想（过去）时

look everywhere for sth. 到处寻找某物

look further and further back into the past 回顾过去越来越远

look back into history 回顾历史

look out of the window 朝窗外看

look pale 看上去脸色苍白

look back and look forward 回顾过去,展望未来

look back upon these years 回顾这些年

look for an answer 寻找;期待着回答

look up at him 抬起头来看他

be looked upon with disapproval 被不满意地看待

be looked upon as... 被看作为……

lose

　　get lost 迷路

　　lose heart 灰心,泄气

loss

　　She was at a loss. 她不知所措。

love

　　be in love with sb. 爱上某人

　　fall in love with sb. 爱上某人

luck

wish each other luck　互祝好运

try my luck　碰碰运气

M

mail

mail these letters for me　为我寄这些信

by mail　通过邮寄

major

major in engineering　主修工程学

make

make these telephone calls for me　为我打这些电话

make him a musician　使他成为音乐家

make a musician of him　使他成为音乐家

All work and no play makes Jack a dull boy.　只干活,不完耍,聪明的孩子要变傻。

Early to bed and early to rise makes a man healthy, wealthy, and wise.　睡得早,起得早,能使一个人健康、富裕和聪敏。

Practice makes perfect.　熟能生巧。

Cartoons are made up of thousands of drawings.　卡通影片是由成千上万张画组成的。

make a note　做笔记

make things out of wood　用木头制成东西

make off with sth.　带了某物匆匆离开

make sure　肯定,设法弄明白

make sure to write everything down　一定要把一切记下来

make up　编造,虚构;化装;打扮

make up the finger alphabet　编成手语

make up for　……弥补

make up for the lost time　弥补失去的时间

make up for one's lack of...　弥补……的不足

have every chair made over　使每张椅子变个样(made over"被更改")

a leather-making shop　一家制革商店

be made up　构成;虚构;编造

Her mind was made up.　她打定了主意。

Life is made up of tears and smiles.　生活是由眼泪和微笑组成的。

Grandfather is a word made up of two parts.　"祖父"这个词是由两个单词组成的。

manner

have good manners　有礼貌

a person with good (bad) manners　一个有(没有)礼貌的人

many

　　many other dance tunes　其他许多舞曲

　　a good many articles about...　大量关于……的文章

　　a great many articles about...　大量关于……的文章

　　made many more important discoveries　又做出更多重要的发现

mark

　　at the boy's last mark　听了那男孩最后的那句话

　　make one's mark　使某人成功或出名

　　be marked with...　被标上……记号

market

　　at the market　在市场上

　　on the market　在市场上

marry

　　married Pierre Curie　与 Pierre Curie 结婚

　　be married to　和……结婚

　　get married to sb.　和某人结婚

marvelous

　　More marvelous than anything is the suffering of men and of women.　那些男男
　　女女的痛苦比任何事情更令人惊异。（这是以形容词开头的倒装句）

match

　　match sth.（＝go well with sth.）　与某物相配

matter

　　Money doesn't matter.　钱不重要。

　　no matter how different the manners are　无论礼貌是怎样不同

　　as a matter of fact　实际上

meadow

　　in the meadow　在草地上

　　make three meals　做三餐饭

　　at each meal　在每一餐

mean

　　mean by　是(什么)意思;指(谁)

　　What does the word "country" mean in English?　在英语中单词"国家"的意思
　　是什么?

　　What do you mean by "population"?　"人口"的意思是什么?

means

　　by no means　决不

　　by means of...　通过……方法

　　by this means　用这样的方法

440

by all means　想尽一切办法,千万,一定要;当然行,请

Try by all means to persuade him to go.　想尽一切办法劝他去。

May I leave? By all means.　我可以走吗? 当然行。

By some means or other　用某种方法

By what means will you go there?　你怎样去那里?

meantime

in the meantime　同时

measure

take your measure　给你量尺寸(做衣服)

take strict measures　采取严格的措施

measure up to　胜任,赶上

He didn't measure up to the job.　他胜任不了这项工作。

meet

meet with difficulties　遇到困难

the first problem for them to meet with　他们碰到的第一个问题

make both ends meet　使收支平衡

meet the changing situations　为了适应(满足)变化的形势

meet the needs of different people　满足不同人的需要

fail to meet the needs of...　没有满足……的需要

meet almost every need　几乎满足了每种需要

memorize

memorize the new words　背单词

memory

in their memory　为了纪念他们

in memory of them　为了纪念他们

mend

mend the lamp　修理灯

mend one's fences　改善关系

mend one's way　改过自新

on the mend　正在痊愈

mention

at the mention of her dead son's name　在提到她死去儿子的名字时

Don't mention it.　不用谢。/不要这样说;哪里哪里(客套话)

mercy

have mercy on...　对……同情,可怜

show mercy on...　对……同情,可怜

at the mercy of sb.　在某人的支配下

without mercy　无情地

merry

   make merry　寻欢作乐，玩得很高兴

message

   take a message to sb. for sb.　为某人带个口信给某人

   leave a message　留个口信

mess

   be in a mess　乱七八糟；狼狈处境

   Don't mess with him　别和他捣乱。

method

   with the new methods　用新的方法

middle

   in the middle　在中间

midnight

   at midnight　在半夜里

mind

   had a quick mind　思维敏捷

   mind doing this for me　介意为我做这件事

   don't mind working　勤奋工作；不介意干活

   Would you mind...? Not at all.　你介意……吗? 不介意。

   bear (keep, carry)... in mind　牢记……

   change (alter) one's mind　改变主意

   make up on's mind to do...　打定主意

   Never mind.　没关系

   To my mind, she was never pleased.　照我来看，他永远不会满意的。

minute

   at 7 o'clock to the minute　七点整

   five hours to the minute　整整五个小时

miss

   miss her train　她没赶上火车

   miss you　想念你

   a missing child　一个迷路的孩子

mistake

   by mistake　错误地，无心(做了某坏事)

   make a mistake　犯错误

   avoid any mistakes about the quantity　避免服用剂量的错误

   Don't make any mistake about me.　不要对我有任何误解。

   make a mistake about the time　把时间搞错了(误解……)

   mistake me for my brother　把我误认为我的兄弟

be mistaken for sweets　被误认为糖果

mix

You can't mix oil with water.　你不能把油和水混合起来。

I am all mixed up.　我被弄糊涂了。

moment

at any moment　在任何时候，随时

at that moment　在那个时刻

for the moment　暂时

the moment...　一……就……

The moment I saw him, I knew that there was no hope.　我一见到他，就知道没有希望了。

money

make a lot of money　赚了很多钱

mood

be in an especially cheerful mood　心情特别愉快

I am not in the mood for joking.　我没心情开玩笑。

moonlight

in the moonlight　在月光下

more

what's more　还有

more than a place where books are stored　不只是一个藏书的地方

more than a place of business　不只是一个做生意的地方

more than provide grades to students　不只是提供学生成绩

more than provide students with grades　不只是提供学生成绩

one more lion　再有一只狮子

There were four more stops.　还有四次停航。

a few more times　再几遍

A dog can do all that and much more.　狗能胜任所有那些工作，并还能做更多工作。

talk some more　再谈一些

morning

early in the morning　清晨

most

most of the time　其中大部分时间

a most popular game　一项很受欢迎的运动

make the most of　充分利用……

mother

mother tongue (＝native language)　母语

mountainous

    in a mountainous country　在一个多山的国家里

move

    He was much moved at the story.　他听了这故事很受感动。

    move sth. from... to...　把某物从……搬到……

    move on　朝前走;晋级;谈别的

    move away　离开;搬走

    move out of the station　开出车站

    move over any kind of surface　在任何一种表面的上方移动

    earth-moving machines　挖土机

much

    be (not) much of a musician　(不)是很好的音乐家,(不)是一个什么了不起的
    音乐家

music

    face the music　承担后果;受处罚

must

    That is a must.　那是件必须要(做)的事。

murmur

    murmur to oneself　嘟哝着

myself

    I'll do it by myself.　我将独自做这事。

    I'm not myself today.　今天我感到不舒服。

N

nap

    take a nap　打瞌睡

narrowly

    narrowly miss striking the boy　差点儿击中那个男孩

    narrowly escaping being killed　差点儿被杀死

name

    make quite a name (for oneself)　成名;成功

    in the name of...　以……名义

    call one names　骂人

    I hear him calling me names.　我听见他在骂我。

    name after...　用……的名字作名字。

    The girl was named after her mother.　这女孩用母亲的名字作名字。

    name for...　(美)按……的名字命名

    The college is named for George Washington.　这所大学按乔治·华盛顿的名

字命名。

nation

　　the United Nations　联合国

　　in a different host nation　在不同的东道主国家

nature

　　by nature　天生地

　　It is not in my nature to be jealous of others.　妒忌别人不是我的本性。

　　about the nature of time and space　关于时间和空间的性质

near

　　The New Year is near.（drawing near/near at hand）　新年即将来临。

　　be near death　快要死了

　　be near to the place　离那地方很近

nearby

　　on the nearby hills　在附近的山上

nearly

　　Twenty pounds is not nearly enough for my journey.　二十英镑远不够我的旅
　　　行费。

necessarily

　　isn't necessarily so　未必如此

need

　　There is no need to do sth.　没有必要做某事。

　　There is no need to feel lonely.　没必要感到孤独。

　　A friend in need is a friend indeed.　患难成知己。

　　Our library is in need of a thorough clean.　我们的图书馆需要大扫除。

nerve

　　get on one's nerves　使我心烦意乱；使我烦恼

nervous

　　Don't be nervous.　别紧张。

　　feel nervous　感到紧张

　　become nervous about making a bad impression　恐怕给人坏影响而变得紧张

never

　　never mind　没关系；不要紧

　　Never had the soup tasted so good to him, nor fruit so juicy.　对他来说，汤的
　　　味道从来没这么好吃过，水果也从来没这么鲜美多汁。（否定词在句首，要倒
　　　装。第二句省掉"had...tasted"）

next

　　live next door to me　住在我的隔壁

　　next to him　在他的旁边

445

next to mine　在我的旁边

newspaper

　　in today's newspaper　在今天的报纸上

night

　　night after night　一夜又一夜

　　all night　整夜

　　through the night　通宵,整夜

　　stay for the night　过夜

no

　　no more（＝not... any more）　再也没有……

　　no longer（＝not... any longer）　不再

　　No pains, no gains　不劳无获

　　no（none）other than...　不是别人,正是……

noise

　　make a great noise　一片欢腾热闹

noodle

　　instant noodles　速食面;方便面

not

　　Thank you. Not at all.　谢谢你。不用谢。

　　not... but...　不是……而是……

　　I do not know about it at all.　我一点也不了解这件事。

note

　　notes to the text　课文注解

　　take notes　记笔记

　　make notes　做笔记

notice

　　two months' notice　两个月的提前解雇通知

　　take little notice of　几乎不注意……;不关心……

　　take（no）notice of him　（没）注意到他

number

　　a number of　一些

　　a number of changes　一些变化

　　The number of supermarkets is...　超市的总数是……（of 后一定要用可数名
　　　词复数）

　　in large numbers　大量地

O

obey

obey the rules　遵守规则

observe

observe the traffic regulation　遵守交通规则

We Chinese also observe Christmas now.　我们中国人现在也庆祝（过）圣诞节。

observe the stars　观察星星

oblige

be obliged to do sth.　被迫做某事

be obliged to sb.　感激某人

occasion

on the occasion of...　在……时刻

occupy

occupy your free time　占用你的空余时间

Is this seat occupied?　这座位已有人坐了吗？

occur

... occur to me　……使我想起；……发生到我身上

An important thing occurred to me.　我突然想起了一件重要的事。

What occurred to you yesterday?　昨天你发生了什么事？

off

take off his shoes　脱掉鞋

off the ground　离开场地

right off　立刻，马上

on his day off　在他休息日

by lifting the box off the ground　通过把盒子从地上抬起

Quite a few books came off the shelf.　很多书从书架上掉下来。

I really should be off.　我真的该走了。

When are you off?　何时动身？

offend

offend against the law　触犯法律

offer

offer him a good post　提供他一个很好的职位

offer to find a job for him　主动提出为他找工作

office

take office　上任，执政

be in office　当权；执政

be out of office　不当权；不执政

on

articles on long life　有关长寿的文章

on a morning　在某个早晨

on the evening of May 1　在五月一日傍晚

I have no money on me.　我身上没带钱。

with 11 men on each team　每队 11 个人

their point of views on important subjects　他们关于重要主题的观点

reports on the Olympics　关于奥林匹克运动会的报道

She wrote a book on public health.　她写了一本关于公共卫生的书。

give a lecture on acid rain　作关于酸雨的讲座

There's a good film on at the Peace Cinema.　在和平电影院上演一部好电影。

on your latest report card　在你最近的成绩报告单上

once

　　once upon a time　从前

　　once (twice, three times, four times) a year　一年一次（两次、三次、四次）

　　once in a while　时不时，偶尔

　　at once　立即；马上

　　all at once　突然

　　once more　再一次；重复

　　once and for all　一劳永逸地；永远地

　　once he made up his mind　一旦他下了决心

one

　　one by one　一个接着一个

　　in one-fifth of the world　在五分之一的世界里

　　one of these days　其中有一天

　　in one　在（某人）身上

only

　　If only...　但愿……

　　If only we had a classroom facing south.　但愿我们有间朝南的教室。

open

　　be open to the public　向公众开放

　　since the reading-room was opened last year　自从阅览室去年开办以来

　　open up new horizons　大开眼界

operate

　　operate a machine　操纵机器

　　operate on the boy's throat　给这个男孩的喉咙动手术

operation

　　had a throat operation　喉咙开了刀

　　put sth. into operation　使某物开始运作（生效）

opinion

　　in my opinion　以我之见

opposite

    the opposite of...　……的对立面

    on the opposite side of the road　在马路的对面

    take a seat opposite them　就坐在他们的对面

or

    in three years or so　大约三年以后

    Hurry up，or we'll be late.　快点，否则我们要迟到了。

order

    Line up and walk to the door in order.　排好队，按次序进去。

    The books are arranged in good order.　这些书被安排得井井有条。

    My car is in good order.　我的汽车性能良好。

    in order to make a score　为了得一分

    place an order for 500 pairs of shoes with this store　向这家商店订 500 双鞋

    Order!　安静!

    take orders from you　听从你的命令

organize

    organize entertainment for sb.　为某人组织娱乐活动

origin

    the origin of music　音乐的起源

    On the Origin of Species　《物种起源》

other

    in other areas　在其他地区

    many other students　其他许多学生

    several other sections　其他几个栏目

    from one end to the other　从一头到另一头

    the other day　前几天

    Many people use it for no other purpose than to send and receive e-mails.　许多
        人使用它只是为了发送和接收电子邮件。

    other than...（＝besides or except）　除……外;不同于……

    some time or other　或迟或早

ought

    ought to be read inside the room　应该在房间（阅览室）里阅读

out

    out of order　坏了;乱七八糟

    out of breath　气喘吁吁

    out of danger　脱险

    be out of work　失业

    The plane was out of sight.　飞机看不见了。

come out of the office　从办公室出来

jump out of bed　跳下床

over

spread the cloth over the table　把这布铺在桌上

all over the world　全世界

take the bus over（across）the bridge　乘那辆公共汽车过桥

over and over again　再三

over the years　经过多年

over the past 40 years　经过 40 多年

I became numb, unable to move and red all over.　我变得麻木,不能动弹,全身发热。

through water or over obstacles　涉水或越过障碍

sail all over the surface　在所有表面的上方航行

a little over half a year　半年多一点

overlie

be overlaid with...　被覆盖着……

owe

owe his success to his teachers　把成绩归功于他的老师们

owing

Owing to ill health, she is not so active in the movement.　由于身体差,她现在参加运动不怎么积极了。

His death is owing to the traffic accident.　他的死是由交通事故造成的。

own

on my own　独自;依靠自己的力量

This is a bike of my own.　这是我自己的自行车。

P

page

on the first page　在头版

pale

She turned pale.　她脸色变得苍白。

paper

my term paper　我的论文

part

on his part　在他本人方面

It's a mistake on the part of sb.　是某人自己的错误

plane

the planes (flights) to Beijing　飞往北京的飞机

450

part

　　play an important part in. . .　　在……方面起了重要作用

participate

　　participate in sth.　参加某事

particular

　　be particular about food　挑剔食物

　　in particular　特别地

partly

　　partly for a rest　一部分是为了休息

pass

　　pass the time in a pleasant way　愉快地度过时光

　　pass away　去世

　　pass by the bookstore every day　每天路过那家书店

　　pass them by　忽略它们

　　The next two hours passed by.　随后的两个小时过去了。

　　pass on from generation to generation　代代相传

　　pass through the street　穿过那条街

　　The rumour passed through the city.　谣言传遍全城。

　　pass through college　上完大学

past

　　in the past　在过去

　　It is half past nine.　现在是九点半。

　　He is far past forty.　他四十多岁了。

　　He walked past my house every day.　他每天从我家经过。

　　in the past one hundred years　在最近一百年来

pain

　　in great pain　极其疼痛

pattern

　　The student patterned himself after his teacher.　那个男孩以他的老师为榜样。

pay

　　How much did you pay me for the book?　这本书你刚才付给我多少钱?

　　I paid 3 dollars for this book.　这本书我付了 3 美元。

　　pay for fire insurance　付火灾保险费

　　pay a visit to London　参观伦敦

　　pay the debts off　还清债务

　　pay attention to doing. . .　注意做……

peace

　　in peace　在和平时期

perform

    perform on musical instruments　演奏乐器

performance

    His performance in the exam is not good.　他在考试中的表现不好。

    continue to improve the product performance and after-sales service　继续改进
       产品性能和售后服务

period

    a long period of time　很长一段时间

    after periods of hard work　在一段艰苦工作后

permanent

    make new knowledge permanent　使新知识巩固下来

permit

    permit us to see the performer　允许我们看到表演者

persevere

    persevere in doing sth.　坚持做某事

persist

    persist in doing...　坚持,固执己见做……

persistence

    need persistence　需要毅力

person

    in person　当面;亲自;本人

    I'll thank him in person.　我要当面感谢他。

personal

    This is my personal opinion.　这是我个人的观点。

personality

    change his personality　改变他的个性

persuade

    persuade the city to pave and light its streets　说服了城里人铺设道路和设置路灯

picture

    take a picture　拍照

    be the picture of...　长得像……

    She was the picture of beauty.　她非常漂亮。

    John was the picture of his grandfather.　约翰长得像他爷爷。

photo

    take photos/photographs for you　给你拍照

    I want a photo taken.　我要拍张照。

pick

    pick out a present for his birthday　为他的生日挑选了一件礼物

pick out the items they need 挑选出他们需要的项目

pick up the book 捡起那本书

pick up new vocabulary 学一点新的词汇

pick you up 接你

piece

The teapot was broken into pieces. 那茶壶被打得粉碎。

The vase fell in to pieces. 这花瓶摔得粉碎。

pin

He was on pins and needles all day. 他整天坐立不安。

pity

It is a pity that... 可惜……

take pity on the poor 同情穷人

For pity's sake, help me. 求求你,请帮个忙吧。

place

in its usual place 在它平常的地方,在老地方

Leave these books in place. 请把这些书放在原来的地方。

place all hopes on sb. 把所有的希望寄托在某人身上

take place 发生;举行

Take your place. 请入座。

be in place of... 代替……

take the place of... 代替……

take first place 得第一名

plan

plan for the future 为未来作计划

plan to do sh. 计划做某事

start planning for the party 开始为晚会制订计划

plaster

His leg is in plaster. 他的腿上了石膏。

play

at play 在玩耍

child's play 容易的事

Solving the problem should be child's play for you. 解决这个问题对你来说应
  该是件容易的事。

play an important part (role) in... 在……方面起重要的作用

play each other 参赛,互相比赛

play games for money 赌钱

play a trick on sb. 捉弄某人

play... with sb. 与某人一起玩……

play with his toys　玩他的玩具

play for them　代替他们进行比赛

please

　　so pleased with Johann's music　对 Johann 的乐曲如此满意

pleasure

　　It's a (my) pleasure.　不用谢。

　　with pleasure　高兴地；愉快地

　　I have had the pleasure of reading all your articles.　我有幸拜读了你的文章。

plenty

　　plenty of snow　大量的雪

　　There are plenty of books.　有大量的书。

plunge

　　plunge into the cool of the sea　跳进凉快的海水里

popular

　　a flow of popular music　一组流行歌曲

　　be popular with/among sb.　受某人欢迎

　　grow popular as a sport　成为一个受欢迎的体育项目

　　His orchestra and music was very popular with the public.　他的交响乐队和音乐极受公众欢迎。

population

　　with the largest population in the world　有世界上最多的人口

　　2% of the total population　总人口的百分之二

　　with a population of 15 million　有一千五百万人口

　　with a growing population　由于人口的不断增长

　　The population in these villages has to get its water from wells.　这些村庄的居民(群众)只能喝井水。

point

　　at one point　在某一时刻

　　at this point　在这时候

　　make one's point　立论，证明论点

　　point to the next word with your finger　用手指指着下一个词

　　point the gun at him　用枪对准他

　　point of view　观点

polish

　　a highly polished surface　很光滑的表面

position

　　He is not in a position to criticize me.　他没有权力批评我。

possible

as. . . as possible　尽可能……

do everything possible　做有可能做的事

pour

be poured into rivers　被排入河里

Factory chimneys pour black smoke into the sky.　工厂的烟囱把黑烟排入空中。

power

in his power　力所能及

within his power　在他的权力范围内

come into power　上任,执政

practise

practise using. . .　练习使用……

practice

be put into practice　被付诸实践

prefer

I prefer. . . to. . .　我宁可……也不……

prefer the lakes to the seaside for a holiday　宁可到湖泊地区度假,也不去海滨度假

preparation

make preparations for. . .　为……做准备

have enough preparation　有足够的准备

prepare

prepare sb. to do sth.　准备做某事

be prepared for sth.　准备好某事

prepare himself for life in the future　为他自己未来的生活做准备

presence

in the presence of. . .　在……面前

present

at present　在目前

be present at. . .　出席……

people present　在场的人

preserve

preserve rare animals from extinction　保护稀有动物免于绝种

president

be elected President of the United States　被选为美国总统

pressure

be under great pressure　在很大的压力下

stop the bleeding by putting pressure over the part which is bleeding　通过在流血处加压来制止流血

455

pretend

    pretend to do sth.　　假装做某事

prevent

    prevent the other from scoring goals　阻止对方得分

prevention

    Prevention is better than cure.　　预防胜于治疗。/预防比治疗更好。

    An ounce of prevention is worth a pound of cure.　　预防胜于治疗。

price

    at a low price　最低的价格

    at reasonable prices　以合理的价格

primary

    a primary school　一所小学

    The primary colours are red, yellow and blue.　　红、黄、蓝是三原色。

print

    be printed in a separate part of the paper　被刊载在报纸的专栏里

prison

    be put in prison for a year　坐牢一年

    be sent to prison for a year　坐牢一年

    be thrown into prison for a year　坐牢一年

prisoner

    prisoners of war　战犯

private

    in private　私下地

    private cars　私人轿车

prize

    (the) first prize　第一名

    the Nobel Prize for Physics　诺贝尔物理奖

problem

    There will be no problem in passing the tests.　　通过考试不成问题。

product

    the finished products　成品

profit

    He profited from his own mistakes.　　他从错误中得到好处。

    His own mistakes profited him.　　他从错误中得到好处。

    make a profit　获利

    draw the quick profit from the trees　从树木中迅速得益

progress

    I have made rapid progress in English.　　我英语进步很快。

be in progress　在进行中

promise

It promises to be fine.　可望天好。

It promises that there will be a good harvest this year.　有望今年又有一个大丰收。

be promised to sb.　被许配给某人

She has been promised to Bill.　她已与比尔订婚了。

propose

Mary proposes to have a get-together　玛丽建议开个聚会

protect

protect rare animals from dying out　保护稀有动物免于绝种

protect themselves against large losses　保护他们自己免受重大损失

ways to protect men from the sun's dangerous rays　保护人们免受太阳危险光
线之害

proud

be proud of...　以……自豪；以……骄傲

be proud to tell... in the past　自豪地讲述过去的……

provide

provide them with money　提供给他们钱

provide money to them　提供给他们钱

provide materials for young readers　为少年读者提供材料

provide us with up-to-the-minute news　提供我们最新的消息

provide a constant flow of music around us　不断地在我们周围播送音乐

provide a balance between work and play　在工作和玩耍间的平衡

be provided free to sb.　（某物）被免费提供给某人

prove

He proved to be a very difficult man to please.　他被证明是个难以取悦的人。

P. S.　P. S.（＝postscript）　附笔；又启

puff

a puff of smoke　一阵烟

pull

He pulls ahead of me.　他超过了我。

pull down　拆毁

be pulled down　被拆掉

pull out a plug from a wall socket　从插座里拔出插头

pull the two cars off the road　把两辆车从马路上拉走

pull through　渡过难关，脱离险境

purchase

purchase freedom with one's head　用鲜血换来自由

457

purpose

    with a purpose　有目的地

    on purpose　故意地

    accomplish his purpose　达到目的

push

    push against a diver deep in the sea　（水）压向深水中的潜水员

    push to the front　挤到前面

    push his way in...　挤入……

    push his way through...　挤过……

    I pushed him to do his homework.　我催他快做功课。

put

    put away　收藏好

    put away our Christmas gifts　把我们的圣诞礼物收藏好

    put down the rebellion　镇压叛乱

    put forward...　提出……

    put off...　推迟;延期

    put on　穿上

    she's put on weight.　她发胖了。

    put the fire out　把火扑灭了

    put out heavy ray　释放出强的射线

    put me to sleep　使我入睡

    put up...　建造……

    put up with...　忍受……

puzzle

    I am puzzled about electricity.　我对电有疑虑。

Q

qualify

    His training qualifies him as a teacher of English.　培训使他成为称职的英语教师。

    He is well qualified for the job.　他完全胜任这份工作。

    He is well qualified to do the job.　他完全胜任这份工作。

quality

    choose the best in quality and the lowest in price　在质量上挑选最好的，价格上挑选最便宜的

    The meat is of a very high quality.　这肉质量很高。

quantity

    Quantities of food are on the table.　桌子上有大量的食物。

    in small quantities　小剂量

quarrel

quarrel about... with her   为……和她争吵

question

Without a passport, leaving the country is out of the question.   如果没有护照，离开这个国家是不可能的。

He is out of question the greatest authority on this subject now.   毫无疑问他就是这门学科的权威。

My health is out of question, so I don't have to be examined.   我的健康没问题，所以我不必检查(身体)。

quick

be quick to do sth.   敏于做某事

quite

for quite a long time   很长时间

quite a lot of people   很多人

quite a few of spelling mistakes   很多错误

quite a bit   很多

quite a birthday party   一次相当不错的生日宴会

R

radio

listen to the news on (over; through) the radio   收听广播新闻

through radio and TV   通过收音机和电视

rain

the wind and light rain   风和小雨

It's raining cats and dogs.   正下着倾盆大雨。

raise

raise your hand   举起你的手

raise pets   饲养宠物

raise money to build the Nightingale Home   筹款建造 Nightingale 护士之家

growing food and raising animals   种植植物，饲养动物

The dots and dashes were raised on the paper.   纸上凸起点和横。

random

at random   随便地；无目的地

range

a range of low mountains   一系列低矮的山脉

a wide range of knowledge   浩瀚的知识

range in ages from 12 to 83   年龄(范围)从 12 岁到 83 岁

The bird is out of range.   那只鸟在射程之外。

rate

    At any rate, I determined to wait for you.　不管怎样，我决心等你。

    a first-rate singer　一流歌手

rather

    rather busy　相当忙

    I am rather better today.　今天我身体好多了。

    This hat is rather more expensive than that one.　这顶帽子比那顶贵得多。

    rather than admit. . .　而不承认……

    I would rather stay at home and watch TV.　我宁可在家里看电视。

    I'd rather do it myself.　我宁可自己做。

reach

    reach different conclusions　得出不同的结论

    reach for the sky　耸入云霄

    I reached for a book.　我伸手去取一本书。

    reach for his gun　伸手去拿他的枪

    reach for his spoon　伸手去拿勺子

    put the bottle of pills out of reach　把药瓶放在够不到的地方

read

    The notice reads. . .　通知说……

    be easy to read　便于阅读，容易被理解

    The letter is read out.　大声宣读这封信。

    read a book through from cover to cover　从头到尾地阅读某本书

ready

    be ready to learn about. . .　准备好了解……

    Don't be ready to cross the street.　不要轻易过马路。

    be ready to journey to the ends of the earth　乐意奔赴天涯海角

realize

    realize a dream　实现个梦想

rear

    at the rear of　在……的后面

reason

    reason out what to do　推断将干什么

    reason with him　和他讲道理

recite

    recite a poem　朗诵一首诗

    recite the text　背诵课文

recent

    the most recent advancement of significance　最新的重要进展

recognize

    recognize 26 letters of the alphabet　辨认字母表里的 26 个字母

    recognize this as a problem　把这当作一个问题看待

    We recognized the new government.　我们承认那个新政府(是合法的)。

record

    set a new record　创新纪录

    keep a record of...　把……记录下来;保存……的记录

recover

    recover from physical or mental illness　从生理或心理疾病中恢复了健康

red

    He will be in the red.　他要负债了。

    out of red　还清债务

reduce

    He was reduced to a beggar then.　他那时落到乞丐的境地。

refer

    refer to...　指向;涉及;谈论到;参考

    He referred his success to his own hard work.　他把成功归功于他自己的努力。

    refer to... as...　把……称作为……

reference

    in the reference room of the library　在图书馆的参考阅览室里

reflect

    Please reflect on what I said to you.　请仔细思考我对你说的话。

reform

    reform and opening up policy　改革开放政策

    with the reform and opening up of our country　随着我国的改革开放

regard

    with (in) regard to our business　关于我们的事情

    as regards to our business　关于我们的事情

    regard A as B　把 A 看作 B

    be regarded as...　被看作为……

    Give my best regards to him.　代我向他问候。

relate

    be related to food　与食物有关

    be related to one's career　与一个人的生涯有关系

    There are magazines relating to different subjects.　有与不同课题有关系的杂志。

relief

    much to everyone's relief　使大家感到宽慰的是

rely

rely on a supply of pure water to live　依靠大量的纯水生存

rely upon it for food　依靠它得到食物

remember

Remember me to your father.　请向你父亲问好。

remind

remind me of sth.　提醒我某事

remind me of the appointment　提醒我有个约会

remind me to have an appointment　提醒我的约会

remove

remove the poison from their wastes　把废弃物中的有毒物质去掉

repair

be under repair　在修理中

reply

reply to it　回答它

report

a report for the year on sth.　一份关于某事的年度报告

rescue

go to their rescue　去营救他们

take a rescue craft　乘一艘救生艇

resolution

The students present all made a New Year's resolution to study harder.　在场的
学生都表了更加努力学习的新年决心。

resistant

resistant to fire, water and electricity　耐火、防水和绝缘

Plastic products can be made resistant to fire.　塑料产品能用来防火。

respond

Please respond to my question.　请回答我的问题。

response

in response to the moment　为了对运动作出反应

responsible

be responsible for...　对……负责;是造成……的原因

rest

take a rest　进行休息

take a short rest　进行短时间的休息

Don't rest your head on your hand.　别把头靠在手上。

The rest (apples) are mine.　剩下的苹果是我的。

The rest (beef) comes from Europe.　剩下的牛肉来自欧洲。

Tom was laid to rest at the foot of the hill.　汤姆被安葬在那座山脚下。

restrict

    We are restricted to 30 kilometres an hour.　我们被限制在每小时 30 公里。

result

    as a result　结果

    as a result of fact　实际上；事实是

    result in serious injures or death　结果导致重伤或死亡

    result from...　是……的结果；由……产生

    His failure resulted from his laziness.　他的失败是他懒惰的结果。

return

    return to the air hostess　回到空姐身边

    in return for his kindness to us　为了报答对我们的好意

    in return for work done　作为对所做工作的报答

    Many happy returns (of the day).　祝你长寿。

reward

    in reward for...　作为……的报酬

    reward him for his help　酬谢他的帮助

    reward him with...　用……酬谢他

rich

    grow rich on...　靠……发财

    rich food　油腻的食物

    the rich top-soil　肥沃的土壤

    The region was rich in natural resources.　这个地区自然资源丰富。

ride

    ride a train　乘火车

    an hour's ride (walk)　一个小时的乘车(步行)路程

    come riding by　骑马路过

    He is taking me for a ride.　他在哄骗我。

right

    All right.　身体正常无事；(情况)顺利正常,没问题；可以

    put... to rights　把……整理好,使……痊愈

    We have a right of way.　我们有通行权。

    be in the right　正确的

    a right angle　一个直角

    right after that　就在那以后；接着

    Are you all right (OK)?　出事了吗?

ring

    He rang off before I could ask his name.　我还来不及问他名字他就放下电话。

    ring me up　打电话给我

ripe

The time was not ripe for election.　选举的时机不成熟。

rise

Prices are rapidly on the rise.　价格在迅速上涨。

ask for a rise　要求增加工资

rise above...　克服……（缺点）

risk

risk doing...　冒险做……

Anyone swimming here does so at one's own risk.　在这里游泳的人风险自己负责。

take a risk of doing...　冒险做……

run a risk　进行冒险

run the risk of killing themselves　冒丧生危险

roar

The engine roared to life.　引擎立刻轰鸣起来。

rob

rob sb. of sth.　抢劫某人的某物

role

play an important role in...　在……方面起了重要作用

room

in the Ladies' Room　在女厕所里

It takes up only a little room.　它只占用一点点空间。

round

all the year round　整年

sit round a stove　坐在火炉四周

The New Year is round.　新年即将来临。

go straight round to the back of the house　一直绕到房子的后面

The doctor soon brought her round.　那位医生很快使她苏醒过来。

route

the Eighth Route Army　八路军

take a shortest route　抄小道

rude

Don't be too rude to him.　别对他太粗鲁。

run

run about　四处奔跑

be run at local government levels　被以当地政府的级别管理

The dog ran at me.　那条狗向我冲过来。

run after...　追赶……

run away from them　逃避它们
run a hospital　管理一所医院
run back inside　跑回里面
run for about 2 weeks　持续大约两周
run on money　涉及钱
run over...　从……上开过去；压死
We ran out of water.　我们昨天把水都用完了。
Water has run out.　水已用完了。
run out into the street　跑到马路上
run short of...　快用完……
run parallel to the Atlantic coast　走向与大西洋海岸平行
in the long run　从长远来说；最后通牒
in the short run　从短期来说
rush
rush out of the house　冲出屋子
rush to the emergency ward　匆匆赶到急诊室（病房）
during the Christmas rush　在圣诞节购物繁忙期间
in the rush hour　上下班时间；交通繁忙时间

S

sack
a sack of wheat　一袋小麦
sadden
sadden sb.（＝make sb. sad）　使某人难过
safety
take sb. to safety　把某人带到安全处
with no thought for one's own safety　不顾自己的安危
sake
for their own sake　出于自己的爱好
sale
for sale　供出售；待售
on sale　出售；（削价）出售
same
do the same for him　同样地对待他
at the same time　同时
Thank you all the same.　仍然要感谢你。
Thank you just the same.　仍然要谢谢你。
I'm in the same boat as you.　我和你处境相同。

sank

　　One's heart sank.　失望了，某人的心凉了半截

Santa

　　Santa Claus（＝Christmas father）　圣诞老人

satisfaction

　　He nodded in satisfaction.　他满意地点了点头。

satisfactory

　　His answer is far from satisfactory.　他的回答远不令人满意。

satisfy

　　The outcome will never satisfy everyone.　其结果永远不会使人人满意。

　　He was satisfied with my answer.　他对我的回答很满意。

save

　　save him a lot of time　节省他许多时间

　　save trouble　省去麻烦

　　save my face　保全我的面子

　　save some of the cakes for tomorrow　留一些蛋糕明天用

say

　　say to yourself　对自己说，轻轻地说

scatter

　　be scattered over the earth　被分散在地球各处

scene

　　on the scene　在现场

　　at the scene of a crime　在犯罪现场

school

　　after school　放学后

　　No school today!　今天没课!

　　The whole school hopes that...　全体师(学)生希望……

　　school board　校管会

　　a school of fish　一群鱼

scream

　　an excited scream of joy　一声欢乐，激动的喊叫

screen

　　on the TV screen　在电视屏幕上

seal

　　be sealed off　被封锁起来

seaside

　　in one seaside holiday town　在一个海边度假镇

search

in search of 为了探索;为了寻找

in order to search for... 为了探索;为了寻找

search his pocket for sth. 搜他的口袋找某物

search through the briefcase 翻那只公文包

I searched all over town for it. 我为它找遍了全城。

seat

Be seated.（＝Sit down.） 请坐下。

invite him to be seated（＝to sit down） 邀请他坐下

second

for the second time 第二次

They use English as a second language. 他们把英语作为另一门外语。

second-hand clothes （二手)旧衣服

Swimming is second to track and field events. 游泳仅次于田径项目。

second only to Chinese in number of speakers 仅次于讲汉语的人数

I am second to none. 我第一名。

section

in the first section 在第一个栏目里

a small section on photography 关于摄影的小栏目

see

I see. 我明白了。

I'll see what flight there are. 我了解一下有什么航班。

April 2nd saw the opening of the meeting 四月二日会议开幕了。

see to the visitors 照顾客人

see to it that... 保证;注意

Could you see to it that...? 你务必做到(保证做到)……?

see you off at the station 到车站给你送行

Seeing that it is ten oclock, we... 既然时间十点了,我们……

send

send back some food 送回一些食物

send the dog away 把那条狗送走

send for a doctor 派人去请医生来

send us floating off 使我们漂离

be sent to sb. 被送给某人

Please send my love to your father.（＝give my warmest regards to your father.) 请向你父亲问好。

send them into the air or the rivers 把它们排入空气中或河里

senior

Senior High School One, Class One 高一(1)班

467

He is three years senior to me.　他比我大三岁。

sense

　　the sense of hearing　听觉

　　the sense of sight　视觉

　　the sense of smell　嗅觉

　　the sense of taste　味觉

　　the sense of touch　触觉

　　the sense of true and false　是非观

　　the sense of pride　自豪感

　　the sense of humour　幽默感

sentence

　　He was sentenced to death.　他被判处死刑。

separate

　　separate A from B　把 A 和 B 分开

series

　　a series of...　一系列的……

serve

　　He will serve as mayor.　他将当市长。

　　serve the people　为人民服务

　　Dinner is served here.　这儿供应饭。

　　serve to show...　有助于显示出……

　　serve to help him　有助于帮助他

　　serve to strengthen Britain's link with the continent　起到加强英国和欧洲大陆
　　　的联系作用

service

　　Will you do me a service?　请你帮个忙好吗？

　　service to the sick and suffering　对病人和受难者的服务

set

　　The sun sets in the west.　太阳在西边落下。

　　set about doing sth.　着手做某事

　　set about preparing for forthcoming game　着手准备即将来临的比赛

　　Be sure to set aside enough time.　一定要留出足够的时间。

　　set out to conquer a mountain　出发去征服一座山

　　set out the facts　阐明这些事实

　　set out to do sth.　着手做某事

　　A new set of film actors appeared.　一批新的电影演员涌现出来了。

　　be set free　被释放了

　　set up　建立

settle

    settle down in Vienna   在维也纳定居

shall

    You shall have a computer if you do it better.   如果干好了，我给你台电脑。

    You shall have your wish.   你定要实现你的愿望。

shame

    What a shame!、   多遗憾！

shape

    be odd in shape   形状奇怪的

    a huge kite in the shape of a phoenix   一只巨大的凤凰形状的风筝

    take shape（＝come into being）   形成了

share

    share the Noble Prizes for physics with sb.   与某人共享诺贝尔物理奖

    share the blame   承担责备

    share in one's troubles as well as his happiness   同甘共苦

    share with him   与他共享

sharp

    make many sharp turns   做许多急转弯

    It is nine o'clock sharp.   时间 9 点整。

    a sharp contrast   鲜明的对照

shake

    shook hands with him   和他握手

    shook the other Hunter by the hand   握着另一个亨特的手

    shake some salt on...   洒些盐在……上

shoot

    shoot at a lion   向一只狮子射击

    shoot a lion   射中(死)一只狮子

    shoot out of the window   （火焰)蹿出窗户

shop

    do some shopping   购物

shore

    get the man to shore   把那个人救到岸上

short

    be short of something   短缺某物

    make a shortcut   走近路,走捷径

    in short   总之

shout

    shout to him   向他大叫

shout at him　愤怒地向他大叫

shout the question again　又大声问那个问题

shoulder

shoulder to shoulder　肩并肩

have a satchel on one's shoulders　肩上背着书包

show

on show　展出;陈列出来

show your student's card　出示你的学生证

show off　炫耀

He always shows off with his knowledge of literature.　他只是炫耀自己的文学知识。

shower

take a shower　洗淋浴

be caught in a shower　淋到了阵雨

skim

skim it through　浏览一遍

side

side effect　副作用

side by side　肩并肩

take the side of you　站在你一边;支持你

at her side　在她的旁边

on the other side of the street　在马路的对面

The side streets were repaired.　那些小马路在修理。

sight

in sight　在视线内;可以看见

out of sight　看不见了

The plane is out of sight.　那架飞机看不见了。

at the sight of him　一看到他

catch sight of him　看见他

at first sight　乍一看（第一眼）

sign

traffic signs　交通标志

in sign language　用手语

a solid sign of Shanghai　上海的坚实的象征

sign up for an interview with...　报名参加……面试

sign out　登记离开

sign to us with his hand　做手势

similar

The climate is similar to that of other continental areas. 这里的气候与其他大陆地区的气候相同。

simplify

some simplified stories 一些被简写了的故事

They are all simplified versions. 它们都是简写本。

sink

sink in 渗透下去,下沉

sit

sit about 坐着没事干

sit round 坐着没事干

She could do nothing but sit down. 她只能坐下来。

sit on a cushion of air 坐在一个气垫上

sit up（＝stay up） 坐起来,熬夜

sit up late（＝stay up late） 熬夜到很晚

sit up till after midnight 守过午夜

site

the site of her old house 她的老房子的旧址（遗址）

size

become small in size 尺寸上变小了

a hole the size of an orange 一个橘子大小的洞

slave

be slaves to... 全力尽忠于……

sleep

The man is in a sound sleep. 这个人睡得正熟（香）。

go to sleep 入睡

the deepest level of sleep 睡得最熟

the lightest level of sleep 睡眠不酣

sleepy

The village is too sleepy. 这个村庄太宁静了。

be sleepy 有睡意,困倦的

slip

slip from his grasp and fell to the floor 没有抓牢,滑到地上

slipped from his horse 从马背上滑下来

smile

smile at sb. 向某人微笑

smile wisely at the king 机智地向国王笑了笑

with a smile 带着微笑

smoke

smoke one's head off　不停地抽烟

so

in doing so　在这么做的时候

be so kind as to open the window　请把窗打开（如此善良以至于把窗打开）

so large an ocean　那么大的海洋

So I have heard.　这情况我确实听说过。

So Della did.　Della 确实这么做了

As..., so...　就像……一样

As bees love sweetness, so flies love rottenness.　苍蝇就像蜜蜂喜欢甜食一样喜欢腐烂的东西。

so much... as...　与其说是……，倒不如说……

He isn't so much ill as depressed.（＝He is depressed rather than ill.）　与其说他病了，倒不如说感到沮丧……

not so much as...　连……都不（肯）

He won't so much as look at me.　他连看我一眼都不肯。

soft

the soft breeze on the skin　微风拂面

solve

solve problems　解决问题

some

some thirty years ago　大约 30 年前

something

He is something of a singer.　他是个相当不错的歌手。

have something to do with everyone's lives　与每个人的生活有关系

sorrow

be in deep sorrow　沉浸在悲哀中

sound

That sounds splendid.　那一切听起来很好。

source

a great source of nutrition　一个很大的营养源泉

south

in 17 counties south of a line from Liverpoor to Humber　在从 Liverpoor 到 Humber 这一线南面的 17 个郡内

sow

As a man sows, so he shall reap.　种瓜得瓜，种豆得豆。

space

in space　在宇宙里

within a small space　在一个小空间里

spare

   in his spare time　在业余时间

   during our spare time　在我们的业余时间

   spare time to do sth.　挤出时间

   a spare tyre　一只备用轮胎

speak

   speak highly of him　高度评价他

   speak ill of him　讲他坏话

   can't speak too highly of him　再表扬他也不会过分

   speak out against...　大胆反对……

   speak up　坦率说出自己的看法;说大声点

   tend to speak like a book　滔滔不绝地发言

   generally speaking　一般来说

   strictly speaking　严格地讲

   English-speaking people　讲英语的人

specialize

   specialize in medicine　专攻医学

   The company is specializing in books.　这家公司专门营销图书。

   specialized persons　专业人员

   specialized high schools　中等专科学校

species

   certain species of birds　某些种类的鸟

speed

   with lightning speed　有闪电般的速度

   with very great speed　(动作)快速地

   at a great speed　以很快的速度;迅速地(奔;跑;行;驶)

   speed up　加速

spend

   spend a few days with an American　和一位美国人一起度过几天

   spend his childhood in hard work　在艰苦的工作中度过他的童年

   spend their money on candy　花很多钱买糖果

   spend time on it　把时间花在它上面

   Many happy hours she had spent trying to think of something nice for him.　她花了许多小时愉快地考虑着为他买的东西(此句倒装,many happy hours 是 spent 的宾语)

spilt

   spilt milk over your composition paper　把牛奶泼在你的作文纸上

spin

473

She spinned up her hair again.　她又把头发用发夹夹好。

spot

  a scenic spot　一个景点

  on the spot　在现场

spread

  Word spread quickly.　消息很快传开。

  The disease has spread over the whole country.　这种疾病在全国蔓延。

  spread from country to country　从一个国家传到另一个国家

  spread the world map out flat　把世界地图摊平

spring

  in spring　在春天

  in the spring　在这年春天

squash

  I feel squashed all over.　我感到全身受挤压。

squeeze

  manage to squeeze through　设法挤进去

stand

  stand about　站在四周

  stand for　代表,象征

  The stands were packed.　座无虚席。

  stand up to...　经得起……;敢于面对……

stare

  stare at Della　盯着黛拉看

start

  in order to get an early start　为了早动身

  Your life started as a single cell.　你的生命由一个单细胞开始。

  start out　出发

  woke up with a start　惊醒过来

state

  He is in a strange state of mind.　他精神状态不正常。

  Matter has three states, solid, liquid and gas.　物质有三种状态:固态、液态和
    气态。

stay

  stay healthy　保持健康

  stay at home　待在家里(过平静的生活)

  stay in bed　躺在床上

  stay for another cup of tea　留下来再喝一杯茶

  stay up（＝sit up）　熬夜

step

  watch your step   走路小心

  step by step   一步步地

  take steps（a step）to improve their school   采取措施改善他们的学校

  make big steps in doing sth.   在做某事方面已迈进几大步

  at a step in the process   整个过程中的每一步

  The door opened and Jim stepped in.   门开了,吉姆跨进来了。

  step on the gas   踩油门；加快

stick

  stick to doing sth.   坚持做某事

  A bone stuck in my throat.   一块骨头卡在我的喉咙里。

  still

  stood still   静静地站在那儿

  sit still   坐着不动

  Still waters run deep.   大智若愚。

stock

  on the stock market   在股票市场

  be stocked with printed works   备有出版

  Red ink is out of stock.   红墨水没有存货。

stone

  A hotel is only a stone's throw away.   旅馆只离投掷一石之遥。

  within a stone's throw of the station   离车站很近

stop

  stop smoking   停止抽烟

  stop a passing car   拦一辆过路轿车

  stop Marie from continuing their work   阻止 Marie 继续工作

store

  store up   储备起来

storey

  the five-storeyed building   那幢五层大楼

stove

  She had the pots and pans on the stove.   她把罐和锅放在炉子上。

strand

  be stranded in deserts   被困在沙漠里

street

  on the street   在街上

  in the street   在街上

stretch

475

stretch oneself 伸懒腰

stretch one's arms and legs 伸懒腰

stretch your shoes 把你的鞋撑大

strict

    be strict with him 对他严格要求

    be strict in his work 对他的工作严格要求

strike

    The clock struck twelve. 钟敲十二点。

    as the clock strikes midnight 当钟敲响午夜十二点时

    He was struck by... 他被……迷住了

    He was struck by her wisdom. 他被她的智慧迷住了。

    The little girl struck（擦）the matches one by one. 小女孩一根一根地擦亮火柴。

    He struck a light. 他擦了根火柴。/他打了个火。

    He struck me on the head. 他打我的头。

    a hunger strike 一次绝食斗争

    All the railway workers struck（罢工）in August. 八月所有铁道工人罢工。

    It struck（使……突然想到）me that I would have a meeting. 我突然想到我要开个会。

    The enemy struck（袭击）the village at dawn. 黎明时分敌人袭击了村庄。

    The sun struck（照射）the hill top. 太阳照在山顶上。

    The strains of music struck（吸引）his ear. 音乐的曲调吸引了他的耳朵。

    The ship struck（触）an iceberg (on a rock). 轮船触到冰山（触礁）了。

    The snake struck（咬）me. 蛇咬了我一口。

strive

    strive to do it well 努力把它做好

style

    different styles of rituals 不同的礼仪方式

substitute

    substitute a donut and a cup of coffee for a well balanced meal 用一只油炸面圈和一杯咖啡代替一餐均衡的膳食

    substitute for other players 代替其他队员

succeed

    succeed in passing the gate 成功地通过那扇门

    succeed in getting the prize 成功地得到奖金

successful

    be less than successful 不太成功

such

    a sport such as bowling 像保龄球一类的运动

I like such sports as basketball and football.　我喜欢像篮球、足球这一类的运动。

suffer

　　suffer from a serious disease　身体患有疾病,受尽疾病痛苦

　　suffer from cold and hunger　受饥寒交迫之苦

suggestion

　　I have a suggestion for you.　我给你提个建议。

suit

　　Does it suit me?　它适合我吗?

　　if the blood type does not suit him　假如血型不适合他

suitable

　　Only a few breeds are suitable for police work.　只有几种狗适合警务工作。

　　He is suitable for the job.　他(在能力上)适合这工作。

sum

　　a large sum of money　一大笔钱

　　small sums of money　少量的钱

　　large sums of money　大笔大笔的钱

supply

　　supply sb. with. . .　用……供应某人

　　supply. . . to sb.　用……供应某人

　　. . . be supplied to animals for their health　为了动物的健康,……被供应给动物

　　a plentiful supply of trees　大量的树

support

　　support his family　维持他的家庭

　　support from the fans　来自球迷的支持

suppose

　　be supposed to help him　应该帮助他

sure

　　be sure of. . .　相信……

　　be sure about. . .　对……有把握

　　Don't be so sure of yourself.　不要那么自信。

　　I am sure/certain that. . .　我相信……肯定……/务必……

　　be sure to fail　一定(将)失败

　　be sure to conquer sth.　一定会克服(困难)

　　make sure that. . .　(把)……查明;(把)……弄清楚;设法确保

　　make sure of. . .　(把)……查明;(把)……弄清楚;设法确保

　　He went round, making sure that all the windows were closed.　他巡视了一遍,看看所有的窗都已关上。

　　for sure(＝for certain＝surely)　肯定

477

surface

  on the surface of water　在水面上

surprise

  be surprised to see...　惊奇地看见……

  in surprise　惊奇地

  We are surprised at his appearance.　我们对他的出现感到很吃惊。

surrounding

  in certain surroundings　在某些周围环境里

  in our surroundings　在我们的环境中

suspect

  suspect sb. of doing...　怀疑某人做……

  He was suspected of stealing...　他被怀疑偷了……

suspense

  be in suspense　担心,焦虑

swallow

  swallow up their homes　吞没了他们的家

  His heart jumped into his mouth and then he swallowed it.　他那时很激动,后来才平静下来。

  swallow a smile　忍住不笑

switch

  switch the light off　关灯

  switch the light on　开灯

symbol

  H is the symbol for hydrogen.　H 是氢的化学符号。

T

table

  sit at a table　坐在桌旁

  be at table　在(餐桌边)吃饭

  be at table having supper　在餐桌边吃晚饭

tailor

  tailor... to...　使……适合……

  The program was tailored to the needs of young children.　这个节目适合小孩的需要。

  a tailor's (shop)　一家服装店

take

  take a cake along　随身带块蛋糕去

  Learning to swim takes time and effort.　学游泳需要时间和精力。

take after sb.　长得像某人

take away with them memories of its beauty　把美丽景色的记忆带回去

Take it easy, please.　请不要紧张。

take on　雇用;开始具有

take on a new look　呈现出新面貌

take in　吸收;欺骗;(把衣服)改小

take in the most of the mountainous areas　包括大多数的山区

take...lying down　甘心接受不愉快的情况

He didn't take his defeat lying down.　他不甘心失败。

take off　起飞;营救;脱(衣,帽,鞋);模仿(别人的讲话)

before the take-off time　在起飞时间以前

take over...　接管;接受

take part in　参加

take the boy to the hospital　带这个男孩去医院

take my grandpa to the hospital　带我爷爷到医院里去

take some medicine　吃一些药

take steps to prevent the river from being polluted　采取措施阻止河流被污染

take 2 pounds out of the pocket　从口袋里拿出两英镑

take time out to do sth.　挤出时间

take a No. 10 bus　乘十路公共汽车

take a bus to cross the bridge　乘公共汽车过桥

take the 12:30 train for Beijing　乘十二点半开往北京的火车

take the elevator　乘电梯

be taken from...　摘自于……

be taken from a fairy tale　摘自于一个神话故事

be taken out　被带出去

take up...　从事;占有,占用(时间或空间);接受

take up hobbies　从事业余爱好

talk

talk over the matter with Mary　和玛丽商量那件事

talk over it with him　和他商量这事

talk it with him　和他商量这事

talk shows　访谈节目

taxi

get a taxi　雇一辆出租车

Let's take a taxi.　让我们乘出租车吧。

teach

teach sth. to sb.　把某事教给某人

I taught myself English last year. 我去年自学英语。

tear

  tear at the string and paper 扯断了绳子,撕开了包装纸

  tear up grass 把草拔起

tear

  Tears came to his eyes. 他热泪盈眶。

  bring tears to her eyes 使她热泪盈眶

  A tear or two ran down her face. 一两滴眼泪从她脸颊上淌下来。

telephone

  telephone for an ambulance 打电话叫救护车

tell

  tell one from the other 区别两者

  tell the difference between them 区别两者

  tell sb. the truth 跟某人说实话

  tell them apart 区别(分辨)它们

temper

  get into a temper 突然发脾气

  lose one's temper 发脾气

temperate

  in the temperate zone 在温带

temperature

  have a temperature 发烧

terminal

  Let's meet at the terminal of Bus No. 26. 我们在 26 路公共汽车终点站见面。

ten

  nine out of ten 十有八九

test

  a simple blood test 一项简单的血液测试

  be tested on the same questions 被以同样的问题测试

  test a large number of people 对大量的人进行测试

than

  better than any other painting 比其他油画更好

  better than the other paintings 比其他油画更好

thank

  Thank goodness! 谢天谢地!

  thank sb. for sth. 感谢某人某事

  Thank you once again. 再次感谢你。

  Many thanks indeed. 真的很感谢。

thanks to... (＝because of...)　多亏……

I owe thanks to you for this priceless gift.　感谢你这无价之宝。

thankful

　　be thankful to sb. for the news　因那则消息感谢某人

that

　　That is (＝That is to say)　也就是说

　　That's it! (＝That's just right!)　就是这样！(那正是合适的！)

　　That's that!　就这样！

　　that much　那么多

then

　　from then on　从那时起(用过去时)

There

　　There on the ground lay a boy.　一个男孩躺在那儿的地上。

think

　　think back to the end of the Ice Age　回顾到冰川时期末

　　Think before you act.　三思而后行。

　　think of anything to say　想到要讲的事

　　think only of sth.　只想到某事

　　think of... as...　把……看作……

　　Think nothing of it.　不用谢。/请别想这件事。

　　think of building a free state　考虑建立一个自由的国家

　　What did you think of it?　你怎样想这件事？

　　What do you think of all the tests at school?　你对学校里所有的测验是怎样想的？

　　think highly of　高度评价

thought

　　He is in deep thought.　他在沉思中。

　　have no thought of...　没想到……

　　It was thoughtful of you to do sth.　你做事考虑很周到。

thousand

　　thousands of tons of earth　成千上万吨土

threaten

　　be threatened with extinction　受到灭绝的威胁

three

　　three-fifths of...　五分之三的……

through

　　understand each other through English　通过英语互相理解

　　pass through the canal　通过了这条运河

serve others through her work as a nurse　通过她的护士工作为别人服务

go through the gate　穿过那扇门

get through...　通过,完成,到达

throw

throw light on sth.　阐明某事

be kidnapped and thrown into prison　被绑架并打入监狱

throw the bag out of the window　把那只包扔出窗外

throw sth. over the side of his ship　把……越过船沿扔过去

throw cold water over it　把冷水泼在岩石上

throw a stone at the dog　用一块石头砸那条狗

thrust

thrust at sb.　用刀、剑等向某人猛刺

tie

The horse was tied to the tree.　那匹马被系在树上。

tide

tide over difficulties　克服困难

time

time and again　再

all the time　一直

have no time for doing　没时间做……

in a short time　在短时间内

The sun is about 250,000 times closer to the earth than any other star.　太阳离
　　地球比其他星球近 25 万倍。

time table　时刻表

in his time　在他的时代

from the beginning of time　历来;从有时代开始以来

from time to time　有时,时而

at times　有时

at that time　在那时

by that time　到那时为止

have a good time　玩得很高兴

have a wonderful time　玩得很高兴

in ancient times　在古代

in no time　立刻,马上

in time　及时,终于

on time　准时

at the right time　就在那时候

at such times　此时此刻

at other times　在其他时候

at these times　在这些时候

at all times　任何时候；经常

at the same time　同时

at some time（＝sometimes）　有时

at a time　每一次

at one time　一度

at no time　决不

for the tenth time　第十次

This is the third time that I have cried.　这是我第三次哭了。

against time　抢时间；尽快地

Take your time about it, please.　请别着急，慢慢来。

part time and flexible working pattern　部分时间弹性工作制

tip

on the tip of my tongue　就在舌尖上；几乎记得

tiptoe

on tiptoe　踮着脚尖

tired

feel tired and dizzy　感到又累又头晕

be tired　累了

be tired of...　对……厌倦

They are tired of mending...　他们厌倦修理……

begin to grow tired of it　开始厌倦它

too

ask too much　要求太高

too busy making a living to have many hobbies　太忙于谋生，以致于没有业余爱好

two inches too long　长了两英寸

Students can't be too careful in the examination.　学生考试时越仔细越好。

top

at the top of a giant mountain　在高山之巅

at the top of her voice　声嘶力竭地

on the top of the building　在大楼顶部

They felt on top of the world.　他们感到高兴之极（兴高采烈）。

at the topmost　最顶层，最上面的

touch

keep in touch with...　保持联系

tour

make a concert tour　进行巡回演出

make a successful tour of Austria　做一次去奥地利的成功的巡回演出

touch

    touch on everyone's lives　与每个人的生活有关系

    get people in touch with...　使人们与……取得联系

    keep people in touch with...　使人们与……保持联系

    keep in touch with sb. by telephone　通过电话保持联系

    bring me into touch with...　使我与……有接触

    touch him on the shoulder　触摸他的肩膀(一定要用"the")

towards

    towards evening　快到傍晚的时候

town

    in town and in suburbs　在市区和郊区

trace

    trace... back to the sun　追溯……到太阳

traditional

    traditional downtown area　传统市区

trade

    trade sth. for sth.　用……换取……

traffic

    at the traffic lights　在红绿灯处

train

    a slow train　一列慢车

    an express train　一列快车

    a non-stop train　一列直达车

translate

    translate it into Japanese　把它译成日文

    translate the passage into English word for word　把短文逐词逐句地译成英语

trap

    be trapped in...　被困在(……地方)

treat

    treat you as one of my family　像自己人一样对待

    treat with...　与……贸易;与……谈判;与……商谈

    treat you to lunch　请客吃饭

trick

    trick and treating　不请吃就捣蛋

trembling

    in a trembling voice　用颤抖的声音

trip

This is our first trip away from home.　这是我们第一次离家旅游。

organize a short trip to...　组织到……短途旅游

take a trip　进行旅游

make a trip　进行旅游

go on a trip　进行旅游

go on long trips through space　作太空长途旅行

tropic

in the tropic　在热带

trouble

be in trouble　在困境中；遇难

have no trouble doing...　做……没困难，做……不费劲

trouble in doing sth.　费劲做某事

have trouble with spelling　拼写有困难

have trouble with those male students　与那些男学生有麻烦事

Have you any trouble?　你有什么困难/麻烦吗?

put you to trouble（of doing sth.）　为做某事给你增添麻烦

have trouble（difficulty 不可数）in doing sth.　费劲做某事

trouser

a new pair of trousers　一条新裤子

truant

play truant　逃学

true

His dream has come true.　他的梦想已实现了。

true-to-life images　身临其境的影像

truth

to tell you the truth　说老实话

This is very far from the truth.　这远非事实。/这根本不是事实。

try

try his best to finish the task　尽最大努力完成这项任务

try out　试用

try putting on the pair of shoes　试穿这双鞋

try to find the patterns and the rules for themselves　自己设法找到句型和语法规则

turn

be turned away　被撵走

turn away from the man-made town to the untouched country　从人工创造的城镇转向未被开发的乡村

turn rain into acid　把雨变成酸

turn the radio down a bit　把收音机关得轻一点

turn the radio up a bit　把收音机开得响一点

turn on the power socket　开启电源

turn off the power socket　关掉电源

I'd better turn it off.　我最好把它关掉。

turn out　结果是;证明是;生产出

stay warm by turning up the heat　通过扭开取暖器取暖

It turned to gold.　它就变成了黄金。

turn to the left　向左转

turn to Channel 20　转到二十频道

turn to sb. (for help)　求助于某人

She turned away from the window.　她从窗户那儿转过身来。

turn out his pockets　翻遍他的口袋

take the first turning　转第一个弯

take a wrong turning　走错了路,转错了弯

turn right and go straight on　右转弯,然后一直朝前走

take his turn　轮到他

Her face turned red.　她的脸变红了。

in one's turn　轮到某人

It turns out that...　结果是……

turn over　移交;翻(页);翻转

turn up　来赴约;出席;赶到场

TV

stop watching news on TV　停止看电视新闻

type

Tom is a person with type A B.　汤姆是个 AB 血型的人。

a type of...　一类……

U

unable

be unable to do sth.　不能(无能力)做某事

under

be under way　在进行中

be under repair　正在修理

have a conversation under water　在水下进行谈话

go far under the water　到深水处去

by tunnel under the river　通过水下隧道

understand

reach my understanding　成功地使我理解

　　be difficult to understand　理解起来很难

　　He can make himself understood.　他能让别人理解自己的意思。

union

　　a trade union　工会

unequal

　　be unequal to the task　不能胜任这项工作

unsporting

　　an unsporting player　一个无运动道德的运动员

unaware

　　be unaware of...　未认识到；未觉察到

up

　　go up　上升

　　up and down the river　在河里川流不息

　　move up and down the street　在马路上川流不息

　　carry up to 30 million passengers a year　一年运送多达三百万乘客

　　It is up to me to decide.　这由我来决定。

　　up-to-date　最新的，现代的

upon

　　upon the thin layer of air　在这么一薄层空气上

　　place her hand upon my shoulder　把她的手放在我的肩上

　　upon completion of the subways　这些地铁一完成

upside

　　The head is upside down.　头朝下。

upstairs

　　go upstairs/go downstairs　上楼/下楼

use

　　have some practical use　有某些实际的用途

　　be in use　被使用

　　put the station into use　这车站交付使用了

　　use the power within their own minds to stop the disease　用他们头脑中蕴藏的
　　　力量治愈疾病

　　make use of...　利用……

　　make good use of...　充分利用……

　　make the most of...　充分利用……

　　use their own minds to fight their diseases　用他们的意志与疾病作斗争

　　use college students as volunteers　使用大学生做志愿者

　　be used as a pen　被用作笔

be used for writing 被用来书写

It is used for surveying. 它被用来测量。

use the money for further experiment on the uses of radium 把这笔钱用于进一步试验镭元素的用途

use the money on further experiments on the uses of radium 把钱用在镭元素使用的进一步实验上

be used in studies 被使用在学习上

be used to treat pneumonia 被用来治疗肺炎

be used to measure the ocean 被用来测量海洋

be used to giving... 习惯于给……

get used to their way of living 习惯于他们的生活方式

used to go a long way 过去要走很长的路

used to leave your bike here 过去把自行车停放在这里

used to play quite a lot 过去放录音带放得很多;玩得很多

until

until a little while ago 直到刚才;一会儿前

usual

as usual 像平常一样

V

vapour

with vapour 精力充沛地

vain

in vain 徒劳;白费力气

He waited in vain. 他白等了。

variety

a variety of breakfasts 各式各样的早饭

very

the very same day 恰恰/正好就在同一天

video

video and audio tapes 音像带

views

to get better views 得到更好的视野

have a definite objective in view 心里有一个明确的目的

be viewed as... 被看作为……

A long 60-degree right hand turn comes into view. 一个高难度的60度转弯出现在眼前。

Have you had a clear view of the princess? 你们看清了公主没有?

violence

    do violence to prisoners　凶暴地虐待俘虏

visit

    visit with sb.　和某人交谈

    visiting hours　探望病人的时间

    pay a visit to China　访问中国

vital

    These matters are vital for（或 to）national economy.　这些事对国民经济至关
      重要。

voyage

    go on a voyage　去航行

    take a voyage　进行旅游

    make a voyage　进行旅游

W

wait

    wait a long time for him　等了他好长时间

    wait for　等候……

    wait for the teacher to explain　等候老师解释

wake

    wake him up　叫醒他

    wake quickly out of dream　从迷惘中很快清醒过来

    wake up in his bed　在床上醒着

walk

    only 10 minutes' walk　只有十分钟的步行路程

    It is five minutes' walk away　距离只有五分钟的步行路程

    walk straight ahead　笔直朝前走

    walk along the river　沿着河散步

    walk into the room　走进教室

    walk over to sb.　向某人走去

    walk around the room　在阅览室里走动（兜圈子）

    walk round the huge department store　在百货商店里东游西逛

wander

    wander through the city　在城里闲逛

want

    want sth. done　要（某人）做某事

    You are wanted by the New York police.　你是被纽约警察当局通缉的人。

warn

warn sb. of... 警告某人当心……

　　warn sb. not to do... 警告某人不做……

　　warn sb. against doing... 警告某人不做……

wash

　　wash over a wide, low plain （洪水）冲上了一片宽阔的低地

　　wash up 洗（餐具）

　　do the washing up 洗餐具

watch

　　watch him repairing the bike 注视着他修理自行车

　　watch TV 看电视

　　Watch out! 当心！

waterhole

　　by the waterhole 在水坑边

wave

　　wave to sb. 向某人挥手

way

　　the way to the station 到车站的路

　　in his way 挡他的路

　　in this way 用这样的方法

　　（in）this way 用这样的方法

　　in many other ways 在其他许多方面

　　in no way 决不

　　make her way to the library 前往图书馆

　　make her way back to the snack bar 走回到点心店

　　in a number of ways 在许多方面，用几种方法

　　in many different ways 用许多不同的方法

　　that way 那样地；用那样的方法

　　in its own way 用它自己独特的方法

　　by the way 顺便问一下

　　By the way, how old are you? 顺便问一下，你几岁了？

　　get in one's way 挡路

　　go back the same way 原路返回

　　be already under way 已在进行中

　　in some way 在某种程度上，在某方面

　　Help is on the way for sb. 对某人的帮助正在展开

　　I'll be on my way. 我要走了。

　　continue on his way 继续上了路

　　in a way 以某种方法；在某种程度上

490

take me far out of my way   带我兜大圈子

weak

Betty is weak in (at) judgment.   贝蒂不善于判断。

wear

wear it in her beautiful hair   把它戴在她漂亮的头发上

wear her hair short   留着短头发

wear his beard short   留着短胡须

weather

What's the weather forecast for today?   今天的天气预报怎样?

What will the weather be like today?   今天的天气怎样?

work in all weathers   在各种天气里工作

weekend

especially at weekends   特别在周末

for the weekend   过周末

weigh

Water weighs 800 times as much as air.   水的重量是空气的八百倍。

have to weigh at first this parcel   得先称一称这个包裹

welcome

welcome the new family to our neighbourhood   欢迎新业主入住我们的街区。

well

as well as   除了……外(也)……

Mr. Li as well as his students goes to the cinema every Sunday.   除了李先生的
学生每星期日去看电影外,李先生也去看电影。

Well begun is half done.   良好的开始,成功的一半。

western

The western third of the country   靠西边三分之一的国土

what

What a pity!   多遗憾!

What's the postage on/for this parcel?   这件包裹的邮资多少?

What's the price of this one?   这张画的价格是多少?

when

There will be times when   有时

where

Where there's a will, there's a way.   有志者,事竟成。

whether

whether you are awake or asleep   不管你睡着还是醒着(作状语从句)

while

for a while   一会儿

after a while　一会儿后

whistles

　blow whistles　吹口哨,鸣汽笛

whisper

　whisper about me　低声谈论我的事

　in a whisper　用(耳语)很轻的声音

went

　She went very white.　她脸色变得苍白。

who

　I know who's who on the screen.　我知道银幕上的名人。

whole

　on the whole　大体上

　as a whole　总体上

　for three whole days　三整天

willing

　be willing to do sth.　愿意做某事;决心做某事

win

　We won at volleyball, but lost at tennis.　排球我们赢了,但网球输了。

　win top honours　赢得最高荣誉

　win the hearts of the audience　赢得听众们的爱戴

　have two ways to win　有两种方法取胜

window

　stood by the window　站在窗户旁

wine

　how to make wine　怎样酿酒

wisdom

　be of great wisdom　很聪敏

wish

　It is my wish (hope) to do sth.　我希望做某事。

　Let's make a wish that...　让我们祝愿……

　Wish her good health and a long life.　祝她健康长寿。

with

　together with their patients　和他们的病人一起

　His ambition to be a musician was still with him.　他想当音乐家的志向未变。

　with it held tightly in her hand　紧紧地把它握在手中

　with my ears and neck burning　我的耳朵和脖子红了

　with a lot of food in it　里面有很多食物

　The hill is green with trees.　这山上都是树。

with the great increase in... 随着……的增加

with the development of... 随着……发展

with patients in the treatment of their disorders 病人在身心机能失调的治疗时

a girl with red hair 一个长着红头发的女孩

with his head lower than his body 头要低于身体

with no time to play 没时间玩耍

with a lighted cigarette in his mouth 嘴里叼着支已被点燃的香烟

with these six holes in different positions 在不同的位置有六个洞

with every member of the family participating 全家参与

with the wind on your face 风迎面吹来

with a lamp past each bed 掌着一盏灯走过每一张病床

with an unlighted cigar in his mouth 口中衔着一支未被点燃的雪茄

with the money to buy Jim a present 用这笔钱为吉姆买礼物

want wood to cook their food with 需要用来做饭的木头

within an hour 在一小时内

witness

a witness to a car accident 一名汽车事故的目击者

wonder

no wonder 难怪

accomplish wonders 创造奇迹

work (do) wonders 创造奇迹

It's nothing to wonder at... ……不足为奇

word

build my word power 为了增强我的词汇能力

copy it down word for word 把它一个词一个词地抄下来

have a word with Jane 和简交谈

with words （口头上）用语言

in words （书面上）用语言

in a word 总之

in other words 换言之

work

by working hard at sth. 通过努力干某事

a hard-working people 一个勤劳的民族

work on my vocabulary （从事于）扩大我的词汇量

The body is continually at work. 身体仍在不停地工作。

be out of work 失业

work out a system of marks for music 解决一个音乐符号系统

works of arts and crafts 工艺品

493

world

    throughout the world　全世界

    all over the world　全世界

    by people the world over　被全世界的人

    around the world　全世界

    the world's saltiest ocean　世界上最咸的海洋

    be world-famous for sth.　以……闻名世界

worry

    worry about...　为……感到担忧

    He was worried about his son.　他为他儿子担忧。

    never need to worry about what to do with their leisure hours　从来不必为怎样
        处理他们的业余时间而发愁

worse

    what was worse　更糟糕的事情是

worth

    be worth one point　值一分

    I bought ten dollars' worth of food.　我买了价值 10 美元的食物。

    An ounce of prevention is worth a pound of cure.　预防胜于治疗。

    A bird in hand is worth two in the bush.　多得，不如现得。

    They are not worth a penny more than two pounds.　它们只值两英镑。

    be well worth buying　很值得买

    do sth. worthwhile　做值得做的事（意译：有所成就）

    be worth mentioning again　值得再提一下

    a worthless desert　毫无用处的沙漠

worthy

    The film is worthy of being seen again.　这部电影值得再看一遍。

    The film is worthy to be seen again.　这部电影值得再看一遍。

    be worthy of sth.　与某物相配

wrap

    be wrapped in a blanket　被毯子裹上

    The earth is wrapped in a blanket of air.　地球被裹上了一层空气。

write

    write in　填写；写进去

    write down　写下来

    write back to him　写回信给他

wrong

    take the wrong bus　乘错了车

    be in the wrong　错误的

go wrong 出了毛病,变坏了
There is something wrong with his bike. 他的自行车出毛病了。
Something is wrong with his bike. 他的自行车出毛病了。
do him wrong (＝do wrong to him) 冤枉他;委屈他

X

X-mas is short for Christmas. X-mas 是 Christmas 的缩写。
X-ray X 射线

Y

year
　the 27-year-old Darwin 那位 27 岁的达尔文
youth
　in their youth 在年轻的时候
　yes-man 唯唯诺诺的人

Z

zero
　−8℃ (＝eight degrees centigrade below zero) 零下八度
　zebra crossing 人行横道
　zero growth (人口)零增长

单项练习答案

第一讲　三种基本句型

1—5	DDBAC	6—10	DADDC	11—15	ABABA
16—20	CCBBC	21—25	BABCB	26—30	CBCCD
31—35	AABBD	36—40	AABDC	41—45	CABBC
46—50	CCDDC	51—55	DDBCC	56—60	DADAA
61—65	AADCB	66—70	CCDCD	71—75	DBADA

第二讲　倒　装　句

1—5	BADBB	6—10	DCADA	11—15	CCBAC
16—20	BACCC	21—25	BCCDD	26—30	BBAAD
31—35	BBDDD	36—40	BACCC	41—45	BDCDC
46—50	CDBAA	51—55	BACAA	56—60	BBCCC
61—65	BCBAB	66—70	ABCBD	71—75	ABAAC
76—80	BDDBB	81—85	CADDC	86—90	DDACB
91—95	BBCDB	96—100	ACCCC		

第三讲　十六种时态和它们的时间状语

1—5	CDAAC	6—10	BBBBA	11—15	DAADA
16—20	AAABC	21—25	BBCBB	26—30	DBADA
31—35	ADACB	36—40	DCBDB	41—45	ABCCB
46—50	DABAD	51—55	CDDCB	56—60	AACAD
61—65	CDABD	66—70	CCCAC	71—75	DCCDA
76—80	BBCBA	81—85	ACAAD	86—90	CAAAC
91—95	CCCBC	96—100	CBAAB	101—105	BDBAC
106—110	DDCBB	111—115	CADBC	116—120	DBCCC
121—125	DDADC	126—130	BBBAB	131—135	DCCBA
136—140	BABDA	141—145	CBBAA	146—150	DBACA

496

第四讲 虚 拟 语 气

1—5	CCCBB	6—10	BACCB	11—15	ABDDB
16—20	BBADD	21—25	ACBBC	26—30	ACCBD
31—35	BDABB	36—40	CDCCC	41—45	DABDA
46—50	AAACC	51—55	BCBBC	56—60	AABCB
61—65	CCBDD	66—70	CBDBD	71—75	CDDDA
76—80	ABDAA	81—85	ADCCC	86—90	ACBAB
91—95	BCCBC	96—100	BABBD		

第五讲 被 动 语 态

1—5	CDDBB	6—10	CDBBC	11—15	CDCBA
16—20	BBDCD	21—25	CBABC	26—30	AAACD
31—35	CCCBA	36—40	ABCDB	41—45	CDADD
46—50	CBBCB	51—55	CDCCD	56—60	CCDCC

第六讲 主谓语一致的规则

1—5	BAABC	6—10	BADCC	11—15	AAAAA
16—20	AACBC	21—25	DBBBD	26—30	AABBC
31—35	ACABB	36—40	ABDCA	41—45	BBABC
46—50	CABBC	51—55	ABAAB	56—60	BDADB
61—65	BACCA	66—70	CCCBB	71—75	DABDD
76—80	BACCC	81—85	CDCAA	86—90	DABCA
91—95	DCCBA				

第七讲 四 种 疑 问 句

1—5	CCBBC	6—10	CDCDD	11—15	BDCBA
16—20	BBCDD	21—25	DBACB	26—30	CBCAB
31—35	DABCC	36—40	CDDCB	41—45	BADAD
46—50	BBBBD	51—55	CDADB	56—60	AAADA
61—65	CCCCB	66—70	AADCC		

第八讲 否 定 句

1—5	DBBAC	6—10	AACBA	11—15	ABBAD

16—20	CCAAC	21—25	CDDCC	26—30	DACBB
31—35	AADAC	36—40	BBABC	41—45	ABDCD
46—50	BACAB	51—55	CDABD	56—60	ACDDC

第九讲 感 叹 句

1—5	AADBA	6—10	CCABB	11—15	CDDDA

第十讲 祈使句和命令句

1—5	CCBBB	6—10	DABAA	11—15	BDAAA
16—20	BADBB	21—25	BCBBB	26—30	BDBBD
31—35	ACCCA				

第十一讲 情 态 助 动 词

1—5	AACCD	6—10	CDDCD	11—15	BBACB
16—20	DACCD	21—25	BACAA	26—30	BADAC
31—35	ABBBD	36—40	CDDBB	41—45	DDBAD
46—50	BADDA	51—55	CBBDB	56—60	CACCC
61—65	DCCBA	66—70	BBCDA	71—75	DDCCB
76—80	DCADB	81—85	ABDCC	86—90	BCCDD

第十二讲 并 列 句

1—5	AAADC	6—10	BBCCA	11—15	DDDDC
16—20	DDADA	21—25	AABAA	26—30	ADCBD
31—35	BBABB	36—40	BADDC		

第十三讲 宾 语 从 句

1—5	CABAD	6—10	ABDBA	11—15	CCAAA
16—20	BDAAC	21—25	DDADD	26—30	CABAD
31—35	DACAD	36—40	ADDBD	41—45	BBDCC
46—50	DACBC	51—55	DCCCB	56—60	ABBBC
61—65	BDADB	66—70	BCBAA	71—75	BBCBD
76—80	CADCD	81—85	DDACB		

第十四讲　主 语 从 句

1—5	BADDC	6—10	DCCAC	11—15	DBDCC
16—20	ABDDB	21—25	CADBC	26—30	AAABA
31—35	CBABA	36—40	DDBDB	41—45	AABBA
46—50	DBDCB				

第十五讲　表 语 从 句

1—5	CDAAC	6—10	BBDCB	11—15	AABDA
16—20	DDDBA	21—25	CABDC		

第十六讲　同 位 语 从 句

1—5	BDBDB	6—10	CCDCB	11—15	AABCA
16—20	DBADC	21—25	DBBCD	26—30	ACACB

第十七讲　状 语 从 句

1—5	DDBBD	6—10	BBDCD	11—15	BADAD
16—20	BDCAD	21—25	ABDCA	26—30	CBCCC
31—35	CBCAA	36—40	CBACA	41—45	DDDBB
46—50	ADDAD	51—55	CDBDA	56—60	BADBD
61—65	DDBCC	66—70	DBCBD	71—75	BBDDC
76—80	BDBCA	81—85	CBCDB	86—90	DABCC
91—95	DCDCC	96—100	BADCC	101—105	BDCDB
106—110	BCCCD	111—115	CABCC	116—120	DCCAC
121—125	BBAAC	126—130	BCAAA	131—135	CBABB
136—140	DAAAA	141—145	CCBAD	146—150	AABAD
151—155	CDDAD	156—160	BCCCB	161 165	ACBAD
166—170	BAADA	171—175	DCAAC	176—180	CCDDC
181—185	BADCB	186—190	DCBDA	191—195	CDABA
196—200	CDDDC				

第十八讲　定 语 从 句

1—5	DCBCA	6—10	DCABC	11—15	ACDBD

499

16—20	BABBB	21—25	BADCC	26—30	BACAC
31—35	ADBDB	36—40	BCCCC	41—45	BDABC
46—50	ACBCC	51—55	ADBCA	56—60	BACAD
61—65	CBADD	66—70	BAAAB	71—75	CBBDA
76—80	BCBDC	81—85	DDBDA	86—90	DBBCD
91—95	ACBAC	96—100	ABBAD	101—105	DADAC
106—110	CCBCC	111—115	DBBAD	116—120	BABAC
121—125	DBCBB	126—130	CBCDB	131—135	CDABD
136—140	DACDC	141—145	ADBAD	146—150	DBABA
151—155	CADCC	156—160	ADCDB	161—165	DDBCA
166—170	ADDBA	171—175	DBCAA	176—180	DABDB
181—185	ABDCD	186—190	BABCD	191—195	AABBC

第十九讲　非谓语动词（一）　分词和独立主格结构

1—5	ACADA	6—10	CBBBD	11—15	BCAAA
16—20	AADCA	21—25	BCADD	26—30	ACDDB
31—35	CCADD	36—40	CDDDB	41—45	ACBAD
46—50	BDACD	51—55	CDCDB	56—60	CCDDC
61—65	ABDDB	66—70	DBBAA	71—75	CBADD
76—80	ACCCA	81—85	ADACC	86—90	DDAAD
91—95	AABCA	96—100	CCBCB	101—105	ABDBD
106—110	CACDB	111—115	BADBC	116—120	ABABB
121—125	ACCDB	126—130	CBCDA	131—135	CBBBD
136—140	CBAAA	141—145	BABBC	146—150	ADBDC
151—155	ABAAA	156—160	BDACB	161—165	CCACC
166—170	CBBDC	171—175	DCBAB	176—180	CBDAC
181—185	DDABC	186—190	BCACB	191—195	BACCC
196—200	BDADC				

第二十讲　非谓语动词（二）　动名词

1—5	CCBBA	6—10	BCBDB	11—15	CAACB
16—20	DCDBB	21—25	CBBDC	26—30	CCBDD
31—35	BBBDC	36—40	CCADB	41—45	ACDDB
46—50	DDACB	51—55	BBABD	56—60	ACCBD

61—65	CAADC	66—70	BBCBA	71—75	BDACA
76—80	BCCDB	81—85	DAABD	86—90	BCCCD
91—95	ABCCB	96—100	DADBA	101—105	BAAAB
106—110	ADCBA	111—115	CBBBA	116—120	DBDDD
121—125	CCACA	126—130	ADDCB	131—135	DDBAA

第二十一讲　非谓语动词（三）　动词不定式

1—5	BBBAA	6—10	DBACC	11—15	BBCBD
16—20	ACBBB	21—25	DDCBC	26—30	BDABC
31—35	ABDBA	36—40	DBAAD	41—45	CABAD
46—50	BBCBC	51—55	CAAAB	56—60	BBACB
61—65	BABBA	66—70	AABBA	71—75	CABCC
76—80	AACDB	81—85	ABBAB	86—90	CBBAA
91—95	CBCDB	96—100	CCBAB	101—105	DCBAB
106—110	CAAAC	111—115	CBCCC	116—120	DCBBC
121—125	DAACA	126—130	ACBCC	131—135	BCBDB
136—140	ABBAD	141—145	ACDDA	146—150	BDDBB
151—155	BAABC	156—160	DBBAC	161—165	CABCC
166—170	DABAC	171—175	BADCC	176—180	ACBBD
181—185	ACBDC	186—190	CABAC	191—195	CCABA

第二十二讲　直接引语和间接引语

| 1—5 | BCCBA | 6—10 | ADBDD |

第二十三讲　"IT"的用法

| 1—5 | CDDDD | 6—10 | BBBCB | 11—15 | CDCAD |
| 16—20 | BCCCB | | | | |

第二十四讲　强　调　句

1—5	ACDBD	6—10	BAACA	11—15	BBDBD
16—20	CDDAA	21—25	ABADD	26—30	BDCCD
31—35	CAABC	36—40	AABBC	41—45	DCACB

501

第二十五讲　词类（一）　名词

1—5	ACCBD	6—10	BCCBB	11—15	BCBCD
16—20	DDBBD	21—25	CDBDB	26—30	ACDBB
31—35	ABCDC	36—40	ABDAA		

第二十六讲　词类（二）　代词

1—5	BDDDC	6—10	DCDDA	11—15	ABBDD
16—20	BABAA	21—25	BACBA	26—30	BACBC
31—35	BCAAA	36—40	CCBCD	41—45	BBBCA
46—50	ACBCD	51—55	CBBDD	56—60	DDCCA
61—65	CCBCC	66—70	ACAAC	71—75	ADCDB
76—80	ACDCB	81—85	CADAA	86—90	BDAAD
91—95	DBCBD	96—100	BBCBC	101—105	CBCAD
106—110	ACABA	111—115	BCCDA	116—120	BBADC
121—125	DAADB				

第二十七讲　词类（三）　形容词和副词

1—5	BCBBD	6—10	CDCCB	11—15	ADCBA
16—20	BCDDC	21—25	CDBCB	26—30	CDCBC
31—35	ABDBA	36—40	BCBDA	41—45	CDDBB
46—50	CCCDA	51—55	CBBDA	56—60	CCCDB
61—65	BBCCC	66—70	CBDBB	71—75	BCDBB
76—80	DACDA	81—85	DDADC	86—90	CBABB
91—95	DAACB	96—100	ABADC	101—105	BBACB
106—110	DDCAB	111—115	BACBC	116—120	DDABA
121—125	DDDCB	126—130	DDCDB	131—135	BCAAC

第二十八讲　词类（四）　数词

1—5	CAACD	6—10	ABACD	11—15	DCCAC
16—20	CBDDC	21—25	ADBAA	26—30	BCCDC
31—35	CDADB	36—40	BAACC	41—45	CADDA
46—50	AACCB				

第二十九讲　词类（五）　冠词

1—5	AAABA	6—10	BCABC	11—15	CCCCD
16—20	BDCCB	21—25	BADDD	26—30	CBAAD
31—35	ADABC	36—40	DAABB	41—45	DBBDA
46—50	BDACC	51—55	CAADD	56—60	CCBBD
61—65	BBCAB	66—70	ADABA	71—75	ACDCD
76—80	BABBB	81—85	CCABA	86—90	BCCAD
91—95	ABDBB	96—100	ACCDA		

第三十讲　词类（六）　介词

1—5	DDADC	6—10	BADBA	11—15	BBCAC
16—20	CADDC	21—25	ADDAC	26—30	BBBDD
31—35	DCDBA	36—40	ADACA	41—45	ACABB
46—50	BABBD	51—55	BAADC	56—60	BCBBB
61—65	BACAB	66—70	ACDDD	71—75	BBDCD
76—80	ACCAD	81—85	DAACC	86—90	BADDA
91—95	BBDCC	96—100	ABACD	101—105	BDACD
106—110	DACAB	111—115	CAAAD	116—120	BDCCD
121—125	ABBBD	126—130	DACAC	131—135	DADDD
136—140	DADBC	141—145	BADAC	146—150	CDDAD

综合练习答案

2014年上海高考英语试题(语法新题型)

(A)

25. where 26. To learn 27. as soon as/as long as 28. exhausted
29. if 30. what 31. adapting 32. did

(B)

33. an 34. is equipped 35. which 36. myself
37. appropriate 38. has forced 39. urging 40. to

第一套

(A)

1. on 2. that 3. causing 4. called 5. but 6. Getting
7. Though 8. necessarily

(B)

9. Following 10. were seen 11. were blocked 12. to
13. whether 14. on 15. to 16. to observe

第二套

(A)

1. grows 2. off 3. is watched 4. The other 5. to 6. to
turn 7. that

(B)

8. have 9. has been told 10. finding 11. what 12. who
13. gives 14. in 15. staying 16. when

第三套

(A)

1. from 2. who 3. to create 4. goes 5. have been arrested
6. have been transferred 7. of 8. that

(B)

9. that 10. to spoil 11. how 12. for 13. others 14. those/
people 15. It 16. fully

504

第四套

(A)

1. what   2. hundreds   3. with   4. are exposed   5. being committed   6. could   7. that/who   8. that

(B)

9. it   10. But   11. hide   12. allowing   13. at   14. what 15. to do   16. trust/being trusted

第五套

(A)

1. to encourage   2. could   3. slipped   4. before   5. playing 6. a   7. with/by

(B)

8. better   9. featuring   10. was changed   11. its   12. what 13. when   14. which   15. based   16. If

第六套

(A)

1. visiting   2. In   3. off   4. to show   5. was requested 6. as   7. smiled   8. must

(B)

9. that   10. What   11. that   12. a   13. is called   14. on 15. are supposed   16. If

第七套

(A)

1. which/that/不填   2. to generalize   3. that   4. more 5. being given   6. so   7. is doing   8. that

(B)

9. at   10. the first time   11. to get   12. calling   13. pointing 14. open   15. will continue   16. what

第八套

(A)

1. there   2. called   3. on   4. where   5. a   6. Every one 7. Since   8. send

(B)

9. in spite of   10. has devoted   11. gathering   12. to help

13. of 14. on 15. hearing 16. much/far/even

第九套

(A)

1. writers 2. seriously 3. so 4. to discover 5. from 6. were described 7. baby's 8. Once

(B)

9. drifting 10. When 11. that 12. why 13. might 14. used 15. From 16. is still used

第十套

(A)

1. problems 2. faces/is faced with 3. know 4. to face 5. Choosing 6. when 7. to 8. helping

(B)

9. being 10. Without 11. why 12. which 13. because 14. are found 15. to spoil 16. though

第十一套

(A)

1. it 2. requires 3. made 4. sleeping 5. But 6. be considered 7. to be forgotten 8. who

(B)

9. covered 10. because 11. with 12. which/that 13. at 14. looking 15. During 16. but

第十二套

(A)

1. named 2. saying 3. but 4. leave 5. Yet 6. It 7. in 8. (should) be

(B)

9. so 10. are experiencing 11. to protect 12. called 13. to 14. off 15. how 16. blown

第十三套

(A)

1. that 2. was shopping 3. about 4. to 5. what 6. to tell 7. in 8. had expected 9. scared 10. stealing 11. for 12. having 13. On 14. had learned 15. enjoy 16. that/in

which/不填

(B)

1. eating   2. in   3. it   4. Eating   5. if   6. to like   7. to
8. winning   9. disqualified   10. are tied   11. of   12. to show
13. better   14. on   15. what   16. stimulate

第十四套

(A)

1. studying   2. it   3. because   4. involved   5. to bring
6. and   7. When   8. who   9. could

(B)

10. growing   11. even though/if   12. what   13. for   14. were
paid   15. that   16. encouraged

第十五套

(A)

1. If   2. herself   3. had to   4. where   5. to find   6. although/
though   7. had parked   8. singing

(B)

9. consists   10. who   11. known   12. were omitted   13. on
14. before   15. when   16. reciting

第十六套

(A)

1. can   2. in   3. expressing   4. to learn   5. and   6. once
7. checked   8. who

(B)

9. if   10. so that   11. why   12. However   13. his   14. has
caught   15. under   16. more importantly

第十七套

(A)

1. to fly   2. approaching   3. towards   4. that   5. to live
6. as   7. a   8. has continued

(B)

9. However   10. denying   11. can   12. To illustrate   13. which/
that   14. are devoted   15. What   16. the fullest

第十八套

(A)

1. for 2. to generate 3. where 4. living 5. ones 6. more effective 7. what 8. should

(B)

9. them 10. in 11. aged 12. even if/even though 13. when 14. can 15. that/which 16. trying

2015 年上海高考英语试题(语法新题型)

(A)

25. As/Because/Since 26. emptied 27. an 28. looking 29. might/may 30. like 31. Shocked 32. the nicest

(B)

33. to check 34. that 35. as if/as though 36. who 37. ignoring 38. someone/somebody 39. has been interrupted/is being interrupted/is interrupted 40. which